Ernst von Dobschutz

The Influence of the Bible on Civilisation

Ernst von Dobschutz

The Influence of the Bible on Civilisation

1st Edition | ISBN: 978-3-75238-300-3

Place of Publication: Frankfurt am Main, Germany

Year of Publication: 2020

Outlook Verlag GmbH, Germany.

Reproduction of the original.

THE INFLUENCE OF THE BIBLE ON CIVILISATION

BY
ERNST VON DOBSCHÜTZ

I

THE BIBLE MAKES ITSELF INDISPENSABLE FOR THE CHURCH (UNTIL 325 A. D.)

There is a small book; one can put it in one's pocket, and yet all the libraries of America, numerous as they are, would hardly be large enough to hold all the books which have been inspired by this one little volume. The reader will know what I am speaking of; it is the Bible, as we are used to call it—the Book, the book of mankind, as it has properly been called. It has been commented upon, treated in every way, but, curious to say, hardly any one has attempted to trace its history through the centuries and mark the influence which it exerted upon our civilisation.

In order to do this we follow the traces of the Bible through the different periods of human or, to speak more accurately, of Christian civilisation. In the first period of Christian history, the time of persecutions during the first three centuries of our era, there is not much to say about the Bible as influencing civilisation. Christianity was but starting on its way and fighting for its place in the world. The Bible could not exert a civilising influence upon a hostile world. But by impressing its value upon the Christian mind it made itself indispensable for the church and thereby laid the foundation for the future development.

Christianity was a living religion. The first congregations were dwelling in an atmosphere of enthusiasm. There was a general outpouring of the Holy Spirit. The prophet's words seemed to be fulfilled: "They shall teach no more every man his neighbour and every man his brother, saying: know the Lord; for they shall all know me." Christianity was not a religion of a sacred book, whose dead letter was to be artificially kept alive by learned men. It was a religion of living experiences. Nevertheless, Christianity from the beginning had a sacred book. Jesus and his disciples used the Bible of their people, the Old Testament, and Saint Paul carried it to the Christian communities of gentile origin, which had not known of it before.

Christianity could not do without it. If it was necessary to convince Jews that Jesus was the Messiah, how could this be done without arguing from the Scriptures as proof? If the gospel was to be announced to the heathen they would give less heed to the new tidings than to the statement that it was really the most ancient form of religion as attested by this sacred book, which was superior to all the books of poets and philosophers and legislators by reason of its venerable age. Christianity without any hesitation claimed the Old Testament as its own book, its own Bible. Not only was Jesus the content of this book, he was even believed to be its author. It was the spirit of Jesus which dwelt in the prophets and made them seek and search concerning the salvation offered by Christ (I Peter 1 : 10-11). "The prophets having their grace from him, did prophesy unto him," we are told in the so-called letter of Barnabas. So the Old Testament seemed to be a Christian book both in content and in origin, and it was easy enough to add some properly Christian pamphlets, as Saint Paul's letters and some gospels, the Acts and other letters, and some books of revelation. It was as necessary as it was easy, if Christianity was not to lose contact with its proper origin.

The New Testament, as we have it now, was not complete at the start. It was a collection of primitive Christian writings, larger in some ways than it is now; on the other hand lacking some of its present elements. Its precise content did not become finally established until a very late period, not earlier than the end of the fourth century.

So also the size of the Old Testament was not quite fixed. There were more books in the Greek Bible of the Alexandrian Jews than in the Hebrew Bible of the Palestinian rabbis. The Christian church at first adopted the Greek Bible, but from time to time some scholar pointed out the difference, and many people thought they had better keep to the Hebrew canon. This view, championed by Saint Jerome, led to a partial rejection of the books which nowadays we usually call the Old Testament Apocrypha, until in the sixteenth century the churches accentuated their difference by a different attitude toward these books, the Calvinists rejecting them altogether, the Roman church including them as an integral part of the Bible, and the Lutherans giving them an intermediate position as books to be read with safety but without canonical authority. When, in 1902, King Edward VII was to be crowned, the British and Foreign Bible Society intended to present to his Majesty the copy of the Bible on which he was to take his oath. Then it was discovered that according to the old regulations the king of England had to take his oath on a complete Bible, that is a Bible containing the Apocrypha. The British and Foreign Bible Society on its part, by its statutes, was prevented from printing Bibles including the Apocrypha; so they presented to the king a most beautiful copy, but the king did not use it for the coronation service. It is the difference between the Alexandrian and the Palestinian canon which reappears in this little struggle and thereby is seen surviving to our own time.

Unsettled as the size of the Old and of the New Testament may have been,

3

nevertheless the principle was established at a very early date that Christianity was to have a holy Scripture in two parts, one taken over from Judaism, the other added from its own stores.

Let us stop here for a moment and try to realise what this meant. Mohammed, when founding his new religion, acknowledged, it is true, the books of the former religions, but for his own believers the unique authority is the Koran, a book which originated within a single generation and therefore is pervaded by one uniform spirit. Christianity adhered to a Bible whose larger part originated in a period much anterior to its own and in a religion inferior to Christianity. The Bible covers a period of over a thousand years. What a difference in civilisation between the nomadic life of the patriarchs and the time of Jesus! What a difference in spirit between the sons of Jacob killing the whole population of Sichem in order to avenge their sister and Jesus' parable of the good Samaritan! or between the prophet Elijah killing four hundred and fifty prophets of Baal and Jesus preaching the love of one's enemies! In fact, it was possible to overcome this difference only in an age which did not read the Bible with historical notions. Even so, the juxtaposition caused much difficulty. We shall see the problem of the Law troubling the church through all the centuries. We shall find the notions of sacrifice and priesthood adapted to Christian institutions. Looking at Charlemagne or Calvin, we realise that the Old Testament is ever introducing its views into Christian minds, as authoritative as any word of the gospel.

Now, at the beginning the influence was rather the other way; the Old Testament was to be interpreted in the light of the New. And, in truth, much light came from the life of Jesus to the history of the ancient people and to the prophecies. We do not wonder that Christian minds were excited by all this fresh illumination, and we must not wonder that sometimes they remodelled the tradition of the life of Christ to accord with the Old Testament.

The harmony between the two Testaments soon became a leading idea in Christian doctrine. Some heretics, indeed, would not accept the Old Testament. Marcion maintained that it came from an inferior god, while the supreme God, the father of our Lord Jesus Christ, had revealed himself only through his Son. He found a great many contrasts between the Old and the New Testament, and this criticism was supported by pagan philosophers, as, for example, Porphyry. The church, therefore, was most anxious to establish the harmony of the Testaments by any means at its command. Taste varies from century to century; the minute parallelism constructed by some early Christian writers, and evidently much admired by their contemporaries, seems to us rather ridiculous and fanciful. On the other hand, the church was right in maintaining the harmony. The New Testament needs to be explained from the

Old Testament; it is open to much misunderstanding when taken apart. There was almost no sense for historical development at that time; the criticism of Ptolemæus, in his famous letter to Flora, where he speaks of several strata of revelation running through the Old and the New Testament, is an exceptional one. For most of the faithful the Christian doctrine was directly looked for and found in the Old Testament; the gospel was contained in every one of its books, from Genesis to Malachi. Unity was conceived as uniformity.

This was the system which appealed most to the average Christian mind. And the Bible was open to all Christians, as Harnack has brilliantly demonstrated in a recent publication. The ancient church laid stress upon this publicity and never tried to withdraw the Bible from the people. There was no hidden mystery regarding the Bible. On the contrary, all members of the church were anxiously urged to make themselves as familiar with the Bible as possible. They were supposed to have copies of their own and to read them privately as well as in the congregation. Even when the struggles about the right doctrine began and the heretics sometimes held to the Bible as their champion against the doctrine of the church, the church did not remove the Bible from public discussion. The ecclesiastical party maintained that the Bible was always in favour of the true doctrine; one needs but to know how to read it. Tertullian, it is true, once in the heat of controversy declared that it was no use arguing against heretics from the Bible, but he did it, nevertheless, and so did the other fathers.

The Bible proved its spiritual value to the experience of every reader. A man familiar with the Psalms has a treasure which cannot be lost; in any situation he will find what is suitable for his needs. If one looks for examples of faith, the author of the epistle to the Hebrews in his eleventh chapter gives a splendid model for finding heroes of faith all through the Bible. The book of Genesis, especially its first chapters, was of particular interest for most of the readers on account of the sublime description there given of the beginnings of mankind. The creation story in Genesis implies much more than even the finest of all Greek myths, namely, the myth in Plato's Timæus, with which it was compared by the emperor Julian. The mighty words, "In the beginning God created heaven and earth," proved to be the one true answer to all the cosmological questions of Greek philosophy, and besides there was ample room for introducing whatever was wanted—such as the creation and the fall of the angels—if only one knew how to read between the lines.

In an old Christian book dealing with church regulations and the rules for individual Christian life we find the following admonition to use no other book at all except the Bible, because, as the author says, the Bible contains literature of every kind. The passage runs:[1]

Stay at home and read in the Law and in the Book of the Kings and in the Prophets and in the Gospel (which is) the fulness of these things. Keep far away from all the books of the heathen; for what hast thou to do with foreign words or with false laws or prophecies which also easily cause young people to wander from the faith? What then is wanting to thee in the Word of God, that thou throwest thyself upon these myths of the heathen? If thou wishest to read the tales of the fathers, thou hast the Book of the Kings; or of wise men and philosophers, thou hast the Prophets amongst whom thou wilt find more wisdom and science than among the wise men and the philosophers, because they are the words of God, of the one only wise God. If thou desirest song, thou hast the Psalms of David or if the beginning of the world, thou hast the Genesis of great Moses; if law and commandments, thou hast the book of Exodus of the Lord our God. Therefore keep entirely away from all these foreign things, which are contrary to them.

[1] Didascalia, ch. ii, p. 5 in Mrs. M. D. Gibson's translation.

The Bible, in fact, pervaded the whole life of a Christian. It was the Bible, its history, its commandments, that he was taught as a child in his parents' home. When the girls gathered in the women's hall to spin, they would sing and talk about God's revelations more eagerly than even Sappho had praised her luxurious love—according to an expression used by Tatian in his Apology. The prayers, private as well as ecclesiastical, all echoed Biblical phrases, and even at burials the Christians sang joyful psalms.

So the Bible became familiar to the Christians of that time. We are astonished to find how well they knew it. The sermons of this period are full of Biblical allusions, and evidently the preacher could expect them to be understood.

This is the more remarkable as the circulating of the Bible in this time met with the greatest difficulties. There was, of course, a large amount of Bible reading in the congregations. According to Justin's description of early Christian worship about 150 A. D., the service began with continuous reading of the Bible through many chapters, as far as time would allow. Then an officer, bishop or elder, would begin to preach. The office of reading was esteemed so highly that it was regarded as based on a special spiritual gift; the anagnostes, i. e., the reader, in the earliest time had his place among the prophets and spirit-gifted teachers. And, in fact, if we look at the earliest manuscripts of the Bible which have come down to us, we shall almost think that supernatural assistance was necessary for reading them: no punctuation, no accent, no space between the words, no breaking off at the end of a sentence. The reader had to know his text almost entirely by heart to do it well. From the "Shepherd of Hermas," a very interesting book written by a Roman layman about 140 A. D., we learn that some people gathered often, probably daily, for the special purpose of common reading and learning. But even granted that the memory of these men was not spoiled by too much reading, as is ours, so that by hearing they were able to learn by heart—it is said of some rabbis that they did not lose one word of all their master had told them, and, in fact, the Talmudic literature was transmitted orally for centuries —nevertheless, we must assume that these Christians had their private copies of the Bible at home. The evidence from the allusions of preachers to private reading is strong. Cyprian addresses a Christian: "Your life should be one of assiduous prayer or reading (of the Bible): now you speaking to God, now God to you."

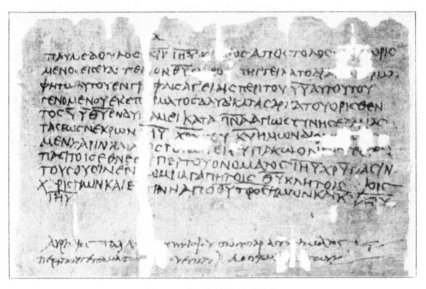

PLATE I—HARVARD PAPYRUS

An attempt to copy the letters of St. Paul (Romans counts as A = first letter) giving the text only unto Romans 1 : 7; late third or early fourth century.

From Oxyrhynchus Papyri, Vol. II, PI. II, Egypt Exploration Fund—London.

7

Here begins our difficulty: how did they get so many copies? There was an organised book-trade in the ancient world; publishers had their offices, using (instead of printing-presses) slaves who were trained in copying; they had shorthand writers, as well as calligraphers to do the fine writing. But as long as Christianity was still an oppressed religion it is doubtful if the Bible was among the books which publishers would care to take. The Christians were, most of them, poor people who could not spend much money for procuring Bibles. Besides, it was no easy thing to get a complete Bible. At that time the books were still written on papyrus rolls, not in book form. Only one side of the papyrus could be used; the roll would become unwieldy if too long. So, in order to get all the books of the Old and the New Testament, at least two dozen rolls had to be written. Maybe a simple Christian copied for himself one gospel or some letters or even one or more books from the Old Testament. There are preserved on papyrus some unfinished attempts which show what hard work it was (Plate I). We can scarcely imagine a man going with this heavy hand through all the books of the Bible.

We are told that wealthy Christians helped their brethren by procuring copies for them. Origen, the greatest Bible scholar of the ancient church, is said to have been supported by a rich admirer, who put at his disposal a number of slave copyists. With their help he succeeded in creating one of the greatest works which Bible criticism ever undertook, his so-called Hexapla, which is a comparison of more than six various Greek translations of the Old Testament. Scholars in the nineteenth century held that scarcely more than one copy of this enormous work had ever been written, but by recent discoveries we know that it was copied several times (Plate II). A later admirer of Origen, Pamphilus, is said always to have carried with him several rolls in order to provide poor brethren. Now that was the third century. Christianity had already begun to spread among the higher classes and to become a feature in the world's life.

PLATE II—ORIGEN'S HEXAPLA

Fragment found in the Cairo-Genizah and published by E. Taylor in 1900; parchment, fifth century, with part of second, third, and fourth columns: Ps 22 : 25-28; used later for copying Hebrew texts.

From "Hexapla of Origen," by E. Taylor, published by G. P. Putnam's Sons.

Devotional reading of the Bible was accompanied by scholarly interpretation. We mentioned Origen as the greatest Bible scholar of his time, if not of all times. It may be worth while to insert here a few words on his life. A native of Alexandria, he saw as a boy his father dying as a martyr for his Christian faith; he longed to become a martyr himself, and was only prevented from giving himself up by a trick of his mother's, who concealed all his clothes. He got a good training at the catechetical school of Alexandria, not restricting himself to mere Christian and Biblical studies, but reading the pagan philosophers of his time as well as the Greek classics. A youth of only eighteen years, he became the head of the school, and his fame spread all over the empire. He travelled to Rome, to Greece; he was even asked by the Roman governor to come to Arabia to settle certain questions. So zealous was he to fulfil the commandments of the gospel that, misunderstanding one of the Lord's sayings, he made himself a eunuch for the kingdom of heaven's sake, which brought him into trouble in his later life. When once on a journey through Palestine he, being still a layman, had preached before the bishop of Cæsarea, he was summoned by his own bishop and ordered not to preach. Some years afterward the bishop of Cæsarea, who was among his strongest admirers, ordained him a priest, which caused his bishop to banish him from Alexandria. He settled at Cæsarea and lived there for twenty years without ever aiming at any ecclesiastical position, pursuing his study of the Bible and gathering around his chair the best men from every part of Christianity. So great was his fame that the empress Julia Mammæa, being still a pagan, asked him to see her when she was travelling in the East. He was the one man to refute the vigorous attack made against the truth of Christian doctrine by the philosopher Celsus. When persecution began again he wrote a tractate of comfort, "On Martyrdom," and another, "On Prayer." He himself suffered imprisonment and torture, and died after his release, as a result of these sufferings, at the age of sixty-nine.

We can scarcely do honour enough to this man, who three centuries after his death was proclaimed to be one of the most dangerous heretics, the church, however, using his learning in the form of extracts. The vast amount of reading, the sagacity, and the perspicuity of the man are alike admirable. He is said to have commented upon nearly all the books of the Bible, and this three times. He wrote short annotations, he compiled large and learned commentaries, and he preached before the congregation. Only a small part of his works has come down to us, but this fills volumes. Origen's great merit is that he brought Christian interpretation to a system which enabled the church to retain the plain historical sense alongside the so-called higher meaning.

For a long time gentile philosophers as well as Jewish preachers had adopted the method of treating their sacred books allegorically. Homer, it was assumed, in telling his stories of battles of gods and heroes, meant quite another thing; otherwise he would be guilty of irreligion. He meant that the powers of nature and the energies of the human soul came into struggle, and therefore virtues and vices were fighting one with another. The same thing was done by Philo for the Old Testament. There was no real history; all was symbolical, allegory. Christianity tried to follow in this path. The gnostics indulged in the wildest form of allegory. But it was not safe to give up the idea of historicity altogether. Jesus and his gospel were historical facts, not mere ideas; they were emptied of all meaning if turned into allegory. And likewise the history of the Old Testament could not simply be reduced to allegorical metaphors. Origen saved the situation by asserting that each of these two views had its proper place. His theory is that as man consists of body, soul, and spirit, so the holy Scripture has a threefold nature, to which corresponds a threefold interpretation. The body stands for the plain historical meaning: Jesus did cast out of the temple those that sold oxen and sheep and doves and the changers of money. There are some historical difficulties, Origen admits, if we compare the different gospel narratives and if we take account of the fact that a single man did this; Origen explains that it was a miracle showing the divine power in Jesus. But there are other aspects too. The soul represents the higher moral view: Christ is always casting out of his church, which belongs to the heavenly Jerusalem, the men who are profaning it by their money-making. And, lastly, there is the spirit, that is, the supreme mystical understanding. The spirit of Christ, entering its temple, the man's soul, casts out of it all earthly desires and makes it a house of prayer. Now that is very ingenious. These three strata of interpretation allow for a great variety in explanation and adaptation. Origen succeeds by this method in keeping the essential historical basis and adding what in those days was thought to be most significant. The Bible, being a divine book, seemed to require a higher form of interpretation; the Holy Ghost of God was supposed to be a spirit of mysteries; it was assumed that to interpret the Bible in a plain way was to think of God meanly.

Of course, the Bible contained some allegories which might seem to support this theory of allegorical interpretation; for instance, the beautiful vision of Ezekiel, told in the thirty-seventh chapter of his book: he sees the valley full of dry bones, and at the command of God he prophesies over them and they begin to come together, and flesh came up and skin covered them above and at last breath came into them and they lived. It is a magnificent allegory of the people of Israel, scattered in the exile and brought to life again by the power of God. It is irritating to see the fathers just at this point declining to follow the path of allegorical interpretation. They insist upon the reality of the occurrence; it is to be taken literally as resurrection of the dead —so it has influenced all mediæval pictures of the last judgment! I need only add that the rabbis took Ezekiel's description in the same way, as a real occurrence, arguing for the historicity by showing the phylacteries which the risen persons had worn—and one feels what a pity it is to treat allegory as history. But the opposite fault is still worse: the spiritualising and allegorising of real history is the greatest damage ever done to religion.

Theologians tried to establish the authority of the Bible. This had already been done in some measure by the rabbis of the synagogue. In taking over the Bible the Christians had only to accept their estimate of it, but they were not quite satisfied with it. The rabbinical doctrine was a rather mechanical one: God had used men, just as a man uses a pencil to write with. The pencil does not act consciously: so the Old Testament writers, according to this theory, did not take any part in what they were writing; it was to them as another man's script. Commenting upon the last chapter of Deuteronomy, where the death of Moses is described, a rabbinical authority remarks: "Until this passage God dictated and Moses wrote; henceforth God dictated and Moses wrote weeping"—namely, the account of his own death. There was so little interest in the human author that he could be eliminated altogether. We are told by an early Jewish legend that all books of the Old Testament had been destroyed at the time of Nebuchadnezzar, when the temple was burned; so God dictated them all to Ezra. According to this theory Ezra would be the real author of the whole Old Testament. This is the most mechanical way of representing the equal inspiration of all parts of the Old Testament. The Jews of the dispersion had a somewhat similar theory about the inspiration of their Greek Bible; when Ptolemy Philadelphus, king of Egypt, gathered at Alexandria seventy elders of the Jews to make the Greek translation of their law, he put each one of them in a separate cell in order to avoid any communication between them, so the legend runs. Then, after working for seventy days, all at once they shouted "Amen" from their cells, having accomplished their task, and when the seventy copies had been compared they were found to agree even in the smallest detail. Here we have again an attempt to assert inspiration not only for the book itself but also for its translation. It is as mechanical as the former, all human co-operation being excluded.

Christians did not want this. In Jesus they had experienced living revelation; they had prophets among themselves. So, at least at the beginning, they had a much higher view of inspiration. God enters a man's soul and fills it with his spirit; now the man acts and speaks in the power of this spirit, and yet he is not unconscious of his own doing and speaking. There are two ways of inspiration, we are told by Clement of Alexandria: either God snatches up the man's soul and conducts it to the unseen world and shows to it whatever he wishes it to know—this is ecstasy—or God enters the man and fills him and makes him his organ. The latter, less striking though it appears, is nevertheless the higher and more valuable concept. Therefore the fathers do not so much use the metaphor of the pencil as the similitude of a musical instrument, whether a flute through which the Holy Spirit is playing, or a harp which he touches with a plectrum.

Much as they appreciate the holy Scripture, the early fathers usually talk about it in a very unpretentious manner. They have not yet developed those gorgeous formulas of quotation which are used in later times. They quote simply: "Scripture says," or "Paul says," not "the holy and glorious apostle in his most excellent epistle to the Romans says exceedingly well." They talk in simple words, but they are prepared even to die for this Bible.

Eusebius, the first historian of the Christian church, to whom we are indebted for so much invaluable information, tells us a moving story about Marinus, a young Christian officer in the Roman army, at Cæsarea, in Palestine. He had the confidence of his superiors and was to be promoted to the higher rank of captain. Then out of jealousy one of his comrades denounced him as a Christian. Summoned before his colonel, he was asked if this was true, and when he confessed he was urged to abjure his faith. The colonel gave him three hours' time. So he went to the small Christian church, where he found the venerable old bishop. The bishop, hearing his story, took the Bible in one hand and the soldier's sword in the other. "This is your choice," he said. And the soldier, without hesitating, grasped the Bible, went back, and declared himself to be and to remain a Christian. And instead of receiving military promotion he became a martyr.

It is a significant little story. Indeed, after a hard struggle, lasting through nearly three centuries, when the Roman empire found it necessary to attempt the final destruction of Christianity the attack was mostly directed against the Bible. Diocletian, in 303 A. D., on the 24th of February, issued an edict ordering all Christian churches to be destroyed and all Bibles to be burned. He relied on the Roman law, which forbids not only the exercise of magical arts, but the science of magic, too, and therefore condemns all books of magic to be burned. The Christians were accused of employing magic, and their Bible was treated as a magical book.

We have thrilling accounts of Christians trying to conceal their treasured Bible rolls from the eyes of the inquiring officials. They took them from the church into their private homes, securing the Bible in safety but many a time bringing persecution upon themselves. To the officials they surrendered books of various kinds in order to escape from surrendering the Scriptures. Asked if they had sacred books in their houses, many of them would answer: "Yes, in our hearts." The enthusiasm was so great that they believed the story of any miracle in support of the Bible. They maintained that copies of the Bible which had been thrown into the fire by the heathen were not burned or even touched by the flame.

Naturally there were others who were not strong enough in their faith to resist, but these "surrenderers," as they were called, were cast out of the church and never admitted again. During the fourth century to bring against a clergyman the charge of having surrendered sacred books at that period of persecution was felt to be the most serious accusation possible. Even to be ordained by a bishop who was under suspicion of having surrendered his church's holy Scriptures was held a disgrace by a large party of zealous Christians who demanded that orders of this kind be invalidated. The records of a trial held at Carthage in 329 A. D. dealing with this question have come down to us. Here documents from 303 A. D. were introduced as evidence against the clergy, and the whole forms one of the most illuminating pages of church history.

Even to be found reading the Bible made a man guilty of obstinate resistance to the emperor's law and involved him in penalty. There was a deacon at Catania in Sicily named Euplus. He was reading the holy Scripture when the sheriff laid hold of him. Brought before the judge he takes his copy of the Gospel and reads from it (Matt. 5 : 10): "Blessed are they that have been persecuted for righteousness' sake, for theirs is the kingdom of heaven," and (Matt. 10 : 38): "And he that doth not take his cross and follow after me, is not worthy of me." The judge asks him: "Why did you not surrender those volumes which the emperors forbade?" "Because," he replies, "I am a Christian and it was not loyal to surrender. It is better to die than to surrender." We do not need the addition made by a late Byzantine hagiographer that the copy of the Gospels was hung on his neck when he was conducted to execution. It is clear enough that he was suffering for his devotion toward the Bible and that it was the gospel which inspired his boldness.

Euplus does not stand alone. I could mention a dozen martyrs whose acts all give the same impression. Sometimes a gathering of men and women is apprehended while reading the Bible, and the whole company is forthwith carried away to the most painful tortures.

These Christians knew what the Bible was to them. All declamations of later theologians about the inspiration and the authority of the Bible count for nothing compared with this testimony.

After all, we do not wonder that the Bible became a civilising power as

14

soon as Christianity had won its victory.

II

THE BIBLE BEGINS TO RULE
THE CHRISTIAN EMPIRE (325-600
A. D.)

After the persecution by Diocletian a new era began. Constantine proclaimed tolerance, and by and by Christianity became the religion of the empire. The victory of Christianity was a victory of the Bible as well. This finds its expression in the remarkable fact that the first Christian emperor, the immediate successor of those who persecuted the Bible and tried to destroy it, ordered fifty splendid copies of the Bible to be prepared at his expense for the churches of the newly founded capital, Constantinople. Some scholars have thought that one or two of these copies still survive in the famous manuscript discovered by Tischendorf in the Convent of Mount Sinai (Plate III), or in the Codex Vaticanus at Rome. I venture rather to think that both copies belong to the period of Constantine's sons. But the fact that the Bible, after a period of destruction when most of the earlier copies were burned, got a surprising circulation under official direction accounts, I think, for a puzzling feature in the transmission of the text. From the Old Latin and the Old Syriac, as well as from the testimony of the fathers, we can infer that various forms of the Greek text must once have been widely circulated, which have now almost disappeared, whereas most of our present Greek manuscripts give a text evidently based on a late official recension. Looking at Diocletian's attempt to destroy the Bible altogether and at Constantine's official order to provide a large number of manuscripts, we easily understand the situation. The older forms of text had been swept away; now there was room to supply their place with the learned attempts of later scholars from the schools of Origen or Lucian who endeavoured to bring in more critical texts.

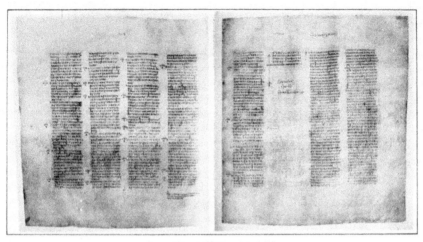

Plate III—CODEX SINAITICUS

End of St. Mark (15 : 16-16 : 8) and beginning of St. Luke (1 : 1-18); Mark 16 : 9-20 is missing; 15 : 47 is added at the lower margin by a later hand; remark the numbers of Eusebius's sections and canons. The eight columns of the open book recall the roll-system.

Reduced one-fifth from the fac-simile edited by Prof. Lake and published by
the Clarendon Press
(Oxford and London).

Another change is to be mentioned at the same time. The old form of papyrus rolls became obsolete and the parchment book took its place. The use of this latter form seems to originate in the law schools; the codex, or parchment book, is at first the designation of a Roman law-book. But at an early date the Christian church adopted this form as the more convenient one and gave it its circulation. We hardly say too much when we call the Bible the means by which our present form of book came into general use. Even if the Bible had done nothing else for civilisation than to give mankind the shape of its books that would be a great deal (Plate IV).

The form of a parchment book, or codex, would admit of the copying of several books in one volume. The great Bibles of the fourth and fifth centuries of which we know contained all the books; they formed one volume. So the internal unity running through the Bible as a whole came to be represented even in the outward form.

PLATE IV—ROLL AND BOOK

St. Luke the Evangelist copying from a roll into a book (codex form):
miniature from a Greek manuscript at the Vatican library (gr. 1158),

18

eleventh century.

The copying of the Bible went on rapidly, monks and noble Christian ladies undertaking it as a form of ascetic work, providing a heavenly merit and sometimes earning bread and butter, too. Instead of the plain copies in an unskilled hand we now find sumptuous books of the finest parchment with purple colouring, in the most luxurious manuscripts the sacred text being written in gold and silver, and the margin sometimes being covered with beautiful paintings. A copy of Genesis in Greek at the Vienna library has forty-eight water-colours, one at the bottom of each page, telling the same story as the text. The manuscript when complete must have had sixty folios: this gives one hundred and twenty of such decorated pages for Genesis, and if it contained the whole Pentateuch we may allow for five hundred and ten illustrations (Plate V). And this manuscript does not stand alone; it is but one of a large group of illuminated manuscripts. This sumptuous appearance may be taken as a sign of the value attached to the Bible. Persecuted hitherto, it became the ruler of the Christian empire, invested with all the glory of royalty.

The place given to the Bible is best shown by the fact that it presided over the great councils, a copy of the Bible lying upon the presidential chair. It was meant as a symbol for Christ himself taking the place of honour and deciding the great questions of faith. The same holds true for non-ecclesiastical assemblies. In an ordinance of the emperor Theodosius it is required that a copy of the Bible be present in every court-room. The Bible, or rather the Gospels, or to speak even more precisely the most prominent page in them, the beginning of the first chapter of St. John's Gospel, was used for taking an oath. The worn condition of this page in many a manuscript still attests this use.

Presiding over the courts, the Bible began at once to exercise its influence upon the Law. We can already trace this influence in the legislation of Constantine himself: when he forbids to brand a criminal on his face, giving as reason that the image of God ought not to be marred, it is the Biblical notion of the man's face being the likeness of God which underlies this law. When, in a law published in 334, he insists that no man, whoever he is and whatever rank he has, shall be admitted as a solitary witness unless supported by another witness, it is the well-known Biblical rule that at the mouth of two or three witnesses every word shall be established. When he makes divorce more difficult, denying the right of remarriage to the man who repudiates his wife without sufficient reason on her part, we feel that it is the injunction of Jesus which is behind this law. I would not say the same of all parts of this legislation which various scholars have adduced as proving Christian influence. Roman law from the second century was influenced to a large extent by the Stoa, all the famous lawyers such as Gaius and Paulus belonging to this school and introducing its ideas into the practice of the courts and into the legislation of the magistrates, especially of the emperor. There is an evident development in the Roman law toward a more humane conception of slavery; this is due to the Stoa. The views on marriage and divorce, the position of "natural children," as the Roman law calls illegitimates, all this is largely due to non-Christian influences. Nevertheless, there are unmistakable traces of a particular influence of the Bible upon the legislation of the Christian emperors, and this influence increases from decade to decade. Constantine gives a rather vague ordinance for keeping Sunday as a day on which courts are not to be held. Theodosius is much stricter; and the climax is reached with Justinian, when Sunday has become a legal holiday.

PLATE V—VIENNA GENESIS

The paradise: Adam and Eve appear three times: (1) under the tree of
knowledge, Gen. 3 : 6; (2) when discovering their nakedness, 3 : 7; (3)

when hiding themselves from the Lord among the trees, 3 : 8. The divine voice, represented by the hand from heaven, belongs to this third scene; it is put in the centre merely for artistic reasons.

From "Die Wiener Genesis." F. Tempsky, Vienna.

Justinian, of course, codifies the Roman law, but his Novellæ, the laws issued by himself, show the new spirit of a legislation ruled by the Bible. He sometimes refers directly to the Bible as authority. Still more is this spirit prevalent in some provincial codes. One of these says that everything has to be judged according to the ancient and to the modern law, i. e., the law of Moses, which antedates the laws of all other nations, and the law of Christ, as it is contained in the laws of the emperors Constantine, Theodosius, and Leo. Lawyers of this period indulge in comparisons between the Roman law and the law of Moses.

The Roman empire was Latin in some respects, Greek in others. Latin was the official language of the court, of the law, of the army. But the population spoke mostly Greek, though from the third century on large parts used their native language, Syriac and Coptic, as well. The Bible had been translated into these languages during the former period. Now the general political situation brings the empire into contact with the Goths in the North, with Armenians and Georgians in the East, with Libyans and Ethiopians in the South. As soon as the empire gains any influence among these neighbouring peoples, the Christian mission tries to get hold of them and we see the Bible translated into these languages, which hitherto have had no writing. The Bible marks for these peoples the beginning of a national literature. Their alphabets were made up from the Greek, thus showing that the reading of the Bible with these nations began in connection with their intercourse with the Roman empire.

The Bible ruled even the Greek language of this empire. There are many changes in the later Greek which are surely due to familiarity with the Bible. Words previously unknown in Greek or used in a different sense became quite familiar; everybody knows what is the meaning of Beelzebub, Messiah, Paradise, Satan, and that an angel is not a mere messenger, but is a messenger from God, a spiritual being, and that the word demon always means an unclean spirit.

Moreover, the Bible influenced the style of the writers, especially of the great preachers. One may distinguish three forms of influence in this department: artificial imitation; naïve use of Biblical names and phrases (what is usually called in Germany the language of Canaan); and, lastly, the unconscious influence which the style of any book exerts upon a careful reader. I do not think that there are many instances of artificial imitation in this period. Sometimes a preacher skilfully composed his whole sermon by adding Biblical quotation to quotation; asked to preach a sermon on a saint's day, he did nothing else than comment upon the saint's life in Biblical phrases. The second type of influence is very common; the present emperor is usually spoken of as the new David; the story of a war is always told as if David were fighting the Philistines; each heretic is entitled to be called the new Judas Iscariot who betrays his Lord. The most famous example of this kind is the sermon attributed to Chrysostom after his first return to Constantinople, when he had fled from the wrath of the empress: "Again Herodias is furious, again she flurries, again she dances, again she desires the Baptist's head to be cut off by Herod." The preacher's own Christian name, of course, was John, and the empress was trying to get rid of him for political reasons.

The most important influence, however, is the unconscious influence simply from the use of the Bible. The great power of Chrysostom's sermons was partly due to his eminent rhetorical talent and training. He knew how to gain his hearers' attention; yet for the greater part his thorough acquaintance with the Bible seems to be responsible. Reading the sermons of those great Greek Christian orators of the fourth century, we are often struck by the embedded quotations from the Bible. In the midst of this fluent Greek there is something quite different, something stern, something austere, something dignified and solemn, which immediately appeals to the hearer. As a matter of fact, the preachers themselves, proud as they were of their classical training, had rather the opposite impression; they apologise for introducing barbarous language. Chrysostom insists, in many a sermon, on the idea that the apostles were fishermen, unskilled in literary style, and that it is one of the proofs of inspiration that those men could write at all. He evidently is not aware of the fact, clear to us, that it is just the vigour and strength of Biblical language which gave to his own sermons their magnificent effect. He was filled with Biblical phraseology as was no other preacher of his time. He himself did not realise it, nor did, I presume, the greater part of his congregation, yet it was this which so impressed them. If only the modern editors would note all the Biblical allusions in his works! Yet they are hardly able even to recognise them. We find preachers noted for their brilliancy in extemporaneous speaking, and usually the remark is added, it was because the speaker knew the Scriptures by heart.

In this way the people became accustomed to Biblical phraseology, and we do not wonder that at last the colloquial Greek also was influenced by the Bible. We can trace its influence even in the romances.

The Bible ruled the home and the daily life; people had their furniture decorated with Biblical symbols; lamps showed Noah's ark or Jonah's whale, Jesus with his disciples in a ship or Jesus treading upon the lion and adder, the serpent and dragon (according to Psalm 91). At the Strassburg Museum there is a beautiful engraved glass cup made probably in a Roman manufactory in Cologne. On one side is engraved Abraham sacrificing Isaac, on the other side Moses striking water from the rock. Rich people wore sumptuous garments embroidered with representations of Biblical scenes. The preachers complain that these people wear the miracles of Christ on their coats instead of taking them to their heart and conscience.

The great officials of the empire used to give to their friends ivory tablets commemorating their honours. In former times they had represented on them the emperor, the empress, or their own portraits, and scenes from the circus; now they chose Biblical subjects. People liked to have long rolls exhibiting the wars and triumphs of an emperor in a continuous series of drawings. Two gigantic rolls of this kind may still be seen at Rome; I mean the columns of Trajan and of Marcus Aurelius. Christian art produced rolls of the same kind, exhibiting the story of Joshua's battles (Plate VI). Senators and noble ladies vied with each other in arranging the history of the Bible and especially the life of Jesus in the form of poems, each word of which was taken either from Homer or from Vergil. It is a wonderful mixture of Bible and classical culture.

PLATE VI—JOSHUA ROLL
(At the Vatican)

Joshua is sending from Jericho (at the left, walls tumbling down) to Ai two men to spy out the land, Joshua 7 : 2. The towns are represented by edifices as well as by allegorical figures (Tyche of the City).
From "Vatikanische Miniaturen," by St. Beissel. Copyright by B. Herder, Freiburg.

24

The Bible rules not only the public and the private life, but also the church and its organisations. At the beginning the Christians were afraid of comparing the Old Testament rites with the ecclesiastical institutions. The Law of the Old Testament belonged to an earlier form of religion; it was abolished by the New Testament. Christ, according to Saint Paul, was the end of the Law. But by and by the Old and the New Testament were brought nearer together. An author of the first century remarks that God by his commandments in the Old Testament has shown himself to be a lover of order, therefore in the Christian congregation, too, order ought to rule. He does not call the Christian communion a sacrifice, the Christian minister a priest; but his parallelism comes very near to this, and a century later the step is taken. It becomes usual to speak of bishop, elders, and deacons as high-priest, priests, and Levites. Later on, even the minor degrees were taken back to Biblical models: the subdeacon, lector, exorcist, acolyte, janitor were found represented in the Old Testament. The clergy formed a separate class as distinct from other people as the tribe of Levi was among the tribes of Israel. It was upon the authority of the Old Testament that they claimed rights and prerogatives to be given and guaranteed by the empire. The monks found their models in Elijah and Elisha; common life was represented by the apostles; penitents were Job, David, and the people of Nineveh; widows (as ecclesiastical functionaries) had their models in Naomi, Hannah, Tabitha, etc. The church was the tabernacle of Moses and the temple of Solomon, and each detail in the description of these Biblical buildings was made to agree with a feature in the Christian church by means of allegorical interpretation. The feasts of the church correspond to the feasts of the Old Testament; Easter is usually called Passover, and Whitsuntide Pentecost. At a rather early date a festival of the dedication of the individual church was introduced to correspond with the festival of the dedication of the temple. As the Jews kept two days in the week for fasting, so did the Christians, choosing Wednesday and Friday instead of Monday and Thursday; and in doing so they remembered that it was on a Wednesday that Jesus was betrayed by Judas and on a Friday that he died on the cross. Even the usual hours for prayers were based on Old Testament authority; David, saying in Psalm 141 : 2 "The lifting up of my hands as the evening sacrifice," means vespers, while in the 131st Psalm he is speaking of compline, in the 63d of matins. The vigil was observed as well as commanded by Christ himself (Luke 6 : 12 and 12 : 37). The whole liturgy was explained as being in every detail a representation of the life of Christ. The sacraments, too, were prefigured in the Old Testament. This symbolism is very old and very commonly used; it has influenced Christian art. We see Noah's ark as a symbol of baptism (*cf.* I Peter 3 : 20); Abel's sacrifice, and Melchisedek offering bread and wine to Abraham, as symbols of the holy eucharist. Abraham entertaining at his home the three angels reveals the holy Trinity. All this is represented in splendid mosaics on the walls of the churches, as for instance in San Vitale at Ravenna.

To us this system of Biblical references for everything in the Christian service seems strange. We feel that the worship of the Christian congregation rests on other principles than the ritual of the Old Testament and does not gain anything by such hazardous comparisons. It looks like comparing the stars in heaven with beasts on earth. But the fathers thought that this was the highest achievement at which they could arrive: to allegorise and spiritualise the Old Testament law in order to deduce from it the Christian liturgy. That was what they called worship in spirit and truth. It is exactly opposite to the great idea which Jesus conveyed in those words; it is one of the greatest confusions to which the juxtaposition of the Old and the New Testament in one Bible was leading. Nevertheless, it was of great influence upon civilisation for centuries.

The church and the laity were ruled by the Bible; but the real Bible folk of this time were the monks. There had been a tendency toward asceticism from the very beginning of Christianity. At the moment when the church came into power this tendency increased rapidly. In Egypt as well as in Syria, wherever there was a desert place hermits gathered and monasteries were built. Now, in these monasteries the life was really filled with the reading of the Bible. Even the poorest monk would have a copy of the Gospels to read. Some of the monks, of course, were very simple, unlearned people. They could not read, so they learned it all by heart. And sometimes—we are told in the legendary tales of the monks—it happened that a monk who never before had learned to read was miraculously given the art of reading, God granting it to him as a recompense for his zeal. The monks had their hours for common worship and reading, but they were supposed to read each by himself as much as possible. "The rising sun shall find the Bible in thy hands," is one of the monastic rules, and legend illustrates how the divine grace recompensed assiduous reading: filled with heavenly light all through the night was the cell of a hermit as long as he was reading the Bible. When visitors came the talk was over questions raised by the Bible. It was with quotations from the Bible that the celebrated anchorite entertained the people who called upon him to ask for spiritual help.

26

Among all Biblical books the Psalter was the one most favoured by the monks. They knew it by heart, almost all of them, and they used to recite it during their manual labour. The Psalter was their spiritual weapon against the temptations of the demons; the demon liked nothing so much as to turn a monk from reciting his Psalter. But besides the Psalter it was the Gospel which prevailed over all other books in these ascetic circles. Many of the hermits were induced to leave the world by attending a Gospel lesson in their church at home. "If thou wouldest be perfect, go, sell that thou hast and give to the poor, and thou shalt have treasure in heaven: and come follow me," or "And every one that hath left houses or brethren or sisters or father or mother or children or lands for my name's sake shall receive a hundredfold and shall inherit eternal life." These are the words which occur again and again in the lives of saints as the decisive ones for their "conversion," that is for leaving the world and going to the desert or entering a monastery. The first saying quoted above is referred to in the life of Saint Anthony, the greatest of all hermits, and Saint Augustine had this in his mind when the time came for him to change his life. The second saying makes Saint Hypatius go away from home; his biographer, however, is honest enough to add that the saint, a youth of eighteen, had just received punishment from his father. An actor living luxuriously with two concubines chances to enter a church, and hears read from the Gospel, "Repent ye, for the kingdom of heaven is at hand"; so he repents and becomes a monk. I do not mean to say that these tales of the monks are historical and trustworthy in every point, but I venture to think that this statement about the motives for conversion is, after all, a correct one. The gospel is what appeals to the human heart, in all centuries and in all nations. And then the man will try to make the gospel the rule of his life. I think it is remarkable that whereas the church and the empire both were ruled mainly by the Old Testament, these ascetic circles took the gospel as their main rule, that is to say, the gospel as understood by the men of that time. It was to them a new law, a law of asceticism, of self-denial, and they kept to it as strictly as possible. Even if for other Christians it meant an almost inaccessible ideal, the monastery ought to be the place to fulfil it literally.

Our picture would be inadequate, however, if we should neglect the abuse of the Bible, the Bible showing its importance and ruling force even by its influence upon the dark domain of human superstition. The ancient world was full of magic. We remember the story in Acts 19 of how Saint Paul overcame some Jewish exorcists, with the result that "not a few of them that practised curious arts brought their books together and burned them in the sight of all, and they counted the price of them and found it fifty thousand pieces of silver." I suspect many a scholar or librarian of to-day would like very much to have those books among his treasures, but they were burned; and

Christianity scored its first triumph over superstition. Superstition, however, did not give way at this first defeat; on the contrary, it made a strenuous effort to draw over all the forces of Christendom to its own side. There was the name of Jesus, frightening the demons; black magic took this name and converted it to its detestable uses. There was the Gospel, representative of Jesus himself in his heavenly power; superstition made it a vehicle of its own magical rites. There was the Bible, the book of divine oracles; human inquisitiveness turned it into a book from which to read the dark future. The heathen had done this with the poems of Homer and Vergil. Turning over the pages they suddenly stopped at a verse and then tried to find in this verse the answer to their question. The fathers of the early church detested this method as something quite alien to a Christian mind, but as early as the end of the fourth century people came to feel that it was all right if only they used the Bible for the same purpose. In the sixth century even church officials kept to this practice. When a bishop had to be elected they almost always consulted the Psalter first on behalf of the man to be elected. Bible verses written on parchment were attached to easy chairs in order to keep away the evil spirits. Gospels in the smallest form were hung on the necks of the babies. It is astonishing to see how great was the esteem in which the Bible was held and how terribly contrary to the spirit of the Bible this practice was, especially when the Bible was used to do harm. Lead, by its dull lustre, always has reminded mankind of the realm of death; so it was used in black magic for bringing upon an enemy a curse from the gods of the underworld. A rolled sheet of lead, inscribed with a psalm and a dreadful curse against any robber, has been found on one of the Ægean Islands hidden in the ground of a vineyard. Evidently the psalm was supposed to be one of the most effective spells. Even the Lord's Prayer and other parts of the Gospels have been abused in the same way (Plate VII). Nothing is so holy that it cannot be turned into a crime by human sin.

It is a dark page of human civilisation. I am afraid it is a large page, too. I could accumulate instance upon instance. But however interesting this might be, it would give a wrong impression. The Bible was not primarily used as a magical means in those centuries. It was acknowledged as something superhuman, bearing supernatural powers, and therefore ruling everything. It ruled the empire as well as the church. It influenced law, language, art, habits, and even magic.

PLATE VII—THE LORD'S PRAYER

On a potsherd found at Megara, sixth century; used probably as a spell.

From "Mitteilungen des K. Deutschen Archaeologischen Instituts," Athen.
Published by G. Reimer, Berlin.

III

THE BIBLE TEACHES THE
GERMAN NATIONS (500-800 A. D.)

From the fourth century on the Germans, tribe by tribe, crossed the Danube and the Rhine and entered the boundaries of the Roman empire. Here part of them settled near the frontier, part took service in the Roman army. But the more numerous they became, the more hostile they were. At last the Roman empire in the West broke down, German kingdoms taking its place. It is a long and cruel history, this period of "Völkerwanderungen" as it is usually called in German, the period of the great migrations. And only after some centuries did the new Roman empire of German nationality come to be established by Charlemagne.

At first the Germans made a brilliant start in taking over Roman civilisation. The Goths had been Christianised and civilised at an early period. While it is true that the Visigoths under Alaric captured Rome and did not refrain from plundering it, the behaviour of the Vandals under Gaiseric was even worse, so that for all time to come their name is connected with the most brutal pillage. But the noble tribe of the Ostrogoths under their celebrated king Theodoric—called Dietrich von Bern in the German songs—tried another plan; they adopted Roman civilisation as far as possible and endeavoured to combine both nations under one dominion. Theodoric had as his minister or secretary of state a member of the Roman nobility, the most cultivated man of letters of the time, Cassiodorus. We have his collection of reports and letters, and we may infer from them how much, aside from his training in the Roman law school, he was influenced by his Christian belief and Biblical reading. Later on, when he retired into the monastery which he had founded on his estates at Vivarium, all his devotion was given to the study of the Bible. He is the man who inculcated on Western monasticism that love for scholarship which has been ever since a characteristic of the Order of Saint Benedict. Cassiodorus was a Roman, of course, but we have ample evidence that even among the Goths the Bible was read and studied. There was a Gothic translation of the Bible, which is supposed to have been made in the fourth century by Ulfilas. In order not to encourage the warlike spirit in his people he is said to have omitted the books of the Kings, wherein so many wars and battles are described. The educational aspect of the Bible as teaching the German nations comes out here distinctly. We are able to trace the history of the Goths by their Bible, which, having been translated in the East from

Greek manuscripts, shows traces of a Latin influence, evidently introduced when the Goths settled in Italy. There still exist some copies, among them the famous Codex Argenteus, now at Upsala, which in its silver writing on purple ground, is a wonderful specimen of luxurious calligraphy, giving testimony to the degree of civilisation which these Ostrogoths had taken over from Rome (Plate VIII).

There was, however, one great difference between the Germans and the Romans; the latter were Catholics, the former Arians. This religious difference is responsible for many troubles and persecutions brought by the Germans upon the population of the conquered land. The Germans had a church organisation of their own; they had their own clergy, and this clergy was well trained in Bible reading. We find the remarkable fact that the German Arian bishops show an even larger knowledge of the Bible than their Roman Catholic colleagues. The complaint was often heard that the watchwords of Catholicism, as, for example, *homoûsios*, had no Biblical foundation, while, on the other hand, the Arians were always ready to fill their creeds with Biblical phrases. These Germans had a profound reverence for the holy Scripture and bowed down to it. It was only by Scriptural proofs that the Catholic clergy of Spain succeeded in converting the Arian king to their faith.

Theodoric built at Ravenna some churches which still exist. Here we see mosaics exhibiting the life of Jesus in a very simple way, but with that unmistakable touch of awe which is so characteristic of German piety. How different are the pictures which were added after Ravenna had become Byzantine! They are highly ceremonial, representing, among others, the emperor Justinian and the empress Theodora with all their suite.

PLATE VIII—GOTHIC BIBLE

Codex Argenteus, now at Upsala. Sixth century, written on purple parchment in
silver and (some words) in gold. The figures at the bottom give Eusebius's
harmony of the Gospels: this particular scheme is found in Syrian manuscripts and in the Old Latin Codex Rehdigerianus at Breslau.

From "Deutsche Kulturgeschichte," by O. Henne am Rhyn. Grote, Berlin,
Germany.

PLATE VIII—GOTHIC BIBLE

Codex Argenteus, now at Upsala. Sixth century, written on purple parchment
in silver and (some words) in gold. The figures at the bottom give
Eusebius's harmony of the Gospels: this particular scheme is found in

32

Syrian manuscripts and in the Old Latin Codex Rehdigerianus at Breslau.

From "Deutsche Kulturgeschichte," by O. Henne am Rhyn. Grote, Berlin, Germany.

These were the first centuries of German invasion. The ancient civilisation, championed by the Roman church, was still strong enough to impose itself upon these invaders. Time went on and civilisation more and more lost its energy. Especially in Gaul, in the kingdom of the Merovingians, intellectual darkness spread all over the country. There was no layman who could read, hardly any member of the clergy. We hear of great monasteries, which were rich royal foundations, where no complete Bible was to be found. We see the troubles of a missionary like Boniface. In order to procure the necessary books, he has to apply to his English lady friends, who send him copies of the books he wants, finely written by their own delicate hands. It was a time when a book, a Bible, was a treasure, and to own one was a fact to be recorded by a biographer. This enables us to trace the history of more than one famous manuscript. We are surprised to find what journeys they made. One was sent from Naples to England, and then a century later again removed to the German shore and finally treasured among the rarities of the Fulda library. Another manuscript, now at Florence, came originally from the monastery of Cassiodorus in the extreme south of Italy and found its way to the monastery of Mount Amiata, near Florence, only by a roundabout route through the famous English monasteries, where it was copied. The few scholars of that period had to go a long way before they could get a copy of the Bible worth their attention, and they had to go a long way to find a monastery with hands able to copy manuscripts.

A new epoch begins with Charlemagne, who has a real right to the name of the Great. If one wants to know a great man, one has only to see what attention he pays to minor things. It is simply wonderful how this German king, who restored the old notion of the Roman empire, whose dominion contained France, Germany, Spain, Italy, was taking care of the schoolboys and fixing his eyes on the way in which the Bible was being copied in the monasteries of his vast realm. In one of his ordinances he complains that they use unskilled boys for copying the most sacred book. It needs, he says, grammar—nay, good grammar—to understand what you are copying. It is no religion to pray to God in ungrammatical language and to have his holy Scriptures in a grammatically incorrect text. From the fact that the monasteries in their letters of application used a bad style he infers that Bible reading here was being neglected. Therefore, Charlemagne tried, in the first place, to bring the schools of his kingdom to a higher standard. Each monastery had to have a well-conducted school for the monks and for the young people who were sent there for education (as they are now sent to public schools). At his own court he had the *Schola palatina* and the great emperor himself went there often and took lessons together with the boys. But he did not stop here. His intention was to secure a really good, trustworthy text of the Bible. He therefore invited scholars from everywhere; even some Orientals are said to have shared in the work. The leading man, the chairman of the Committee for the revision of the Bible, as we should say at present, was Alcuin, a monk from England, who by his great learning had won the confidence of Charlemagne and was appointed by him abbot of the famous monastery of Tours. Here, at the school of Tours, most of the work of revision was done (Plate IX); through Alcuin's influence the revision was mainly based on the text current in England. That this was the best text available at that time is now generally acknowledged by all competent scholars. This was not so in Charlemagne's time; other scholars, Frankish bishops, disapproved of Alcuin's work. They thought the revision would have come out much better if conducted according to the text prevailing in Spain. So Theodulf, bishop of Orleans, issued a version of his own (Plate X). It is always instructive to see how men were the same in former times as they are now: scholars seldom agree one with another. The result was that henceforth two forms of the Latin Bible were used through the next centuries—in the North, Alcuin's revision, in the South, the revision made by Theodulf.

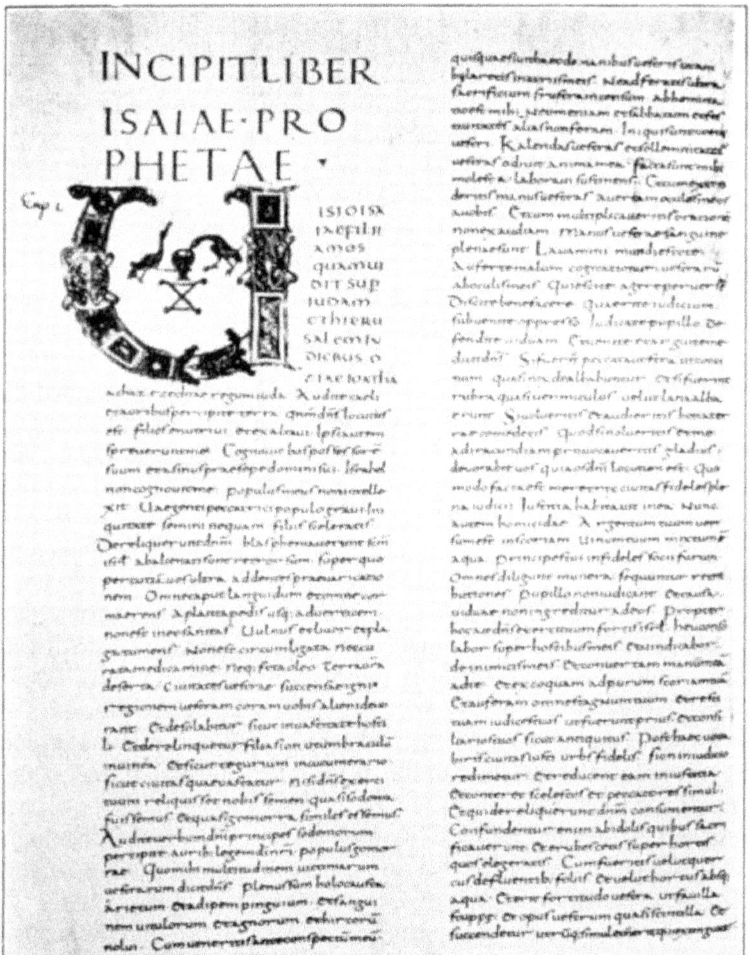

PLATE IX—ALCUIN'S BIBLE
(Brit. Mus. add. 10546)

Written at Tours, soon after Alcuin's death: a very good example of fine Carolingian minuscule. The lines are of equal length.

From F. G. Kenyon, "Fac-similes of Biblical Manuscripts." By permission of the Trustees of the British Museum.

PLATE IX—ALCUIN'S BIBLE

(Brit. Mus. add. 10546)

Written at Tours, soon after Alcuin's death: a very good example of fine

Charlemagne would not have cared so much for the text of the Bible had he not esteemed the Bible to be the one great text-book for his people. He himself was filled with Biblical notions. In his private circle, a club for promoting classical reading, he was called David. And it was, indeed, the Old Testament idea of the theocratic king which governed his mind. The king chosen by God and elected by the people, the king a representative of God and the head of the people, the king a valiant warrior and a royal psalmist at the same time, this was his ideal, in which old German notions were combined with Old Testament views. While revering the priest, he always felt himself superior even to the bishop of Rome. He willingly accepted the rôle of a defender, of a protector; he never would have accepted his crown from the hand of a priest. Nothing is so alien to Charlemagne as the later mediæval theory of the two swords, both given by God to Saint Peter, the one spiritual, kept by himself and his successors, the other worldly, given by them to the emperor. No, he had his sword from God directly, and his royalty included the power and the duty of looking after the church's affairs as well. The Bible tells of a king of Judah, called Josiah, who, on being informed that the book of the Law given by Moses and hidden for a long time had been rediscovered, forthwith ordered everything to be reformed and restored according to this law. That served as the model for Charlemagne's own ecclesiastical work. Being the king, he felt responsible for the purity of worship and of doctrine. Therefore, when the question arose in the East if worship was due to the pictures of Christ and the saints, and the bishop of Rome did not please him in his answer, Charlemagne himself, assisted by Alcuin and other theologians of his staff, wrote a treatise on the subject, which he himself thought to be decisive, the so-called *Libri Carolini*, a document of a rather Puritan character, showing the austere spirit of early Western theology. When in Spain a discussion began about the divine nature of Christ, he again interfered, sending his theologians to discuss the matter according to the true teaching of the Bible—as is said expressly in their instructions—and after they had decided he even took political measures against those whom he believed to be heretics. We can scarcely understand his attitude in those cases without keeping in mind that he felt himself a new David and a new Josiah.

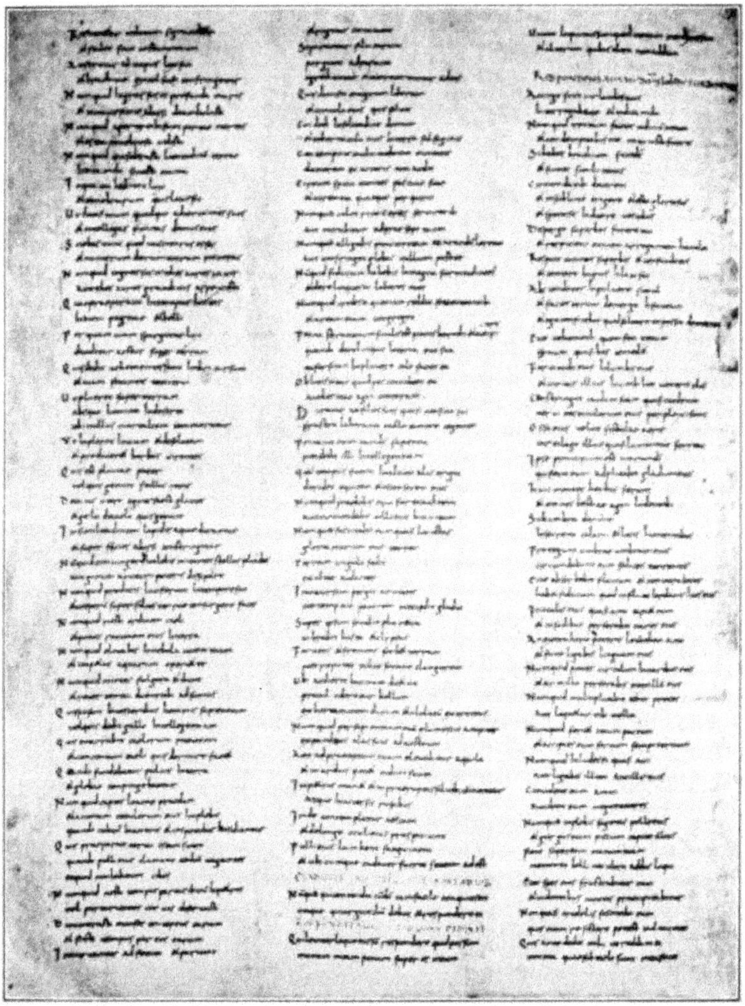

PLATE X—THEODULF'S BIBLE
(Brit. Mus. add. 24142)

Written in three columns like many Spanish manuscripts, and in lines of various length, "cata cola et commata," as St. Jerome says.

From "Fac-similes of Biblical Manuscripts." By permission of the Trustees of the British Museum.

PLATE X—THEODULF'S BIBLE

(Brit. Mus. add. 24142)

Written in three columns like many Spanish manuscripts, and in lines of various length, "cata cola et commata," as St. Jerome says.

Sometimes it is a true evangelical spirit which pervades his ordinances for the church. In a proclamation of 811 he says: "We will ask the clergy themselves, those who are not only to read the holy Scriptures by themselves but are to teach them to others also: who are those to whom the apostle says, Be my imitators? or who is the man of whom he says, No soldier on service entangleth himself with the affairs of this life?—or how to imitate the apostle and how to do service to God? What is it to leave the world? does it mean simply not to wear weapons and not to be married publicly? does it mean to enlarge one's property daily, oppress the poor and induce men to perjury?" Charlemagne is particularly strict about avoiding perjury, not only in the solemn form of public oath, which is taken on the holy Gospel or on the altar or on the relics of the saints, but in common conversation as well. He tries to introduce Matt. 5 : 16, "Even so let your light shine before men that they may see your good works and glorify your father which is in heaven," as the motto for every Christian's life. That is quite evangelical. But it is from the Old Testament that the tenor of his laws comes. They all have a strong mark of severity, in particular the so-called Saxon laws, which were imposed upon the Saxon tribes when after a very hard resistance they were finally defeated and subdued. Through this law runs, like a bloody thread, the frightful menace: *morte moriatur*, by death shall he die. This sounds harsh, but it is nothing else than the adaptation of a well-known Biblical phrase (Ex. 19 : 12; 21 : 12: "He shall surely be put to death," R. V.). That is an example of Biblical phraseology. But the Bible influenced the legislation of Charlemagne also in content. I choose three instances: in all three cases the work of Charlemagne was prepared for by church councils. Christianity had begun by voluntarily adopting Old Testament laws; then the church had made their observance compulsory; now Charlemagne gives to the ecclesiastical ordinances the sanction of the state and inflicts penalty upon trespassers. The first instance is Sunday; it was called the Lord's Day; from the sixth century synods and councils had tried to make the people keep this day in a more solemn fashion. They did not refer to the Old Testament commandment at first; they did not even demand that all manual work should be stopped. The frequent repetition of the decree seems to prove that it was rather unsuccessful even in this limited form. Now the government interferes, and its injunctions secure at once to the Lord's Day the strictest observance. It is remarkable that Charlemagne expressly refers to the Old Testament commandment. It is according to the Bible that the day was counted from sunset to sunset. This is the beginning of the Sabbatarian question in the West, the East preceding the

West, as we have seen, by about two centuries.

Our second instance is the tithe; it was to be paid, according to the Bible, by all the other tribes to the tribe of Levi, who served at the temple. Now Christians began to pay voluntarily a tithe to their priests, accommodating themselves to the Old Testament rule; but by and by the clergy derived from the Old Testament a right of asking for the tithe. The farmer had to pay his tithe to his parish priest. Charlemagne proclaimed this as a law of his kingdom, referring expressly to God's commandments.

The third instance is given in the prohibition against taking interest. It is said in Deut. 23 : 19: "Thou shalt not lend upon usury to thy brother." Ecclesiastical authorities took this as forbidding to take any interest in lending money, and they tried to impress this prohibition upon the minds of the Christian people. Here, again, Charlemagne gave his sanction to this ecclesiastical view and made the prohibition against taking interest a part of the public law. It is obvious that the economic life of the nation was deeply influenced by this compulsory adoption of Old Testament laws.

Justice, with the Germans, was to a large extent exercised by means of the ordeals. We scarcely realise the importance these proceedings had at that time. People believed in a divine power bringing out guilt and innocence by means of these curious trials. It was but natural that the Bible, representing the divine oracles, should be present at the ceremony, that both parties should revere and kiss it. But people did more; they made the Bible itself a means of deciding between guilty and innocent. They had a particular kind of ordeal which they called determining by means of the Gospels, and another which was called the ordeal of the Psalter, a copy of the Psalter being swung over the head of the suspected person.

I have referred to the palace school. This had its continuation in a graduate school, if we may so call a Bible circle among the theologians attending the court. These theologians, headed by Alcuin himself, were first-rate Bible scholars. They knew great parts of the Bible by heart; they had read all accessible commentaries of the fathers. They had ideas of their own, too, but they were traditionalists to such an extent that they would not say anything of their own unless it was said and supported by the fathers. When asked to write brief commentaries on Biblical books, because the patristic commentaries were too large and comprehensive for the students of this time, they simply gave extracts from the fathers and carefully avoided adding anything of their own. One went so far as to take even the connecting words from the works of Saint Augustine; another, whose mental energy was too strong to keep him within the boundaries of pure traditionalism, excuses himself whenever he introduces an interpretation of his own.

In these studies the ladies and gentlemen of the court took part. It is very interesting and often amusing to see what kind of questions they bring before Alcuin as the great oracle of learning. One lady reading her Psalter was puzzled by the words in Psalm 116, "All men are liars." How can babies be liars before they begin to speak, or dumb men? "The sun shall not smite thee by day nor the moon by night" (Psalm 121 : 6) seemed to be incompatible with the fact that the moon never burns. A scholar who had come from Greece troubled the court by putting the question: To whom was paid the price with which we were bought according to I Cor. 6 : 20; 7 : 23. Charlemagne himself has other questions. He is troubled by finding that the hymn sung by Christ and his disciples after the Last Supper has not been recorded by any of the Gospels. I wonder if he really was satisfied by Alcuin's answer. After a very learned explanation of the term hymn, Alcuin gives, first, three views of different interpreters: (1) That there was no special hymn, only a general praisegiving; (2) that they had sung the twenty-second Psalm; (3) that it was some Jewish prayer. Then he proceeds to establish his own solution: that it is, in fact, the prayer of Jesus, recorded in John 17, which was meant by the word hymn here. Incidentally, he makes some important remarks upon the harmony of the Gospels: "Although we see in the Gospels some things told similarly, others in a different way, we nevertheless believe that everything is true." That was the leading idea for the criticism of the fathers, and it was the same for nearly all the mediæval centuries. Historical criticism, directed upon the Gospels, would have seemed to show intolerable lack of piety or certain evidence of heretical views.

Theological thinking does not go beyond the limits of Biblical doctrine. Scarcely one or two men dare to think in their own way or speculate on such problems as darkness and nothing (that is, what was before the creation) or on the nature of miracle. There was hardly any attempt at scientific theories. And the best men, indeed, as, for instance, Alcuin, were proud of basing their theology entirely on Biblical ideas.

―――――――

The one great event in the expansion of Christianity among the German nations is the mission of Saint Augustine to England. When Pope Gregory found some Anglo-Saxon youths at the slave market of Rome and perceived that in the North there was still a pagan nation to be baptised, he sent one of his monks to England, and this monk, who was Saint Augustine, took with him the Bible and introduced it to the Anglo-Saxons, and one of his followers brought with him from Rome pictures showing the Biblical history, and decorated the walls of the church in the monastery of Wearmouth. We do not enter here into the difficult question of the relations between this newly founded Anglo-Saxon church and the old Iro-Scottish church. Differences of Bible text had something to do with the pitiful struggles which arose between the churches and ended in the devastation of the older one. The one point which interests us here is the fact that both Iro-Scottish and Anglo-Saxon monks were driven into missionary work by the Bible. When, in the service, they heard read from the Old Testament or from the epistle to the Hebrews that Abraham and the patriarchs had all left their home, their parents, their native country, and had gone to a foreign land which they did not know, simply in order to please God, then they felt bound to do the same. When at the mass the Gospel was read, "And every one that hath left houses or brethren or sisters or father or mother or children or lands for my name's sake, shall receive a hundredfold and shall inherit eternal life," then they hurried away, not knowing where to go, looking only for a far-distant and desert place. It was this ascetic view of the Bible which drove the Iro-Scottish monks over the sea to France, Italy, Germany, which made them preach the gospel to the Germans who had not yet heard of it. It was this same motive which caused Willibrord and Boniface to cross the North Sea and come to preach among the Frisians and Saxons. Boniface is said to have received the deadly stroke from a pagan while holding his Bible over his head. They still show the copy at Fulda.

Again, it was the Bible which determined Charlemagne to use force against the Saxons in order to bring them to baptism and Christian faith. Saint Augustine had discovered the passage in the Lord's parable of the great supper, where the servant is told to go out into the highways and hedges and "constrain" them to come in. This *coge intrare*, he explained, might excuse the using of secular power for the purpose of bringing heretics back to the church or of causing pagans to join the church. Charlemagne knew no better than to suppose that this was the true meaning of the saying of our Lord, and so he felt in conscience bound to use military force and the full strength of the law in christianising the Saxons.

But it was the Bible itself and not Charlemagne's sharp sword and his cruel law which brought over the wild Saxon tribes into Christendom. They had among themselves a poet who had the gift of singing the gospel into their hearts. Charlemagne himself was fond of the national songs; he loved his German language as much as he esteemed Latin. He was convinced that a man ought to pray to God in his native tongue. There are not only three sacred languages, he says, in which to pray and to praise God—Hebrew, Greek, Latin—you may praise him in your German as well. Therefore he arranged that a priest should translate the Biblical lessons and the sermon to the people who did not understand Latin. He would probably have approved a German translation of the Bible; but the clergy were not prepared to do this. They took Latin as the basis of civilisation, and only a few of them had any regard for the uncultivated people. There are preserved some few attempts at translating parts of the Bible into German; they attest what might have come out of this Carolingian movement if the bigotry and narrowness of Charlemagne's son Louis had not stopped it. Among the Saxons a fresh and vigorous spirit was still alive. Having been introduced to Christianity by brute force of war, they embraced the gospel, trying to make it their own by putting it into the form of their national song. We do not know the name of the poet; he seems to have been a clergyman, instructed in the best commentaries of his time, such as were available at the monastery of Fulda. For the framework he used a Gospel harmony which is contained in the famous Codex Fuldensis of the Vulgate, originating at Capua (in south Italy) and brought probably by Boniface himself from England to Fulda. This Gospel harmony he translated freely into some six thousand Saxon verses. His poem is one of the finest assimilations of the Gospel history to national German feeling, to be compared only with Dürer's engravings and Eduard von Gebhardt's paintings. Christ is the heavenly king; the apostles are his loyal kinsmen; he wanders with them through the Saxon wood; he stops at a native spring; all Oriental character has gone, but the gospel has lost nothing. It is as fresh and as real as it ever had been. The fact our author detests most is Christ's betrayal by one of his own men; nothing is so bad as this according to the German mind. Christ on the cross is not suffering; he dies as a victorious warrior. When he says, "I thirst," he expresses by this the fact that he is thirsting after the souls of men, to bring them into paradise. It is wonderful how the gospel has penetrated the German soul in order to produce a harmony like this.

This "Heliand" by the anonymous Saxon poet we shall admire even more if we compare it with the other attempt at bringing the life of Christ into German poesy. It is by Otfried of Strassburg, whose "Christ" is a very learned elaboration, partly in German, partly in Latin, therefore undoubtedly much preferred in the literary circles of that time, but infinitely inferior to the "Heliand" in freshness and popular quality.

It is remarkable that there is something similar to the "Heliand" in the Anglo-Saxon poem, the "Genesis." The theory has been successfully started and proved by later discoveries that both have the same origin. The Saxons of Germany and the Saxons of England were not so far away one from the other that they could not have intercourse and exchange (Plate XI).

However this may be, it is evident that the Bible had an influence in teaching the German nations from the beginning, and that the new civilisation which was to be built would have the Bible as one of its foundations.

PLATE XI—LINDISFARNE GOSPELS

(Brit. Mus. Cotton: Nero D IV.)

Written about 690 in honour of St. Cuthbert († 687), in English round style.

The interlinear version was added two hundred and fifty years later— remark in the midst of the left-hand column the words: *xpi* (=Christi) *evangelium* with *Cristes godspell* above it.

From "Fac-similes of Biblical Manuscripts." By permission of the Trustees of the British Museum.

IV

THE BIBLE BECOMES ONE BASIS
OF MEDIÆVAL CIVILISATION
(800-1150 A. D.)

The Middle Ages, the dark Middle Ages, that is what we are wont to call the period we now enter in our journey through the centuries. Scholars of the sixteenth century called it so, when they looked back to the classical period, from which they drew all their light and inspiration. The centuries between counted for nothing; they seemed to be barbarous, uneducated; the humanistic scholar would simply drop them out of the world's history. Time passed and men became enthusiastic about the beauties of these Middle Ages. At the beginning of the nineteenth century Europe was enchanted by romanticism. Nothing was fashionable that was not mediæval in art, customs, manners. At present we view these centuries more calmly in the light of their own time; we see what was their defect, and we see at the same time what was their merit. It is true that civilisation had only begun to recover from the shock which the great migrations had given to it. If a chronicler thinks it worth while to mention that the emperor Henry IV was able to read to himself the petitions brought before him, we must infer that the art of reading was not wide-spread, even among the nobility. And the famous poet Wolfram von Eschenbach tells us himself that he was no friend of this art. On the other hand, I need only remind my readers of the beautiful buildings we still admire at Cologne: the massive old church of Saint Gereon in Romanesque style and the light and airy cathedral, whose Gothic arches and spires reach up toward heaven—to mention only these two well-known examples—in order to make them realise the power and the splendour of this civilisation, which never will cease to impress the human mind. We cannot drop this period from our history; nor can Americans deny that this mediæval civilisation is an element even in their modern civilisation.

There is an ingenious theory that history always repeats itself: the German migrations corresponded to the migrations of the Greek tribes; the time of chivalry was like the time of Homer's heroes; humanism represents the age of Plato and Aristotle; only the repetition always has the advantage of using the results of the former cycle. But we must not forget that from time to time new forces enter those cycles and change their relation. At the end of the classical period Christianity has come in and now runs as a straight line through the parallel cycles; therefore nothing in this parallelism is quite exact.

It was the Christian church which served to keep the old civilisation alive through all troubles and dangers. When classical training had nearly vanished everywhere else, it was found in some remote monasteries. Esteem of good style, love of ancient poetry, some chance bits of philosophy had safely weathered the storm. But it was only in combination with the Bible that those remains of classical reading were allowed to persist. The mediæval civilisation was Biblical at its base.

Saint Jerome, who was a great admirer of classical eloquence but a stern defender of pure Christianity, tells in a friendly letter to a certain lady a sad experience of his own. He had read much of Vergil and Cicero and other pagan books, when one night he found himself suddenly summoned before the heavenly judge. "Who are you?" he was questioned. "I am a Christian," he replied. "Thou liest, thou art a Ciceronian," was the judge's answer. And forthwith he was given over to cruel constables, who beat him frightfully until he promised never to touch a pagan book again. When he awoke in the morning he still felt the blows. The story is mere fancy, and Saint Jerome never proves so guilty of imitating his adored classical models as in this very letter. He was an actor who knew how to pose. But by this letter he has caused plenty of people in later time to dream over again the frightful experience he describes so suggestively. Dozens of monks and nuns have felt blows struck upon them by invisible hands for having given themselves too much to the seduction of reading classical books instead of the Bible. Again and again the leaders of monastic institutions had to insist upon the rule that the Bible must be read and no pagan books. Hrotswitha of Gandersheim, the nun who celebrated the great acts of the emperor Otto I, wrote some Biblical comedies, in order to prevent the nuns from enjoying the comedies of Plautus and Terence.

PLATE XII—BYZANTINE MINIATURE

(Psalter, Paris B. N. gr. 139)

David, playing harp while watching his sheep, looks like Orpheus in Greek
art. The female figure at the left represents Melody, while at the right-
hand corner Echo, also personified, is listening behind a pillar. The man
in the cave to the right is Mount Bethlehem.

47

On the other hand, all the great fathers of the church insisted upon classical training; so did Saint Jerome himself and Saint Augustine, not to speak of the great classical scholars in Christian bishoprics in the East (Plate XII). And even in the later centuries, when classical civilisation had gone and was only kept up artificially by assiduous reading, it was the church which maintained the right and the necessity of a classical training for its clergy. Alcuin was proud of the classical training he had had at home, at the famous monastic school of York under the direction of Abbot Ælbert. He enjoyed finding kernels of truth in the writings of the heathen, and he pointed out that Saint Paul had done the same. There was a time when there was no reading at all outside the clergy and the monasteries, but this reading was a combination of classical and Biblical. That is the great merit of the mediæval church.

Mediæval civilisation had various foundations, but the Bible was one of them, and the most important one. That is what we find wherever we try to analyse mediæval culture.

What was the aspect of the world at this period? The world seemed to be an edifice of three floors. Above was the heaven, a compact dome, in which the stars were fixed, while the planets moved in their own sphere; over the sky was the space where God or, let us say, according to the usual expression of that time, the holy Trinity dwells, surrounded and adored by millions upon millions of angels, who keep heaven and earth in continuous communication. Besides, the heaven can be rent asunder; then the angels look down to earth, and from time to time a pious man is allowed to enter and see the heavenly mysteries and the glory of the saints. The earth, the abode of man, is a large round plane; its centre Jerusalem, where, at the same place, Adam was buried and Christ was crucified, so that the blood of the Saviour dropping down reached Adam's skull. The earth was surrounded by the ocean. At its boundaries all kinds of strange beings—men with dogs' faces, giants, pygmies—were to be found. There was still an earthly paradise—not to be confounded with the paradise in heaven, the goal of human longing. This earthly paradise was unknown and inaccessible to the greater part of men, but from time to time a pious hermit or a favourite of fortune reached it; the lucky man on his return had exciting stories to tell about the wealth and the bliss of this paradise, but he never could find the way again. I have read an accurate description of the way from paradise to Rome, giving the exact number of days and months, but there was nothing said about how to come from Rome to paradise!

Below the earth was the great dark cellar called hell; here the devil was at home with his companions. But these demons did not like their abode; they preferred to roam the earth and play jokes on men and women. As the angels from above were kind and helpful to man, so the devils were cunning and malicious. But many a time the devil showed himself stupid; a clever boy might easily cheat him. The devil's aim was to capture the frivolous and to seduce the pious in order to bring them all into hell. Here the various categories of sinners had their separate compartments, where they were punished according to the varying nature of their sins. Mediæval writers describe these various tortures, and they know more about the geography of hell than they usually know about the geography of the earth.

Now, according to the view of that time this is all Biblical. A modern reader would find difficulties in looking for it in his Bible; but he will recognise some of the motives as clearly Biblical. Further investigation will show him that other notions are brought in from the late classical philosophy, and finally he will discover a large amount of folk-lore, German folk-lore. All this mingled together made a very curious combination, and the most curious point was that this combination was regarded as Biblical. It was upon the authority of the Bible that the church accepted this whole view of the world and put it before the people, judging all doubts and divergences from its teaching as intolerable heresy. It is this naïve way of reading between the lines, this allegorical method of making the Bible say what it does not say, which we have already found in the Greek fathers of the fourth century when, in commenting upon the *hexaëmeron*, the six days' work of creation, they introduced whatever they had read about the world and nature in the works of Plato and Aristotle. In the time of which we are speaking these great Greek philosophers were known only indirectly, but nevertheless they exercised much influence through later imitators. Boëthius was the one great authority of this time, besides the Bible.

The Bible's influence is still more evident if we turn to the mediæval view of history. What was history? People at this time had few notions about what was happening in the world; there were no means of communication, nor had they a conception of history as a coherent series of events in which each link is the effect of what precedes as well as the cause of what comes after. They simply registered the facts which chance made known to them. The chronicle is the form of record which prevails at this period. There was no history of the world; what passed for such was the history of the Jewish people as given in the Bible and the history of the Christian church as recorded by certain chronicles. Both together made up the history of mankind. The first part, the history of the Old Testament, was not regarded as the history of the Jews, but as the history of the people of God; it was the history of our fathers the patriarchs, the history of the first covenant finding its direct continuation in the history of the new covenant and the Christian church. There was only a

49

very slight conception of chronology; everything was arranged according to the system of a week, the duration of the present world corresponding to one week, whose days, according to the 90th Psalm, each counted a thousand years. The world was not expected to endure beyond six thousand years, the seventh day being reserved for the millennium. Into this history of the world a few fragments of Greek and Roman history found their way by means of an odd synchronism: David was said to have been a contemporary of the Trojan War, and a correspondence was invented between the king of Troy and the king of Israel, in which the latter excuses himself for not coming to join the Trojan army. It was in the beginning of the twelfth century that a famous professor of the university of Paris called Petrus Comestor wrote his *Historia Scholastica*, which for all the Middle Ages served as the text-book of Biblical history.

But, like the mediæval aspect of the world, so the history of the world was not purely Biblical. The Bible always had to suffer the strong rivalry of apocryphal and legendary fiction. Already the Jews had invented a life of Adam, full of miraculous events, which appealed to the taste of the average man much more than the simple and severe story of the Bible itself; the lives of Abraham, of Moses, of Solomon were enriched in the same way. Christianity continued this kind of fancy. The story of the holy root was traced back into paradise; it was a branch from the tree of life, given to Adam's son Seth and planted by him on his father's tomb. It had been used as a bridge over the Kidron until the queen of Sheba arrived at Jerusalem. Being a prophetess, she worshipped this holy root; consequently Solomon tried to use it in his temple, but the carpenter did not succeed in cutting it to the necessary length; therefore it lay unused, "rejected by the builders," until the time came when a tree was wanted to crucify Jesus; so Jesus died—on the cross which was the tree of life—a splendid symbolism, indeed, but set forth in a strange legend. Or they investigated the earlier history of the thirty pieces of silver given to Judas Iscariot as the reward for the betrayal of his master, tracing the money back as far as Abraham. The life of Christ was surrounded by apocryphal legends of all kinds: the story of his birth and of his childhood; his stay in Egypt; how in their flight lions and all kinds of wild beasts accompanied the holy family; how a palm-tree bowed down before them in order to provide them with its fruits; how at Jesus' arrival in Egypt all the idols of the Egyptians fell down; how he helped his father Joseph in his carpenter shop; and so on. Again the miracles at his death, the descent to hell, the resurrection and ascension, everything was covered with an abundance of miraculous narratives, partly enlargements, developments of the canonical accounts, partly mere fiction. In addition to this apocryphal life of Jesus there is the life of the Virgin, giving a most curious description of her birth and childhood and again of her death, making every detail parallel to the life of Christ himself and yet keeping hers subordinate. The mediæval life of Christ begins—one may say—with the birth of Mary (or with the story of her parents, Joachim and Anna) and ends with the death and assumption of Mary. The history of the apostles as read in this period is nearly all apocryphal except the few data taken from the canonical book of Acts. Then the history of Christianity is continued as the history of the church according to the scheme of Saint Augustine's *De civitate dei* (the City of God): the church is the city of God and beside it is the city of this age, the kingdom of this world, the one spiritual, the other secular, with two parallel lines of development. This is best shown by the mural decoration in Charlemagne's palace at Ingelheim on the Rhine, where two series of pictures, one giving the Biblical history according to the Old and New Testaments, the other tracing the profane history from Ninus, king of Babylon, down to Charlemagne himself, were painted on opposite walls. That is the mediæval view of history. We may add that, according to this view, history begins in heaven when the holy Trinity conceives the idea of creation, and ends in heaven at the last judgment. Our view of history is a different one, but we cannot help agreeing that this is a magnificent conception and that it is Biblical, too, in its main points.

It is partly built upon the Apocrypha, of course. Regarding these Apocrypha the attitude of the church changed a good deal during our period. The early view is set forth in several utterances from the Roman bishops of the fifth and sixth centuries, and is represented in its sharpest form in the so-called decree of Pope Gelasius, which condemns all Apocrypha as heretical writings totally to be rejected and detested and not to be used in any way by a Catholic Christian. We found this Puritan view prevailing in Charlemagne's *Libri Carolini*. It is predominant among the theologians of the Carolingian time. They scarcely use apocryphal books, and when they do they always refer to them as to doubtful books devoid of all authority. But gradually the Apocrypha came into favour; they are used freely alongside the canonical books. They are very much of the same kind as the legends of the saints; and those legends of the saints are favoured by the people, too. At last, in the thirteenth century, even theologians do not distinguish between canonical and apocryphal books. They quote the Gospel of Nicodemus alongside the Gospel of Matthew or of John; they call it the fifth Gospel and have it copied in their Bible manuscripts. So they have a letter from Saint Paul to the Laodiceans and other Apocrypha inserted in or attached to the Bible. And the common people were fond of these Apocrypha and delighted to hear the preacher quote them because the bizarre miracles appealed to their taste.

There was almost no science, no medicine in this time; the world seemed to be full of miracles having no rational connection with one another. There was no causality, no law of nature. This was exactly the same view that we have in most parts of the Bible. Therefore people did not feel any difficulty in identifying their own notions about miracle and nature with the Biblical ones. Nay, we may say that many of the legendary miracle stories are copied after Biblical patterns. Even the wording is often modelled according to Biblical phraseology. "Healing all manner of disease and all manner of sickness," from Matt. 9 : 35, is repeated in many a saint's life.

Bible history in the embellished form which we have just now observed inspired mediæval art. In the first place, there were the inner walls of the churches, usually painted from top to bottom. If we remember that a Romanesque church had only very small windows, we understand what a large space was given to painting. Pictures are the text-book for those who cannot read; so Pope Gregory the Great had said, and this dictum was repeated many a time. It is true, of course. These plain mural paintings, awkward as they often are, make a greater impression on a simple mind than even the best written account could produce. The art is nothing but illustration; the painter tries to bring before the people who view his work the main features of the Biblical text. One must, indeed, know the text in order to understand the pictures. Sometimes the spectator is helped by additional inscriptions. To the illiterates these may be read and explained by the priest; and then even the simplest peasant will understand and always remember the story. Some churches were decorated in this way twice or even oftener, the first painting being covered with lime and whitewashed and then another painting being put upon it, according to the style of the later time. Here, again, we see the Biblical history, pure and plain at the beginning, but by and by combined with motives taken from the apocryphal sources and the lives of the saints. At the annunciation the angel meets the Virgin Mary at a well; it is to his mother Mary that the risen Christ appears before he reveals himself to his disciples.

In the Gothic period sculpture is more favoured, the walls being broken up into groups of columns and large windows. This arrangement lent itself more to the representation of individual figures of saints; but even so Biblical personalities, and sometimes even Biblical scenes, were chosen, and the large windows, with their stained glass, offered another possibility for decoration based on Bible stories. Besides, the whole building is directed by a scheme of Biblical symbolism difficult for us to understand but dear to the men of that period. They loved symbolism. The cult of the Virgin Mary was surrounded by it. She was the queen of heaven, she was paradise, she was the tower, she was the unicorn, she was the well, and so on, and all these symbols were taken from or related to the Bible.

The growing wealth and the higher standard of civilisation created a new demand for illuminated manuscripts. The artists of this period did not follow the classical scheme of filling the lower margin with representations in water-colour; they put little pictures, framed like those on the walls, into the text itself, or they decorated the initials of each book or chapter (Plate XIII). In turning over the pages we admire the skill of these artists, their simplicity, and sometimes their sense of humour. We seldom recognise what an amount of reading and interpretation of the Bible is contained in these little pictures; and how, on the other hand, they helped and stimulated Bible reading. We are told of King Charles V of France (1364-80), that he read the Bible all through once a year during his reign. This means a period of sixteen years. We are quite sure that he had a beautifully illuminated copy, and we may assume that the pictures helped him in performing this religious exercise.

Plate XIII—ENGLISH MINIATURE
(Latin Bible, Brit. Mus. Royal I D I)

Written in England, early thirteenth century. Initial I, Gen. 1 : 1, shows creation, fall, and redemption.

The three upper little compartments give each of them the work of two days: Christ is the creator; the fourth brings the seventh day's rest: Christ on the throne; the next three compartments contain the story of Adam and Eve: temptation, expulsion, and their working under the curse; the eighth compartment shows the Redemption as prophesied in Gen. 3 : 15.

The grotesque little figures are a beautiful illustration of mediæval sense of humour.

From "Fac-similes of Biblical Manuscripts." By permission of the Trustees of the British Museum.

Plate XIII—ENGLISH MINIATURE
(Latin Bible, Brit. Mus. Royal I D I)

From "Fac-similes of Biblical Manuscripts." By permission of the Trustees of the British Museum.

The art of painting is often accompanied by the art of making verses, as I would rather call this mediæval poesy. And again it is the Bible or, to speak more accurately, the Biblical history which finds its expression in this art. Besides the inscriptions added to the pictures and often given in versified form, there are a number of rhymed Bibles, as these versifications of the Biblical history are called. There are short verses giving the content of each book or chapter of the Bible for mnemonic purposes. There are some real poems, too, dealing with Biblical subjects.

————

The Bible and mediæval art brings before us another feature of civilisation, which is important, indeed, in our own time and which one would scarcely think of as originating with the Bible. I mean the theatre. The old classical drama and comedy had entirely died out. Plautus and Terence were read in the monasteries, not played, and so were the Biblical comedies by Hrotswitha, of which we have spoken, intended to be read only, not played. There was nothing but jugglers, jesters, and dancers. On festival days people amused themselves by frivolous masquerades, which were looked upon by the church authorities with suspicion and contempt as survivals of heathen rites and therefore to be frowned upon and abolished. Things took quite a different turn when some of the clergy began at Christmas and at Easter to present the sacred story in acted form in order to illustrate the lesson. They did it inside the church, directly before the altar. It was nothing but a dialogue, developed out of the lessons from the Scripture, the angel addressing Mary, the shepherds coming to see the child, the three Marys at the tomb and the angel speaking to them, and so on, as simply and plainly as it was told in the Bible and as it was usually painted on the walls of the church. The people took delight in these representations and they were soon enlarged. They had to be removed from the choir to the front of the church, the steps of the entrance forming the stage. Soon more and more persons appeared on the stage; the laity joined the performers; the guilds (the trade-unions) undertook the performance of the play, and out of these naïve little representations of the birth of Christ or his passion and resurrection sprang gorgeous miracle-plays which sometimes lasted four days and brought the whole story from the creation to the last judgment before the bewildered eyes of the spectators.

Nothing could make the Biblical history so familiar to the people as these plays, in which hundreds took part as performers and thousands attended as onlookers. There was but little art. They had no scenery; the actors simply moved about in the open space. But it was highly realistic. We are told that they nearly killed the man who was acting Judas Iscariot. It was also amusing. Mediæval piety did not refrain from putting in just before the crucifixion a sarcastic dialogue between the blacksmith, who had to provide the nails, and his wife, ending in a scuffle between them. People liked to see this. It was on account of these undignified scenes, which kept increasing, that the plays were abolished by secular and ecclesiastical authorities in the sixteenth and seventeenth centuries, when through humanism and the Reformation taste and piety had been refined. There are still a few survivals, such as the Passion Play of Oberammergau, which, however, has undergone a thorough change. There is now a revival of these popular plays, but I doubt if it will be successful. Possibly the film will take the place, as it has entered some churches already.

Men nearly always like to travel and the Germans liked it exceedingly well. This tendency received a special direction from the Bible; there were so many sacred sites in Palestine which a Christian wanted to see. So since the fourth century we see many people from the West—from Gaul, Spain, later on from Germany and England—travelling to the Holy Land in order to visit all the places connected with the sacred history of the Bible. At the end of the eleventh century the pilgrims suddenly turned into crusaders, sailing by thousands, fighting, settling down for a while, going back again. Then after a period of nearly two centuries of vain struggle for the possession of the Holy Land they changed again into pilgrims. Meanwhile, the Holy Land had changed also, and Christian piety, too. They were now not so much interested in visiting the sacred sites themselves as in gaining the indulgences which were granted in abundance to the visitors to each of these places. We still possess a long series of descriptions of these pilgrimages, increasing from century to century not only in number but also in size. The pilgrims did not rest until they had fixed upon a certain location in Palestine for every event in the Bible. Sometimes we seem to catch the process of fixation. The hermit or monk who served as guide had just told the company everything he himself knew about the resurrection of Lazarus. Then suddenly some one broke in with the question, "And where was it that Jesus met Martha?" and the poor hermit would be sure to show him a rock or a doorway, of which he had never thought before. They showed the pilgrims the place where Abraham and Melchisedek met, the tomb of Rachel, the monastery of Elijah on Mount Carmel. They would show also the mantle Elijah left to Elisha or the widow's cruse of oil which was always full. At Nazareth one could see the rock from which the citizens tried to throw down Jesus headlong, and one could see on the rock the imprint of his body, which he left there—according to a legendary addition to the story—when passing through the crowd unhurt. On the Mount of Olives was the Chapel of the Ascension. Here the pilgrims could see and worship the footprints made by Jesus when he leaped up toward heaven. Nay, we are told that people used to carry away dust from this place to use for charms, and yet the footprints never disappeared. I am giving these examples in order to show how even here sacred history and legend were mixed together. It is obvious, however, from what I have said that the pilgrimages contributed a great deal to make people familiar with the Bible stories; for not only the pilgrims themselves but all their people at home were mightily interested in what they had seen and heard in the Holy Land. We see them build churches representing the Holy Sepulchre. In the later centuries they make calvaries and stations on the way to them, representing the main points on Jesus' way to the cross, on the so-called Via Dolorosa at Jerusalem. There is even (as I have pointed out in my book on *Christusbilder*) a mutual influence between the pilgrimages and the passion plays, which accounts for some changes in the order of scenes and the fixing of places at Jerusalem.

The Bible continued to exercise its influence upon the Law. As King Alfred of England when collecting the laws of his people put the ten commandments at the beginning, so likewise the German collections, *Schwabenspiegel*, *Sachsenspiegel*, and so on, have prefaces which present the national law as an emanation from the law of God as contained in the Old and New Testaments. Still more important than these national laws was the so-called canon law, the collection of ecclesiastical canons and decrees of the Roman bishops. It is remarkable that this canon law, while incorporating naturally a good deal of Biblical matter, such as the degrees of relationship within which marriage is forbidden, does not make so much use of Biblical authority as one might expect. The decrees of the popes, it is true, usually begin with a quotation from the Bible, but that is more for the sake of appearances. The fact that the law of the church, in spite of all references to the Bible, was derived essentially from other sources, and that the study and the knowledge of this law were appreciated as the most important attainment of a bishop or even a clergyman, is very striking.

We have already noted the influence which the Bible exerted upon social and commercial life. The German notion of the king as representative of the nation was easily combined with the theocratic theory of the Old Testament. David's court, with his mighty men (II Sam. 23), furnished a good example for any royal court of this period. Feudalism seemed to agree with the stories of the patriarchs, as when Abraham led forth his trained men, three hundred and eighteen in number, and pursued the invaders who had taken captive his brother's son Lot. Bondage, serfdom, even slavery, seemed to be sanctioned by the Bible. The church did not object to slavery provided the Christian faith of the slave was respected; he was never to be sold to a Jew or a pagan. The opposition against slavery in the Middle Ages came from the monasteries. Here the ancient Stoic doctrine that all men are equal and no man is to be treated as a brute animal had been combined with the Christian view of brotherhood that all are children of God, and with the doctrine of the simple life. But this theory, championed by the monasteries, spread only slowly. It did not put an end to slavery in the northern countries of Europe before the thirteenth century. In the eastern and southern countries, where Christianity bordered on Mohammedanism, slavery did not die out before the sixteenth century, and bondage remained everywhere until the eighteenth and nineteenth centuries. The Bible defined the position of the Jews, who as murderers of Jesus were thought of as living under the divine punishment. Whatever happened to them was regarded as a penalty due to the crime of their fathers. So they were exposed to all kinds of insults if they were not protected by the king, whose personal serfs they were held to be. A large part of this general hatred of the Jews was due to the fact that they were making money out of their trade and their medical science, being allowed by their own law to take usury from the Christians. The law of Moses (in Deut. 23 : 20) expressly says that a Jew may lend upon usury to a foreigner, while he is forbidden to do so dealing with a brother. Now, as we have already seen, the Christian church adopted this law as forbidding the Christians to lend at interest. The fatal result was that trade on the basis of credit was made almost impossible, and that the Jew was the only one who could lend money at interest. As he abused this opportunity by taking enormous usury, it became evident that the one remedy to be used from time to time was to take away from him by force all the money he had made, thus restoring it to its proper source. The Jew might be thankful if he got off with his life. Among the many accusations brought against the Jews on such occasions, one of the most effective was the indictment that they had falsified their Bibles, putting in curses against the Christians, or that they had insulted and destroyed Christian Bibles. The criminal charge of falsifying the holy Scriptures had been raised against many heretics, too, and in most cases had been proved to be untrue. It could be retorted that the Christian church itself, during the first centuries, had "improved" the Psalter in many a place by slight Christian interpolations. Destroying books by fire was at this time one of the most common means used by the church in fighting Jews and heretics, and vice versa. The Bible recorded not only the burning of the magical books at Ephesus but also the burning of the holy Scriptures by Antiochus Epiphanes. So this also was "Bible tradition."

To sum up our survey of mediæval civilisation we find the Bible recognised as one, if not as the one, foundation. Its influence was to be seen in every department: the view of the world, the view of history, arts and sciences, social life and commerce. It was to the Bible that people referred, even if the thing had not been deduced from the Bible; they made it appear Biblical, though it was not so in itself, because they felt that it had to be Biblical if it was to be recognised as an integral part of Christian civilisation. That is what makes it so difficult for us to define the real influence of the Bible, there is so much artificial Biblicality.

The Bible was the leading norm, and it was recognised as such. Never had the Bible had a higher estimation or a more undisputed influence.

And yet the real influence of the Bible was a limited one. It had not only to face the rivalry of the classics on one side but of the Apocrypha, legends, ecclesiastical traditions on the other. Its real influence was mostly indirect. Biblical ideas had been incorporated into the works on the world and nature; Biblical history had been used for the text-books of history, and now these books came to be substitutes for the Bible. All read the *Historia Scholastica* of Peter Comestor; very few read the Bible. And those few again read mostly the historical parts of the Bible without caring for the books of the prophets and the letters of the apostles. A wide-spread substitute for the Bible was the so-called *Biblia Historialis*, which gave the Biblical history in a convenient not to say entertaining and even amusing form. Another well-known substitute was the so-called *Biblia Pauperum* ("Bible of the poor)," showing the most important features of the life of Christ, together with typical scenes from the Old Testament and some verses from the Bible. By means of all these substitutes the people became very familiar with Biblical history, but they knew nothing about doctrines. Theologians, of course, did, but their eyes were blinded by the tradition of the church, the doctrine of the fathers. They interpreted the Bible according to tradition. That is the great demerit of this age; the people had free access to the Bible, but the Bible became alien to them by reason of its many substitutes and its successful rivals. The reaction against this will furnish the subject for our next chapter.

V

THE BIBLE STIRS NON-CONFORMIST MOVEMENTS (1150-1450)

Mediæval civilisation has a twofold aspect. It looks backward, to the old church and the old Roman empire; so far it is Biblical and classical. But it also looks forward, to the development of the nations and later to the development of the individual personality, as this has been realised in the Renaissance; so far it is secular and, in a way, modern. In the earlier part of the Middle Ages the nations did not feel strong enough by themselves. They were parts of the empire, and all children of the one mother church. The church was training them, and it fulfilled this task in an admirable way. But the children grew up and the church lost its power over them. They declared themselves of age and independent at the very moment when the church seemed to have the largest and most undoubted influence.

The church was training the nations by means of the Bible, and now it is the Bible which stirs the anti-ecclesiastical movements. The Bible had been used by the church chiefly in an indirect way; parts of the Bible or substitutes for it had taken its place. Now the complete Bible made its appeal to the people and gave directions which were exactly opposite to the training given by the church.

The Bible had originally been accessible to everybody. In the first centuries the church itself had insisted upon this publicity, as we have seen in the first chapter. Then came a time when almost no one could read and the clergy had the Bible practically to themselves. They did not take away the Bible from the hands of the laymen; the laymen themselves did not care for it because they could not read it; they were totally dependent on the clergy. But now civilisation had made a new start; the art of reading became again popular. And suddenly a desire for reading the Bible spread among the people. The clergy were astonished to find the laymen using their right of reading the Bible themselves. That was something new, and we see the clergy puzzled, we hear them complain. They did not want people to read the Bible, for—as they said—this would introduce them to heresy. And so it proved.

The movement starts from the south of France. As early as the eleventh century we hear of people here who gather in order to hear the Bible read. It is the cardinal Pietro Damiani, a friend of Gregory VII, who complains of their presumption. They are plain, simple folk, shopkeepers, farmers, women, having no theological education, and yet aiming at understanding the Bible. The theologians of this period treated the Bible as a book of secrets. In order to understand it aright one had to be initiated into the art of interpreting everything by allegory according to the authority of the fathers. They used to quote Saint Jerome, that the Bible was a mysterious stream; one man can walk through in safety while another would be drowned. They therefore disapproved earnestly of this reading of the Bible by unprepared tradesmen, women, and children. But reading did not stop. The same complaint occurs again and again during the next decades. We hear of people in the diocese of Metz, simple country folk, reading the Bible. The church authorities already began to be alarmed and to take a more severe attitude toward the offenders.

The main movement, to be mentioned here, is the one connected with the name of Peter Waldo, a merchant of Lyons, who was a zealous reader of the Bible himself, and travelling about held frequent meetings with people of the same sort. The story of his "conversion," as given by the best authorities, runs as follows. It was in 1176, the year of a great famine, that one Sunday afternoon he listened to a jongleur reciting the famous legend of Saint Alexis the poor. He was struck by this heroism of poverty, and the next day he asked a well-known master of theology what was the surest way to God. The master, following the best tradition of the mediæval church, told him to follow Christ's advice: "If thou wouldst be perfect, go, sell whatsoever thou hast, and give to the poor." So Peter separates himself from wife and children and begins to live the life of a poor man—a beggar. Others join him; two by two, on foot, they go preaching the gospel. They are not anxious for the morrow; they do not work; they have faith that whatever they need will be supplied to them. Thus they try to fulfil Christ's commandments and to imitate his disciples. They refuse to take an oath; they censure lying as a deadly sin; they condemn all shedding of blood either in war or in the execution of justice. The fraternity called itself the Poor in Spirit. At the beginning they thought themselves to be true members of the church; only later, when the church denied to them the right of preaching, did they form a sect, Peter being ordained bishop and giving orders to other members of the community.

Meanwhile a similar fraternity of poor men, or *humiliati* as they were called here, had made their appearance in the north of Italy. It was a kind of workmen's union. So far as we know there was no connection at the beginning between this movement and the one at Lyons. Both started independently, and it was only later that they came into contact, without, however, amalgamating. The Italian fraternity spread from Milan all through that region and was rapidly extended into Germany, while from Lyons the

Poor went through France and even through Spain. It was an enormous movement among the laity, and it was stirred by the Bible. Peter Waldo desired to have the Bible translated into his own vernacular; and it was by reading the Bible that these people got their enthusiasm and their eagerness even to suffer persecution and death.

Many scholars in former days treated this Waldensian movement as truly Protestant; they used to call Peter Waldo and his followers reformers before the Reformation. The Protestant church in Italy, calling itself Waldensian and growing in our own day more and more vigorously in the spirit of Calvinistic Protestantism, seemed to support this view. And yet it is wrong. The true Protestantism of the Waldensians dates only from the sixteenth century, when they came in contact with Geneva, and then went over to Calvinism. Before this they had been something quite different, a purely mediæval form of Christianity. The characteristic point is that they take the gospel as a law, exactly as the monks did. If the monks kept to poverty, fasting, praying, and so on, in order to fulfil the gospel's commands, these people did the same; only they did not become monks and enter a monastery; they continued to live in the world, carrying on their ordinary business, because, they said, the commands of the gospel were not given to the monks only, but to every Christian. They abolished the double standard of morality which the church had established, the standard of perfection, reached only by the clergy and monks, and the standard of secular morality, kept by the average Christian; but they abolished it in the opposite way from the reformers, by making the ascetic ideal the rule for every Christian. It was from the Bible that they deduced this ideal and its binding force for every Christian, but it was, of course, the mediæval understanding of the Bible which they followed.

It is important to distinguish clearly this Waldensian movement from the so-called Albigensian one. This also has to do with the Bible, and sometimes seems closely akin to the former, but is based on an entirely different principle. It goes back to a very early time and originates outside of Christianity. It was in the third century after Christ in Persia, that a certain Mani tried to reform the religion of Zoroaster by adding Gnostic speculations. He failed, and was put to death together with some of his adherents. But the movement spread and reached as far as Gaul and North Africa in the West. Here this Gnostic doctrine of Persian origin took the form of a Christian heresy. Manicheism, as it was called, accepted the Christian Bible, or at least some parts of it. It accepted still more heartily the Christian Apocrypha, which seemed to be written for the very purpose of supporting its favourite doctrines. Saint Augustine, having been for a long time an adherent of Manicheism, afterward spent a great deal of his energy in arguing with this sect and refuting their theories and their criticism. The leading idea was a strictly dualistic conception of the world such as is characteristic of Persian religion: there are two gods, a good one and a bad one; in other words, God and the devil are of the same rank. The devil is the author of this bodily creation; whatsoever is material comes from him; while God, the good god, is purely spiritual and does not create anything but spiritual beings. So man, who is of a mixed nature, having a divine soul in a material body, is bound to defy the devil by weakening the material part of his being. He has to refrain from meat and wine, from marriage, and from a number of things which belong to the devil's dominion. This highest degree of perfection only few could reach. Therefore the Manicheans had several classes of members: the lower classes living in the world had to support the higher by their manual labour; the higher class of the so-called "perfect" lived entirely for prayer and spiritual exercises. It was a well-organised body, extending over all the countries. They had their own Pope, residing usually in the East. They were persecuted in Persia, persecuted in the Roman empire, persecuted later both by the church and by the secular powers; but in spite of all difficulties they kept on, living in secrecy and trying to conform as much as possible in outward appearance to the requirements for church members. They went to the Catholic church, even attended mass and took the holy communion—one charge brought against them was that instead of eating the consecrated bread they concealed it in their mouth and spit it out afterward—but they had their own clandestine congregations, often by night, often outside of the town. They appear here and there under different names. They call themselves Cathari, or the pure ones, from which is derived "Ketzer," the German word for heretics. In the East they often are called Bogomils or Paulicians; in the West the usual name given to them was Albigensians, from a town, Albi, in the south of France, where they had their headquarters.

The attitude of these Albigensians toward the Bible was a somewhat divided one. They accepted the New Testament and interpreted it according to their dualistic theory as a law of asceticism, herein corresponding to the church's interpretation. They praised exceedingly the fourth Gospel, and used its opening verses at their solemn initiation, the so-called *consolamentum*, by which an adherent got the degree of "perfect" and became a member of the highest class. But they rejected the Old Testament, either the whole of it or the greater part, some admitting that the Psalter, Job, the books of Solomon, and the books of the prophets were inspired by the good god or (as they used to say) were written in heaven. The rest, they said, came from the devil, and they criticised strongly the historical parts of the Old Testament, in particular the account of the creation given in Genesis. They took this and all the other stories in a strictly literal sense, not allowing for any allegorical interpretation. It was in the discussions against the Manicheans that Saint Augustine, and through him the Western church, learned to value the allegorical method of interpretation. It was the easiest way of evading all the difficulties which were raised by the criticism of the Manicheans.

This Manichean or, to use the mediæval expression, Albigensian heresy could hardly be defined as a movement incited by the Bible. It was wholly different from the Waldensian movement and its allies. The Waldensians were at the beginning loyal members of the Catholic church, and were driven into opposition only by the resistance of the clergy, not being allowed to read and to use their Bible and being opposed and disturbed in their harmless meetings; but after having been separated from the church they kept aloof from it. The Albigensians, on the other hand, were at heart opposed to everything in Christianity. They were, in fact, adherents of another religion, pretending for the sake of safety to be members of the Catholic church. Yet just this attitude of the Albigensians was what made it so difficult to distinguish between the two movements, and has caused a curious confusion. The Waldensians, with their frank and open opposition to certain institutions of the church, were taken by many to be the more dangerous, and were therefore attacked and persecuted more severely than the Albigensians, who knew how to conform themselves to the outward appearance of church life.

What was the attitude of the church toward these non-conformist movements? According to the current theory of the time there was no salvation outside the church; there was no room for various denominations. A man belonged to the church by the very fact that he was born in a Catholic community and consequently was baptised. He *had* to attend the church, which procured for him eternal salvation, and if he neglected his duties, he was compelled to perform them by the church authorities perhaps with the help of the secular power. A man had no right to try his own way to salvation; he was forced to use the means provided for him by the church. And if he did not submit he was to be extinguished in order that his devilish spirit of heresy might not infect others; possibly he himself could be saved by being deprived of his sinful body and godless life. This theory gave a legal sanction for using all kinds of persuasion by force, for applying cruel tortures, and for inflicting death by burning, hanging, beheading.

But the church found that the movements could not be mastered in this way. In order to extirpate the evil, the underlying cause had to be rooted out or else its energy turned in another direction.

The first method was tried for the Bible. It was the Bible which had stirred the Waldensian and similar movements; so the Bible was to be kept away from the people. When asked by the bishop of Metz what he ought to do with regard to the associations of Bible readers in his diocese, Pope Innocent III replies (1199) that of course the study of the Bible is to be encouraged among the clergy, but that all laymen are to be kept from it, the Bible being so profound in its mysteries that even scholars sometimes get beyond their depth and are drowned. At the end of his letter he refers to the holiness of Mount Sinai as expressed in Ex. 19 : 12, 13: "Take heed to yourselves, that ye go not up into the mount, or touch the border of it: whosoever toucheth the mount shall be surely put to death: no hand shall touch him, but he shall surely be stoned, or shot through; whether it be beast or man, it shall not live." Likewise, the Pope says, if a layman touches the Bible he is guilty of sacrilege and ought to be stoned or shot through. This amounts to a general prohibition of Bible reading for the laity. It was especially against the translations of the Bible into the vernacular tongues that the church's ordinances were directed. In the later centuries of the Middle Ages the prohibitions against Bible reading by the laity, against translating the Bible, and against selling the Bible became more frequent. But it is exactly this frequent repetition which makes it evident that the prohibitions were for the most part neglected. The best known is a book ordinance, issued by Bishop Berthold of Mainz in 1485-6, in which the bishop forbids the printing and selling of Bibles unless they are annotated by approved church theologians, the Bibles in the vernacular language being forbidden altogether. We know of a Strassburg printer who was at work printing a German Bible at the very time this ordinance was issued. He did not stop printing, he only took care not to mention his name in the book. Evidently he was sure that he could find a sale for his book.

There was another way of overcoming these non-conformist tendencies, and it proved to be more successful; the church tried to direct them and put them to its own service. A good example of this method is given in the history of the movement started by Saint Francis of Assisi. At the beginning this was exactly like the Waldensian movement that spread through the south of France and the north of Italy, and may have received some influence from it; for we know that the family of Saint Francis had French relations and that the business of his father brought him into contact with people from the North. But the conversion of Saint Francis was independent, so far as we know. It again was caused by the Bible. Once at mass he heard the lesson from the Gospel, and was struck by the same words which had struck so many thoughtful Christians before him: "If thou wouldest be perfect, go, sell that which thou hast and give to the poor, and thou shalt have treasure in heaven; and come follow me." He at once throws away stick, bag, purse, shoes to become the true follower of the poor Jesus and of his poor apostles, to be himself the apostle of the gospel of poverty, the lover of his good lady Poverty, as he likes to call her. When the first two disciples had joined him he takes them at daybreak to a small chapel, takes from the altar the book of the Gospels, and (so the legend tells us), opening it three times, every time comes upon the words quoted above. Therefore they were made the basis of Saint Francis' rule for his community, together with the instruction given to Christ's disciples in Luke 9 : 1-6, and Matt. 16 : 24-27: "If any man would come after me, let him deny himself and take up his cross and follow me; for whosoever would save his life shall lose it, and whosoever shall lose his life for my sake shall find it; for what shall a man be profited if he shall gain the whole world and forfeit his life, or what shall a man give in exchange for his life?" It was the desire for martyrdom inspired by this passage which caused Saint Francis to go to Palestine and preach the gospel to the Moslems. In his retreat at Mount Alverno he assiduously read the history of the passion, until he became so deeply impressed by it that it had a corporal effect upon him. He became stigmatised, the five wounds of Christ appeared on his body. Saint Francis composed an interesting paraphrase of the Lord's Prayer, and his famous hymn to the sun is nothing else than a beautiful reproduction of the 148th Psalm. When dying he asked for John 13 to be read to him. Thus all his life is accompanied and profoundly affected by the Bible. His preaching is an attempt at bringing the pure gospel of poverty before the people as simply and plainly as he found it in the Gospels according to the ascetic understanding of that time.

Now this would have turned into a non-conformist movement, like that of the Poor of Lyons or the Poor of Milan, had not the bishop from the beginning protected Saint Francis from his father's wrath. Then at a later period Cardinal Ugolino of Ostia, known from his later life as Pope Gregory IX, became a protector of Saint Francis and his fraternity and managed to make of it a regular order in the service of the church. It was not Saint Francis who founded the order of the Franciscans or Friars, but some of his first pupils and friends, and certain high dignitaries of the church abused him for their own purposes. They put upon Saint Francis and his fraternity the whole machinery of a religious body of the church. There was to be a general, and numerous provincials, and an annual meeting of delegates; there were monasteries ruled by abbots or guardians, and later these monasteries received endowments. Besides the monks and the nuns who formed the first and second orders, there was a third order of Saint Francis including those laymen who wished to belong to the order and enjoy its religious benefits but were prevented by their families from entering the monastery. This comes very near to the ideal put forth by the Poor of Lyons, but the organisation kept the whole body always in touch with the church and its authority. The non-conformist tendency of the movement had been taken out and it had been turned into an instrument of ecclesiastical policy.

To be sure, the spirit of Saint Francis reacted against this system, inspired, as it was, more by ecclesiastical shrewdness than by Christian piety. The saint himself at the end of his life fell out with his friends and especially with the cardinal protector. He felt himself too much the gallant knight of his lady Poverty to make himself a tool of ecclesiastical policy. He detected a spirit of worldliness, and in his last will he warned his monks not to yield themselves to it. Nevertheless, the cardinal when promoted to be Pope ordered Saint Francis, two years after his death, to be worshipped as a saint, in a bull of canonisation very characteristic for the style of this time, filled as it is with Biblical allusions. "From this bull," says one of Saint Francis' recent biographers, "you learn much more about the history of David and the Philistines than about the life of Saint Francis."

But the spirit of Saint Francis reacted even more after his death. One part of his followers insisted upon the strict rule of having no possessions at all; they treated the other part, which permitted possessions in common, as a set of worldly apostates from the master's ideals, far from the law of the gospel. And as the church authorities decided in favour of the less strict group, the spiritual party, as they called themselves, openly rebelled against the church, while the emperor, being on bad terms with the Pope, granted them his protection. From the book of Revelation they deduced that the official church was the great Babylon and the Pope the antichrist. So even this movement, started by the Bible, ended partly as a non-conformist anti-ecclesiastical undertaking.

But the main part of the Franciscans, or Friars, as they are called from the Italian *frari* (brothers), kept to the straight line of ecclesiastical discipline, and, together with the other order founded nearly at the same time by Saint Dominic the Spaniard for the special purpose of repelling heresy, they became the powerful army of the church directed against all non-conformist movements such as the Waldensians and Albigensians. Both orders made themselves at home at the universities—at this period Bologna and Paris, later Oxford and Cambridge—and soon became very influential. They had rich monasteries and great libraries, and made Bible study their favourite subject. It is a remarkable contrast between Saint Francis, who, having only one book, a New Testament, gives this away in order to help a poor widow, and the great stores of books in the convents of Saint Francis' fraternity. The saint himself did not wish his monks to possess, privately, anything, not even a Psalter, and now they owned huge Bibles and commentaries and read and studied like any scholar of the secular clergy. Saint Francis did not wish scholarship among his brethren; it was to him something worldly, opposed to the true principles of poverty. Now members of his order sat in the chairs of the universities and were among the leading teachers of the church.

It is due to the Friars that Bible study is again favoured at the mediæval universities. But even these Friars were taken away from the Bible by the current tendency toward scholasticism. Dogmatics, systematics, dialectics were what everybody wanted. The curriculum of a student of theology required first a training in Biblical studies, then he had to go to attend lectures on the *Sententiæ*, as they called the text-book for systematics. Likewise the professor was bound first for two or three years to teach Biblical matters before he could touch upon systematics. In a number of German universities there still remain some traces of this mediæval regulation. But we are told that both professors and students hurried on to get rid of their Bible course as quickly as possible in order to reach the higher level of dialectics and systematics. The Bible among these theologians was a text-book for the junior classes, but not held in great esteem as compared with the treasured text-book of the senior classes, the *Liber sententiarum.*

It is no wonder that a reaction against this system of scholasticism was stimulated by the Bible itself. Two streams we may distinguish, both starting within the boundaries of the church and of ecclesiastical theology, both inclined to overflow these boundaries, and both ending in non-conformist movements.

One stream is represented by the mystics. They are pious people, led by high-church preachers, Master Eckhard, Tauler, Suso, and others. These preachers are given to thorough study of the Bible. But their allegory turns out to be far different from that traditional with the fathers. They care for God and the soul, and for nothing else in the world. Their favourite text-book is Canticles: the Christian soul as the bride of God or of Christ. This mysticism sometimes comes into collision with the sacramental view of the church. Being in complete spiritual union with God, the mystic wished no outward sign; piety was love, not creed. The church instinctively felt that where these ideas were prevailing the whole ecclesiastical system was in danger, and tried to stop the movement. But by this very opposition the movement became more anti-ecclesiastical than it had been before. The mystic circles withdrew themselves from the superintendence of the church, they read the Bible, they read the books of their spiritual fathers, and they became more and more sure of their own mystical theory as opposed to the doctrine of the church.

The second stream is still more important. Some theologians reading the works of Saint Augustine discovered that the present church doctrine was not what it pretended to be, the true representation of the doctrine of the fathers, that there was a large difference between the real tradition of the old church and the scholastic doctrines of their own time. And, as they went on, they found that the Bible, viewed according to the interpretation of the fathers, did not support the theories of the modern scholars. So they departed from scholasticism and built their own systems on the basis of the Bible as interpreted by Saint Augustine. It was a general movement; men of this kind were found in many places. It is difficult to say how far they were dependent one upon another. Some were quiet men of letters; some gained high positions, like John Gerson, who was elected chancellor of the University of Paris; others were aggressive reformers. Mixing in politics, these became leaders of an anti-hierarchical and at last anti-ecclesiastical movement. We are not concerned here with the political side of the question, which sometimes seems to be predominant. Thus in England John Wycliffe stirred up a long-lived struggle. Influenced by his writings John Huss in Bohemia entered on a campaign for true Christianity which instead led to a national Czech movement. In 1409 the German students of the University of Prague left the city and moved to Leipzig. After the martyrdom of their hero at Constance in 1415 the Hussites became an aggressive national and militant party, constantly invading and devastating Germany. It needed shrewd politics and the united forces of the empire to keep them back from the Silesian and Saxon frontiers.

As so often happens in history, at the end it is hard to recognise the causes which have led to the result. In spite of all political appearances it is true that it was really the Bible which stirred up these two movements, the Wycliffite and the Hussite. The proof is given in the fact that both Wycliffe and Huss not only were fond of reading the Bible, but both tried also to make their people familiar with the Bible by procuring translations into the vernacular. In this way they aimed to provide the laity with the evidence of this one true authority and so to protect them against the adulteration of Christianity due to scholasticism and hierarchy.

The circulation and influence of the English version made by Wycliffe—or, as some scholars think, at Wycliffe's instance—is shown by the fact that in spite of persecution and destruction one hundred and seventy copies are still preserved, one hundred and forty of which belong to a second revision, made by a younger friend of Wycliffe's, John Purvey (Plate XIV). It was the first English translation of the whole Bible, a good specimen of English, but, like most mediæval translations based upon the Latin Vulgate, preserving the faults of that version and adding others of its own. There are numbers of Czech Bibles in existence, both in manuscript and in print, but not yet thoroughly studied. It is remarkable that in this Hussite Bible, as well as in some German translations of the same time, readings are found which go back to the very earliest period of textual development. They belong to the southern branch of French tradition and are supplied probably by Latin, French, or Italian copies which came from Lyons or Milan. This is clear evidence that it was through the Waldensians that the Bible spread in the vernacular of Italy, Bohemia, and Germany, and that the later movements, while originating independently, were in close relation with the earlier ones. It is the Bible which not only stirred all these movements but connected them one with the other.

VI

THE BIBLE TRAINS PRINTERS
AND TRANSLATORS (1450-1611)

We have been led in the last chapters far back into the Middle Ages. Now we approach the great time of discoveries. It is difficult to say who made the most important discovery, Columbus crossing the Atlantic to find a new world, in which a new civilisation was to arise, or Gutenberg inventing the art of printing and thereby revolutionising the world of intellectual life and consequently the history of the Bible.

During the last centuries of the Middle Ages the Bible had been much copied. At the University of Paris booksellers, helped by some scholars, undertook to issue a special edition for the benefit of the students. This Paris edition, easily recognised by its fine type of handwriting and its blue and red decoration, became the standard Bible text for men of learning. At the same time many a pious member of the Fraternity of the Common Life, which was founded by Gerhard de Groot at Zutphen (in Holland), copied the Bible in his miserable cell with great skill. The monasteries began to have large collections of Bible editions. There were large copies consisting of four or eight volumes in folio, for use in chapel, and smaller ones, in one volume, for private reading. We know of a regulation made for all monasteries of the Order of Saint Augustine, that in the catalogues of their libraries all Bibles should be put under the letter A. There was no need for such a regulation in the pre-Carolingian time, when a monastery would scarcely have one complete Bible.

But now let us try to realise what it meant that each copy should be made by itself, the writer painting (as we may say) letter by letter, and this through hundreds and thousands of pages. The copyists showed wonderful skill. Some of these manuscripts look exactly like printed books; one letter is just like the other; no slipping of the pen! Nevertheless it was inevitable that the copyist should make mistakes from time to time. He dropped a letter, a word, even a line; unconsciously he changed the order of the words. He brought in something which he happened to have in his mind. When he was familiar with his Bible, some parallel confused him. It is only natural that in copying a book of this size even the best copyist should make some hundreds of blunders; the next copyist would introduce other hundreds, sometimes even by an unhappy attempt at correcting the blunders of the former. So it went on till in the end the text became filled with mistakes. Of course, there was a remedy. After having finished the copy the writer himself or some one else was expected to compare it carefully with the original and correct all the blunders. But from personal experience in reading proofs we know how easily a real blunder escapes our attention. One ought to go over a proof-sheet three times at least in order to avoid all mistakes. So we cannot wonder that the Bibles copied by hand contained errors, and considering all the difficulties it is surprising that the copies were most of them so nearly correct.

———————

It was Johann Gutenberg, a native of Mainz, residing some time at Strassburg as a silversmith, then again returning to Mainz, who made the great discovery that several copies could be printed at once by using letters cut out of wood or metal. People had used woodcuts before his time. Engraving large blocks of wood with pictures and letters, they printed the so-called block-books, as a cheap substitute for illuminated manuscripts. Gutenberg's great idea was that instead of using a woodcut block for the page one might compose a page by using separate, movable letters, putting them together according to the present need, then separating them and using them again. We are not interested here in the technical part of the work; imperfect as it was, it was surely a great advance. Now one got a hundred copies, two hundred, or even more without any difference between them. When the proofs had been corrected carefully the Bible was sure to have as few mistakes as possible; and if the printer still found some errors, he could easily correct them for the whole edition by adding a printed list of errata, or necessary corrections, at the end of the volume. It was only by printing that uniformity of text became possible.

The important fact for our present investigation is that it was the Bible which Gutenberg chose to be the first printed book. This fact illustrates the estimation in which the Bible was held. It shows at the same time the demand for Bible copies; the printer felt sure that it would sell and pay. It was an enormous enterprise to put the fresh, inexperienced art of printing straightway at a task so big as this. It took four years to print the first Bible, from 1453 to 1456. While working at it Gutenberg had to try some smaller things which would bring him money immediately, school-books, letters of indulgence, and so on, but his main care was given to the Bible. It contained six hundred and forty-one leaves, with two columns on each page, and forty-two lines in each column (Plate XV). The initials were not printed, but were supposed to be illuminated by hand; a small letter was printed in the free space to indicate what kind of letter the illuminator had to paint. Probably not more than one hundred copies were printed, a third part of them on parchment. Out of the thirty-one copies which have been preserved, or, to speak more accurately, are known as such, ten are luxuriously printed on parchment and illuminated, each in a different way, but all very fine and costly. It is obvious that Gutenberg put into this printing not only a great amount of labour but much money, too; and there was no assurance that it would come in again in a short time. Like many ingenious discoverers and inventors, he was no business man; he was always in need of money. So when his first Bible was not yet finished one of his creditors, John Fust, of Mainz, took all his apparatus from him and, associating himself with an apprentice of Gutenberg's, Peter Schöffer by name, brought the printing of the first Bible to completion, thus depriving the inventor of the financial success as well as of the glory. But Gutenberg was not discouraged. He immediately began, with a new set of letters, the printing of a second Bible, containing thirty-six lines in each column and so amounting to eight hundred and eighty-one leaves in size. He printed it in the years 1456 to 1458. Again his rivals, Fust and Schöffer, published, in 1462, a third Bible, called sometimes the Bible of Mainz. It has forty-eight lines in each column.

P I. AT & X, -- O C TE:NDER G'R F'[R:,';T BfBLE

(4i! lines, :lluioz, 1'45!l - 1 156)

Copy at 1_.,ipl.ii:. on purchmcnl. f>ea utilull - illumi t1aktl. Th,, capilal, ,u e
paintrJ1,y ll:11111. hul intlicaLed b · small 11ri1ll,· tl lri ter;i.
From "Er6111.lung der Bud ulruckerkunsl." Puhli, hcd hy V,•lhageu & Klu•ing,
ßidd .-ld, <:t ru umf .

Thus the printing of the Bible was inaugurated. The new art quickly spread
all over Germany, and printing-presses were established at Strassburg,
Bamberg, Nuremberg, Basel, Cologne, Lübeck, and many other places. The
art entered France and England with less success, the government in both
countries being partly opposed to it and partly trying to make it a royal
privilege. Good printers worked at Paris and Lyons. The most splendid
presses were at Venice, where the Doge championed the new art even against
attacks from Rome. Before the year 1500 ninety-two editions of the Latin
Bible were issued by these various presses, according to Mr. Copinger, who
possessed the largest collection of printed Bibles. (He registers four hundred
and thirty-eight editions of the Latin Bible during the sixteenth century.) In
addition to these we have a great number of printed Bibles in the vernacular
of Germany, France, Italy, Bohemia, and so on. There was a sudden
outpouring of Bibles. But we must not overestimate the circulation. These
editions contained scarcely more than two hundred copies each; they were
most of them in large folio, very unwieldy, and the price was enormous,
though, of course, not so high as it is now, when for one copy of Gutenberg's
first Bible $20,000 is paid. The Bible was not available for the average man.
We know of scholars copying for themselves the Bible or the New Testament
from a printed Bible. The clergy were rather opposed to this printing. They
did not in the least encourage the printers; on the contrary, they tried to cause
as many difficulties as possible. Therefore the circulation was a limited one.
Copies were bought by churches for their services, by princes, and by very
rich merchants, as to-day a splendid work is bought more as a luxury than as
something for daily use. One cannot say that at this period the Bible, even by
printing, acquired a circulation among the people.

This was accomplished only through the Reformation. It was Luther's
German translation which made the printed Bible popular and caused a
number of similar translations. In order to make the Bible what it was
destined to be, the book of the people, the printer and the translator had to
work together.

In former times many Protestants held the view that Luther rediscovered
the Bible, which had been almost entirely forgotten. They thought that there

had been a meagre transmission of the Bible and no translation into the vernacular at all. This view, of course, is untenable. We have seen what a circulation the Bible had in the last century before the Reformation, and that it had been translated into almost every vernacular. Nevertheless, Luther's version is a landmark in the history of translation; it marks a new period and represents the beginning of a new sort of translation.

In order to realise this, let us look back over the former history of translations. In the first period we found the Bible translated from the Greek into Latin, Syriac, Coptic; in the next period Gothic, Armenian, Georgian, Libyan, and Ethiopic were added, not to mention the several revisions of the former translations. About 600 A. D. the Bible was known in eight languages; in each of them there had been several attempts at translating. There were different dialects, too; in Coptic no less than five. The spread of Christianity in the next period is shown by the fact that the Bible is translated—and this again several times—into Arabic and Slavonic from the Greek, and into German, Anglo-Saxon, Celtic, and French from the Latin—rather, I should say, parts of the Bible, for it was only parts which people at this period tried to translate. We hear of a Gospel, of a Psalter, of one or another book translated into the vernacular. Only when stimulated by the popular movements of the next period, as we have seen in the fifth chapter, was the work of translating into the vernacular prosecuted on a larger scale; from the thirteenth century on we may speak of Bibles in the vernacular. Beginning in the southeast of France, the tendency spread over Italy and Germany. We can still trace the influence of the French Waldensian Bible in the earliest Italian translations and also in some of the German ones. Another circle is defined by the northern French translation, which influenced the Flemish and Dutch and possibly even the Scandinavian. All these are based not so much upon the Bible itself as on a rearrangement known as the Historical Bible, telling the stories and omitting the doctrinal portions. A new start was made in England by Wycliffe, and this caused the Bohemian translation into Czech, which was again influenced by the Waldensian Bible. It is like a net thrown all over Europe. We may count more than a dozen languages, many of them represented by different dialects and by several separate renditions, which were added to the eight languages of the former periods. The culmination came in the fifteenth century, when everywhere fresh translations were attempted. In Germany more than forty different types of translation can be counted, and one of them, containing the whole Bible, was printed fourteen times before the period of the Reformation (Plate XVI). There was only one translation, however, with a value of its own, and that was the Spanish, for this was made from the Hebrew Old Testament by the help of some Spanish Jews. Both the king of Spain and the high clergy showed at that time a remarkable breadth of view in trying to get a trustworthy translation. All other versions in the West were based upon the Latin Vulgate as the recognised Bible of the church, and they were made with more devotion than knowledge. The translators usually did not know Latin well nor were they masters of their own language. They translated word for word, and the result was sometimes strange. It is of no great importance that, not recognising in "Tertius" and "Quartus" proper names, one of these translators said "the third" and "the fourth." It was worse when another explained "encænia" in John 10 : 22, the feast of dedication, as meaning "wedding," or declared the words in Matt. 27 : 46, "Eli, Eli," to be Greek. Sometimes the translation resulted in pure nonsense, and even where it made sense, it was difficult and often far from the true meaning. Now humanism insisted upon going back to the original languages. Erasmus, in 1516, published the first edition of the New Testament in Greek. We see how Luther, at this time professor at the University of Wittenberg, lecturing upon Romans when this edition came into his hands, was impressed by this new source of information. He eagerly set himself to learn Greek with the help of his friend Melanchthon, and so he was prepared for the great task of translating the New Testament directly out of the Greek into German. It was during his exile in the Wartburg that he found the necessary time to make this translation. It appeared in print in September, 1522, and it is astonishing in how short a time this New Testament circulated all through Germany. It was reprinted everywhere, and often very carelessly, so that Luther had to complain against the printers as falsifying his translation. He himself did not take any payment for his work; he wanted the publishers to sell it as cheaply as possible. And it was a masterpiece, not only for the beauty of the language, which was the best and most popular German that had ever been written but also in the way Luther translated, giving not the single words but the meaning of the sentences, not transferring from one vocabulary to the other but transmuting (if one may say so) the whole expression of thought from Greek into German. The Bible became a German book; one hardly feels that he is reading a translation. Luther had more trouble with the Old Testament. In order to master the Hebrew he had to rely on friends; he even asked some Jewish rabbis to join their meetings. He tells us that they often had to look for a single word three or four weeks; that in particular Job was so difficult that they scarcely finished three lines in four days. The Pentateuch was ready in the year 1523; then year after year the work went on. The prophets were not finished until 1532, and in 1534 the first complete Bible was issued. The work was highly praised by Luther's friends and unduly criticised by his antagonists. He himself replied sharply to such criticism, and he had a right to do so because the attempts made by Eck and Emser, the champions of Roman Catholicism, to translate the Bible themselves were feeble and betrayed much dependence on Luther's translation, which they had so severely criticised. Luther himself never felt satisfied with his own work and always tried to improve it. At two different periods he held meetings with his friends for the purpose of revising the Bible. The records of these meetings of the committee for the revision of the Bible (if one may call it so) have come down to us, and it is highly interesting to see how carefully they discussed every word and how it is always Luther himself who at last finds the most apt expression.

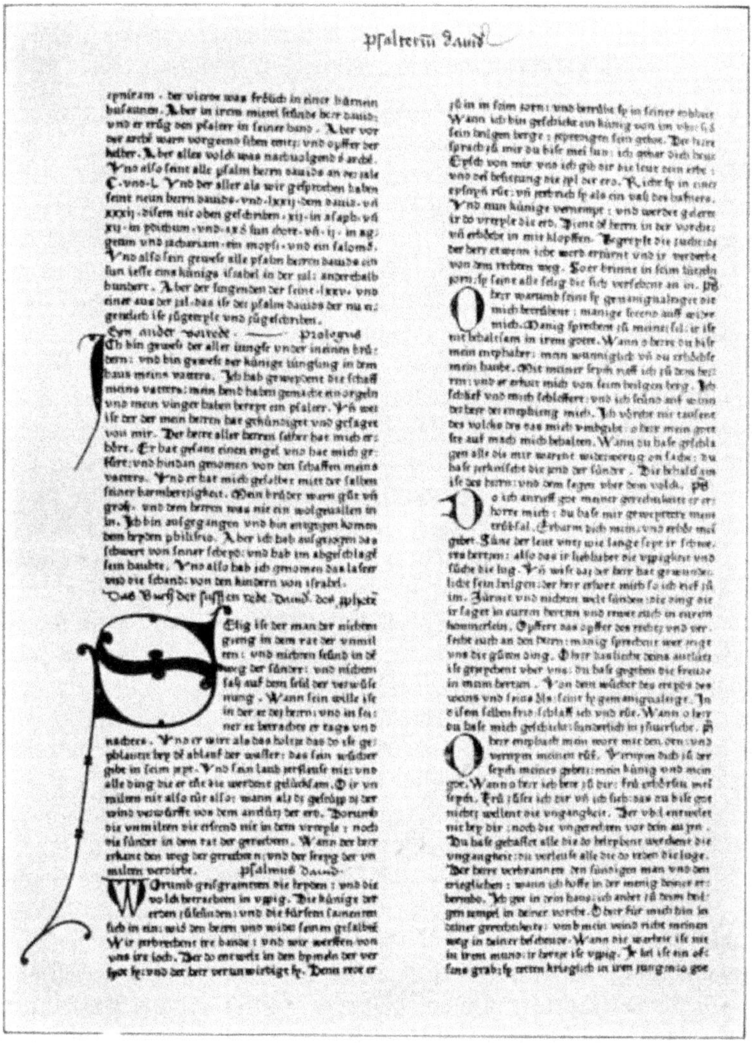

PLATE XVI—FIRST GERMAN BIBLE

Printed at Strassburg by G. Mentell in 1466: the progress in printing made in
these ten years is remarkable.

Entnommen aus W. Walthers "Deutsche Bibelübersetzung des Mittelalters."
Verlag von Hellmuth Wollermann in Braunschweig.

PLATE XVI—FIRST GERMAN BIBLE

Printed at Strassburg by G. Mentell in 1466: the progress in printing made in

81

these ten years is remarkable.

Entnommen aus W. Walthers "Deutsche Bibelübersetzung des Mittelalters." Verlag von Hellmuth Wollermann in Braunschweig.

It is a great privilege of the German nation that it received this excellent Bible at the very beginning of the new era. The German language is moulded by this Bible. In Luther's time the dialects still prevailed. Luther's Bible had to be translated into the dialect of lower Germany. The south of Germany and Switzerland had quite another dialect. The Zürich reformers, in 1529, published a Bible in this dialect, translating from Luther's Bible as far as it existed at this time and providing for the rest a translation of their own. It is unquestionably due to Luther's Bible that the Germans have now one language for all literary purposes. The German classic writers Herder, Wieland, Klopstock, Lessing, Schiller, Goethe were all trained from their childhood by the language of this Bible. Even now there is a remarkable difference in style between authors of Protestant and of Roman Catholic origin in Germany. In the easy and fluent language of the former we see the influence of Luther and Goethe, whereas the latter often show a certain stiffness and a greater number of provincialisms. The attempts to translate the Bible independently of Luther have never succeeded in gaining any large circulation, although there have been many such, not only from the Roman Catholic side but also from Protestants. A famous one is the so-called Berleburg Bible, by certain mystics, published in 1726-42 in eight volumes. In the nineteenth century scholars undertook to give more scientific and more exact translations, but, valuable as these may be for scholarly purposes, the German people will never abandon its classic Bible. It is difficult even to introduce a revision. There was a revision some twenty years ago, but in this Luther's text was retouched and altered only at a very few points, most of the corrections introduced by the revision committee being rather restitutions of Luther's original renderings, which had been badly "improved" by former printers. It is remarkable that even the printed Bible never stands still, but is always changing, the printers acting as the copyists did in former times. The copies of the revised text printed at Stuttgart differ slightly from the copies printed at Halle and Berlin, to mention three of the modern centres of German Bible printing.

Luther's translation was the signal for a general movement in this direction. It is not so much translating the Bible into new languages—only a few which had no Bible before were added to the list given above—as rather the making of new translations in all languages of the Christian world as far as this was influenced by the Reformation. Of course some of these translations were inspired by humanism more than by the spirit of the Reformation. The humanists abhorred the vulgarity of the monkish Latin, and they extended their aversion to the official Bible of the church, the Vulgate of Saint Jerome; therefore they tried to translate the Bible into what they thought to be Ciceronian Latin, and some of them translated this again into French or German. But most of the translators were simply following Luther's model; nay, they used Luther's translation even more than the original. King Christian III of Denmark gave orders that the translators should follow Luther's version as closely as possible. In this way the Dutch, the Danish, the Swedish, the Finnish, the Lettish, and the Lithuanian Bibles were more or less influenced by or even based upon Luther's.

It is different with the English and the French Bible. Wycliffe's translation never had been printed. William Tindale, a pupil of Erasmus, translated the New Testament and parts of the Old during his exile in Germany and Holland, whither he had gone under Henry VIII because, as he says, there was no place to translate the New Testament in all England. Printed copies of them were brought to England, but most of them were confiscated and destroyed. Once again the Bible was burned, but this time by the Christian king in agreement with the bishops of the English church; and with the Bible suffered many of its zealous readers. Tindale himself died a martyr for his faith and his Bible in October, 1536, at the hands of the imperial authorities in Flanders. But the work of Bible translation went on, nevertheless, and Henry VIII was still on the throne when the Bible gained the victory. Miles Coverdale, who had undertaken another translation, issued the year before Tindale's death, failed to get royal sanction for its publication, but the book was not suppressed. John Rogers, a friend of Tindale's, the year after his death, under the assumed name of Thomas Matthew, published a Bible, chiefly made up from Tindale's and Coverdale's work. Through Crumwell's mediation Cranmer secured the king's permission to sell this Bible in the realm. But the convocation was not satisfied with it. It asked for another translation, and therefore the so-called Great Bible was published in 1539, Coverdale revising his former work under the direction of Crumwell, Cranmer, and others. This Great Bible was ordered by a royal warrant to be exhibited in all parish churches; copies were fastened to the pulpits by means of chains, and the public was allowed to read them "with discretion, honest intent, charity, reverence, quiet behavior," as is said in the admonition published by Bishop Bonner. This happened in the last years of Henry VIII. Under Queen Mary—bloody Mary, as she was called— the printing of Bibles was stopped, but the exiles who went to Geneva undertook a new revision, which was much more radical and had the privilege of bearing an introductory letter by Calvin himself. At the very moment of Queen Elizabeth's coronation, among other prisoners (according to the expression of one of her courtiers) the four evangelists and Saint Paul were released, having been long shut up in an unknown tongue, as it were in prison. The Great Bible was revised by some of the bishops under direction of Archbishop Parker, who did not shrink from using improvements from the Geneva Bible. This Bishops' Bible, published in 1568, was the official one, but the Geneva Bible was far more popular, while the Roman Catholics made a translation of their own, printed in France at Rheims and Douai. The rivalry between the Bishops' Bible and the Geneva Bible was confusing. Therefore, in order to overcome it, King James, in 1604, appointed a committee for the revision of the Bible, consisting of about fifty members, and divided into six groups, two of which met at Westminster, Oxford, and Cambridge respectively. They did excellent work, the result of which was published in 1611 and is known as the Authorised Version. It is in this version that the English translation attained its highest excellence. It is this form which gained the largest circulation and the greatest popularity among all English-speaking peoples. It still survives the recent attempt at revision, which was made by an English and an American committee, both working on the same principles and in constant communication with one another. It is a well-known fact that the final corrections were cabled from England to America in order to procure a simultaneous publication on both sides of the Atlantic. Here again, as in the German revision, the two issues are not identical. It marks, however, a clear distinction between the German and the English Bible that the former reached its final form at its very beginning, whereas the latter did not achieve this result until a hundred years later. The Bible of Luther was creative of the German language, as we have seen, while the English Bible is rather a product of the period of highest literary culture in England. Luther produced Goethe. Shakespeare (d. April 23, 1616) is practically contemporaneous with the Authorised Version.

The development of the French Bible is still more slow and varied. There was a pre-Reformation translation, printed several times, at Lyons and at Paris; but it was of a purely mediæval character. Then a humanist, Jacques Lefèvres d'Étaples (Faber Stapulensis, d. 1536), undertook a new French translation from the Vulgate. The first French Bible translated from the original Hebrew and Greek was published in 1535 by Peter Robert Olivetan, a cousin of Calvin. The author himself, and Calvin, and others corrected and improved it from time to time, and nearly every twenty or thirty years a new editor would try to revise it. In this series of revisions one of the most successful was that of Frédéric Ostervald of Neuchâtel, in 1744. But the process is still going on, French and Swiss theologians vying one with another in fair competition. Moreover, the Protestant translation found many rivals in the work of Roman Catholics, especially in the great period of French literature in the reign of Louis XIV. Some of these translators, for example

Bossuet, aimed at making the style of their translation as elegant as possible, while others, under the influence of Port Royal, paraphrased the text with a view rather to clearness. None of these versions had real success; none has become final. France still suffers from the lack of a classic form for its Bible.

The attitude of a nation toward its Bible is largely determined by the development of the translation. It is obvious that the Germans hold to Luther's Bible even more insistently than the English do to their Authorised Version, and that in France there is an open field for every fresh attempt at revising and translating. The nation has not become united with its Bible, and, as regards language, the famous "Dictionnaire de l'Académie," aiming at a standard of literary uniformity, is but a poor and artificial substitute for the influence exercised in a living and natural way by the Bible.

It is not our task here to trace the history of translations in Italy, Spain, Portugal, Hungary, and elsewhere. It is to a large extent a history of enthusiasm, devotion, and martyrdom, and at the same time of failure and oppression. Wherever the so-called Counter-Reformation, started by the Jesuits, gained hold of the people, the vernacular was suppressed and the Bible kept from the laity. So eager were the Jesuits to destroy the authority of the Bible—the paper pope of the Protestants, as they contemptuously called it —that they even did not refrain from criticising its genuineness and historical value.

To sum up: it was the Bible which trained printers and translators and thereby made a noble contribution to modern civilisation and literature; on the other hand, it was printing and translating which made it possible for the Bible to become the popular book that ruled daily life.

VII

THE BIBLE RULES DAILY LIFE
(1550-1850)

The Reformation gave the Bible a new position—not that there had been no Bible before, nor that the Bible had had no influence. We have seen that there were numbers of Bibles, in Latin as well as in the vernacular, and that the Bible had been one of the foundations of mediæval civilisation, yet it was only by Luther's translation and the other versions made on his model that the Bible became a really popular book, and it was only by the Reformation that the Bible was established as the authority for daily life in a modern, that is, non-ascetic, sense.

The two points insisted on by all the reformers were, first, that the Bible is perspicuous, that is, that every reader can by himself find out in his Bible what is essential for salvation; and, secondly, that the Bible is sufficient. The Christian does not need anything else; the Bible tells him everything which he requires—of course in its own domain, religion, or, to use the language of that time, the "doctrine of salvation." By the Reformation the Bible got rid of all its rivals, such as tradition, Apocrypha, legend, canon law, and so on. It is wonderful to see—and I doubt if modern Christianity has realised the fact in all its importance—how by the preaching of the reformers all these things, which hitherto had been thought of as integral parts of Christianity, simply fell away. No cult of the saints, no adoration of their images, no legends, no fancy, no merriment connected with religion, but the pure Bible and the stern doctrine of it and the austere attitude of Puritanism corresponding to it were now uppermost. Nay, the letter of the Bible was binding in a stricter sense than it had ever been before. Catholicism made it possible to mitigate the strictness by allegorical interpretation; Protestantism insisted upon taking the Bible in its literal sense. There was now no way of escape; a man had to take whatever the Bible said or refuse the Bible altogether. In principle the mystery had gone; the Bible was plain and made itself understood.

It was the literal sense, as established by lexicon and grammar, which was to be followed. This caused the reformers to encourage and facilitate the study of the original languages of the Bible. When they tried to improve the grammar-schools and to found as many new ones as possible, it was not so much the humanistic delight in the classical languages as the desire to secure a sure knowledge of Greek and Hebrew which might enable a boy to read and to interpret the Bible. It is evident from many utterances both of Luther and

Calvin that their aim in all their school work was to provide good preachers of the true gospel, or good teachers of the genuine doctrine of the Bible.

To be sure, there are differences of character, both personal and national, between the two great reformers, which account for a somewhat different development of their churches. In Luther's piety the joyful experience of salvation brings in a happy note; the children of God praise his love and grace. In Calvin's devotion the feeling prevails that God's majesty is above all creatures and that his holy will is the supreme rule for our life. Religion with Luther is bright and cheerful, whereas with Calvin it has a darker tinge. But both are building on the same foundation and with the same end in view: from salvation to salvation, from grace to grace. The difference is but one of attitude toward the present life.

The difference finds its best expression in a varying use of the phrase Word of God. Both, of course, believed in an historical revelation of God to mankind, and they were convinced that this revelation was to be found in the holy Scriptures. God had spoken through his prophets; he had given his promises to his people; he had sent his Son and had fulfilled his promises through him. All this was to be found in the Bible and only in the Bible. The reformers refused the authority of tradition, just as they declined to acknowledge the present individual inspiration of enthusiasts, or "Schwarmgeister," as Luther contemptuously called them. It was in the Bible that Christianity had to look for all necessary information about God and salvation. And yet Luther, when using the expression Word of God, scarcely thinks of the written book. It is the living word as represented by the preaching of the prophets and the apostles, and perpetuated by the preaching of the ministers of the church. It is to him not a formal authority but an energising inspiration. Not everything in the Bible is authoritative, merely by the fact that it stands in the Bible; only what witnesses to Christ is authoritative and is to be taken as the Word of God. On the other hand, Zwingli and Calvin frequently use the term Word of God when speaking of the holy Scriptures themselves. It is characteristic that the reformed churches of Switzerland felt it their duty to fix the exact number of writings included in this Word of God, just as the Roman Catholic church did at the Council of Trent, while no Lutheran creed ever defines the exact content of the Bible. To the former it was a book of law, to the latter a book of inspiration.

Luther, owing to his familiarity with Saint Paul, understood that Christianity had nothing to do with the Law; the whole notion of the Law had to be dropped out from the field of religion. Law there must be in the government of the state—it would not be necessary even there, if all people were true Christians—but for the wicked there must be a law and there must be punishment. The Christian's life, however, is not a slave's obedience to injunctions but a child's glad doing of his father's will; he knows what his father wants him to do and he does it joyfully. Luther is especially interested in proving that Jesus' teaching, in particular the Sermon on the Mount, does not exhibit an ascetic law, but gives principles for the moral life of every Christian. One need not enter a monastery in order to fulfil Christ's commandments. It is in the tasks of the daily life that a Christian has to prove himself a true disciple of Jesus. The Bible is to rule the daily life of the Christian, but not in the sense of a law. When, in 1523, a preacher at Weimar aimed to introduce the Mosaic law instead of the common law, Luther treated him as a "Schwarmgeist," and, in fact, it was that proposal which lay at the basis of all the "Schwarmgeisterei." Such experiments, aiming to constitute a kingdom of the Saints on earth, as the Anabaptists made at Münster and elsewhere, always failed, and made Luther and his friends suspicious of any such attempt.

It is different with Calvin. He is interested in realising the kingdom of God in the Christian congregation, or, to put it more accurately, in the commonwealth of Geneva, which is to him identical with the Christian congregation of that place. So it is the commonwealth which is to be ruled by the Bible, and the Bible in this rôle acts as a law to which the whole community as well as the individual has to submit. And again it is characteristic that Calvin takes the Bible as a unit. It is the Old Testament law as well as the gospel which is to be regarded as the indispensable rule both of public and private life. With the Calvinists the ten commandments become an integral part of the regular Sunday service.

Of course there are many gradations between these two positions. Zwingli, the Zürich reformer, was of a different type from Calvin, while he was even more opposed to Luther than was the Genevan. Luther's rule was to abolish whatsoever was contrary to the Bible. Zwingli would permit only what was based upon or commanded by the Bible; he objected to the use of an organ, to the keeping of festival days except Sunday, and so on. Luther even tolerated pictures in the church. He was sure that no one would adore them if pervaded by the true spirit of the gospel, and he was convinced that this spirit could be successfully inculcated by means of preaching. Zwingli and Calvin both did away with all pictures in the churches. They had the walls whitewashed and the ten commandments and other passages from the Bible painted on them. Nothing is so characteristic of this difference between the Lutheran and the Calvinistic feeling as the history of an epitaph in an East Prussian church, the monument of the noble family of the earls of Dohna. At the time of the Reformation they joined the Grand Master, later Duke, Albrecht of Brandenburg in taking Luther's part. The epitaph, which was erected in the church of Mohrungen on the death of Earl Peter in 1553, was decorated with a picture showing the holy Trinity adored by the family of the donor. At the beginning of the seventeenth century the family went over to Calvinism, and the painting was altered by covering the image of the holy Trinity with black varnish and putting over it some Bible verses in gold letters.

The different attitude toward the Bible finds its expression also in the fact that the Lutherans used hymns, whereas the Calvinists adhered to the Biblical Psalter. Of course the vigorous songs composed by Luther are most of them based upon Psalms and other Biblical passages, and so were the greater number of hymns in the Lutheran church. On the other hand, the Calvinists did not agree with the English church in taking over the alternative recitation of the Psalter from the mediæval exercises of the monasteries and large cathedral choirs. They used the Psalter in a rhythmical paraphrase adapted to modern singing, but keeping so near to the wording of the Psalms that they even called it the Psalm-book. The difference was, in fact, slight, but they felt it to be essential. The Lutherans followed the usage of the church, the Calvinists the very word of the Bible. It is remarkable, however, that hymns gradually gained more importance among the Calvinists, especially since the time of the eighteenth-century revivals, and that nowadays the hymn-book, enriched by the contributions of recent time from poets of all denominations, is in favour with all Protestants and in some circles is even in danger of becoming a substitute for the Bible.

In spite of all these differences, these two great forms of Protestantism manifest almost the same attitude toward the Bible, and we see them changing their attitude almost at the same time and in the same direction. The theologians of the orthodox period exaggerated the authority of the Bible to such an extent that critics like Lessing could speak of Bibliolatry or Bible-worship. They extended the notion of inspiration even to the smallest details in the printed text which lay before them, with no regard for the fact that those details were late additions, sometimes even misprints, and that the various editions did not agree in these details. True scholastics as they were, they had no sense for facts but an unlimited desire for theory; the facts had to submit to the theory, and whoever would appeal to the facts against the theory was denounced as a heretic and driven out as a disreputable person. This doctrinal attitude changed when, at the end of the seventeenth century, Pietism in Germany and Methodism in England once again turned religion from ecclesiastical doctrine to personal devotion. The estimation of the Bible is not diminished—quite the contrary; yet it finds its expression not in stiff formulas of dogmatics but in beautiful hymns. Under the direction of P. J. Spener (d. 1705) people once more gather in private circles to read and to interpret the Bible; once more the students are drawn away from dead scholasticism to the living study of the Bible. To the *theologia dogmatica* is opposed a *theologia biblica*. People begin to realise again what is the true use of the Bible, not as a text-book for dogmatic competitions and controversies, but as the divine word of comfort and exhortation, a guide to salvation, and an expression of salvation already gained. There is a beautiful tract written by A. H. Francke of Halle (d. 1727) and very often printed as a preface to the Bible in German, "A brief direction how to read the Bible for edification." It sounds thoroughly modern, as it deals not with questions of theology but entirely with piety. This attitude was again changed by the so-called rationalism. That movement, too, entered the Protestantism of Germany as well as of England and America in various forms and under various names (deism, unitarianism), but with the same tendency. It may be that it had an easier start and a wider spread in the Lutheran church of Germany. We shall speak of its influence in the next chapter. The Bible was submitted to reason or explained according to reason. The Bible was to be followed for the sake of the precepts of reason contained in it or else not at all. It was, however, the common conviction that the Bible gave the most reasonable injunctions, and whereas orthodoxy had been mostly intellectual and Pietism emotional, rationalism by its moral strictness helped the Bible to retain its influence on daily life.

This influence was due to the fact that since Luther's time the Bible was in every house; it was the centre of the regular morning and evening prayers, the father reading and explaining to his family some chapters of the Bible. What a knowledge of the Bible had been gained by the laity soon after the Reformation is shown by the prince elector of Saxony Johann Friedrich, who at the important meetings held at Augsburg in 1530 was able to quote from memory all necessary passages of the Bible.

In Lutheran countries the influence of the Bible found expression in arts and crafts. Not only were the walls of the churches decorated with pictures taken from the Bible but also the walls of private houses. The furniture of a farmhouse was painted with Biblical stories, very awkward paintings, indeed, but showing the spirit of simple and plain devotion. It is otherwise when a rich lady's dressing-table in baroque or rococo is decorated with such scenes. We feel that they are out of place there and that scenes taken from ancient mythology would suit such a purpose much better. We should consider it a little profane that, at a wedding dinner in the sixteenth century, between the several courses elaborate dishes were passed, representing Biblical scenes. We cannot help remembering the remark of that preacher of the old church who exclaimed: "Oh, that they had these stories painted in their hearts!"

Much more important is the art of music. Luther was fond of it; he would never have given up a choir and an organ. He made it possible for the

Lutheran church to produce the greatest masterpieces that music has ever achieved—Bach's oratorios. While the Roman church directed the work of its great musicians toward the glorification of the mass, and the Calvinistic church became rigorously opposed to the very art of music, the Lutheran composers were inspired by the Bible itself. The Biblical sonatas of Johann Kuhnau (d. 1722) seem to us mere trifling. The real work was done by Heinrich Schütz (d. 1672) and Johann Sebastian Bach, the cantor of Saint Thomas in Leipzig (d. 1750), who succeeded in giving to the Bible a new voice, a voice which is still sounding and entering circles where the printed Bible would scarcely be read. The combination in Bach's oratorios is very striking—the majestic church hymns sung by the choir, the simple recitative of Scripture, and, last but not least, the arias giving the response of the pious individual to the words of God in the Bible. This is the most characteristic part of it. Protestant piety cannot be without the personal expression of individual feeling; it is thoroughly subjective in the highest sense. As Luther in his catechism explains the Apostles' Creed thus, "I believe that God has created me...; I believe that Jesus Christ is my Lord, who has saved me...; I believe that it is impossible for me to come to Jesus Christ without the help of the Holy Ghost...," so Protestant piety gives to everything this subjective note. There is a Greek manuscript of the Gospels from the fourteenth century, written in several colours to distinguish the words of Jesus, of his apostles, of his enemies, and of the evangelist. The narrative of the evangelist is given in green ink, the words of the Pharisees and other adversaries of Jesus in black, the words of the disciples in blue, and the sayings of Jesus himself are in red. It is a curious piece of work, showing the tendency of the Greek church to dramatise the sacred history of the Gospel. With this Greek copy we may compare a Protestant family Bible mentioned by a modern German preacher. It is a plain old printed Bible, but the pious great-grandfather has marked it all through with various colours, which he explains in a note: "What touched the sin of my heart:—Black. What inspired me to good:—Blue. What comforted me in sorrow:—Red. What promised me the grace of God in eternity:—Gold." The difference between objective facts and subjective relation to them, between apprehension and appreciation, is evident. This is the new spirit which pervades the Protestant reader of the Bible, and therefore the Bible is much more to him than it had been to Christianity in former times.

Where the Bible was read in such a spirit it was bound to gain an influence upon the daily life. We must admit this even if we have no direct evidence. The inward acting of the spirit in the individual is inaccessible to scientific observation and statistics.

We are in a much better position regarding the Calvinistic circles, for here the influence of the Bible was a public one. The Bible here was recognised as the only rule to be followed in public life as well as in private. The most characteristic feature is the attitude toward the Sabbath. Luther had explained the third commandment (according to his numeration, the fourth according to the Calvinists) as meaning "den Feiertag heiligen," to use the day, granted by God as a holiday, for going to church and listening to the preaching of the gospel; so the Lutherans, who never called it Sabbath, did not insist upon avoiding all work, but upon attending the holy service; besides, human feeling led them to relieve their servants and employees so far as possible from their labour. The Calvinists kept the Sabbath, as they said, exactly according to the Old Testament commandment: "Thou shalt not do any work." It reminds us sometimes of the minuteness of rabbinical Sabbath controversies when we see how carefully the Sabbath is kept as a day for doing no work whatever; even the children are forbidden to play with their toys. It is a concession made to the gospel if works of piety, of charity, or of necessity are permitted.

Another prominent feature is the use of Biblical names. Among Lutherans and members of the English church the use of Christian names, mostly derived from famous saints or kings, as Edward, George, Richard, Robert, Thomas, William, continued; while the Calvinists preferred Biblical names such as Abraham, Isaac, Moses, Joshua, Elijah, Jeremiah, Nathaniel. They often chose the names of obscure persons from the Bible, such as Abia, Abiel, Ammi, Eliphalet, Jared, Jedidiah, Jerathmeel, Reuben, Uriah. It was not so much the admiration for this or that hero in the Bible as the simple demand for something Biblical which gave to the children such unfamiliar names. Parents did not care for the real character of the man to whom the name first belonged provided he was mentioned in the Bible; neither Delilah nor Archelaus had a reputation which would make their names desirable; but, nevertheless, they were given. Gamaliel was a Pharisee, a scribe, very far from being a Christian, but the name, being in the Bible, became a Christian name among the descendants of one of the Pilgrim fathers. Biblical reminiscences also are to be found in Christian names, such as Faithful, Faintnot, Hopestill, Strong; Praise-God Barbone, one of Cromwell's followers, is said to have had two brothers, baptised with the Christian names of "Christ-came-into-the-world-to-save Barbone" and "If-Christ-had-not-died-thou-hadst-been-damned Barbone" respectively; but this is apocryphal, and so is probably the American counterpart: "Through-many-trials-and-tribulations-we-must-enter-into-the-kingdom-of-God" (Acts 15 : 22) as a Christian name.

One can hardly deny that this Biblicism sometimes became an abuse of the Bible. The Scriptures were used for investigating the future. This method, which we have already noted in the second chapter, was made an official one in the Moravian church. People used Bible verses in their games; riddles were taken from the Bible. As the one and only book the Bible had to serve as a whole library and provide all kinds of entertainment. That is the other side of the matter.

The influence of the Bible on public life in the time of Puritanism is illustrated best by the records of the first plantations in New England.[2] When, in June, 1639, "all the free planters" of the colony of New Haven "assembled together in a general meeting to consult about settling civil government according to God," the first question laid before them by John Davenport was: "Whether the Scriptures do hold forth a perfect rule for the direction and government of all men in all duties which they are to perform to God and men as well in the government of families and commonwealth as in matters of the church." "This was assented unto by all, no man dissenting, as was expressed by holding up of hands." The second question was whether all do hold themselves bound by that (plantation) covenant that "in all public offices, etc., we would all of us be ordered by those rules which the Scripture holds forth to us." This was answered in the same way. Therefore it was voted unanimously, "that the Word of God shall be the only rule to be attended unto in ordering the affairs of government in this plantation." Before they go on to select officials from their number, the chapter on the institution of the seventy elders (Ex. 18) is read, together with Deut. 1 : 13 and 17 : 15 and I Cor. 6 : 1-7, and one of the planters declares that he had felt scruples about it, but that these had been removed by reading Deut. 17 : 15 at morning prayers. When a difference arises between two members of the colony they refer it for arbitration to brethren, in accordance with I Cor. 6 : 1-7. A prisoner is pressed to confess his crime by reminding him of that passage of Scripture: "He that hideth his sin shall not prosper, but he that confesseth and forsaketh his sins shall find mercy" (Prov. 28 : 13). When a murder has been committed they sentence the guilty to death "according to the nature of the fact and the rule in that case, He that sheds man's blood, by man shall his blood be shed" (Gen. 9 : 6). They refer to Lev. 20 : 15 in a case of bestiality in order to justify the sentence of death. When questions and scruples arise between New Haven and Massachusetts about the justice of an offensive war, New Haven refers to the story of Jehoshaphat, king of Judah, "who sinned and was rebuked by two prophets Jehu and Eliezer for joining with and helping Ahab and Ahaziah, kings of Israel" (II Chron. 17-20). From this, they say, one might infer that even a defensive war and all leagues are forbidden by the law of God. On the other hand, they rely on the conquest of Canaan and David's war against the Ammonites (II Sam. 10) as examples for the justice of an offensive war and even a vindictive war of revenge.

[2] *Cf.* C. T. Hoadly, *Records of the Colony and Plantation of New Haven from 1638 to 1649*, Hartford, 1857, and *Records of the Colony or Jurisdiction of New Haven from May, 1653, to the Union* (1665), Hartford, 1858.

It is their fundamental agreement, not to be disputed or questioned hereafter, "that the judicial law of God given by Moses and expounded in other parts of Scripture, so far as it is a hedge and a fence to the moral law and neither ceremonial nor typical nor had any reference to Canaan, has an everlasting equity in it and should be the rule of their proceedings." This fundamental law, as it is fixed in 1639 and reinforced in 1642 and 1644, shows clearly the spirit of this legislation. At the same time we learn from the many restrictions how difficult it was to adapt the Old Testament law to the needs of this Christian commonwealth.

The first records of the Massachusetts Bay Company[3] show indeed a marked difference. They are less Scriptural. In the royal charter given to the company by Charles I in 1628 the Bible is not mentioned; the aim of the colony is said to be "to win and incite the natives of the country to the knowledge and obedience of the only true God and Saviour of mankind and the Christian faith." The governor is bound by his oath "to do his best endeavour to draw on the natives of this country, called New England, to the knowledge of the true God and to conserve the planters and others coming hither in the same knowledge and fear of God," or, according to another form of oath, "to act according to the law of God and for the advancement of his Gospel, the laws of this land, and the good of this plantation."

[3] *Records of the Governor and Company of the Massachusetts Bay*, edited by N. B. Shurtleff. Boston, 1853.

But in the laws framed by the colonists themselves, the Bible is constantly appealed to. Passing a law against drinking healths, in 1639, the General Court declared this to be a mere useless ceremony and also the occasion of many sins, "which as they ought in all places and times to be prevented carefully, so especially in plantations of churches and commonwealths wherein the least known evils are not to be tolerated by such as are bound by solemn covenant *to walk by the rule of God's word* in all their conversation." This statement is a solemn one, and they put it into effect as far as possible. When discussing in the General Court the question whether a certain number of magistrates should be chosen for life, a question which had a good deal of importance for the future development of the colony, they decided in favour of it, "for that it was shown from the word of God, etc., that the principal magistrates ought to be for life." Nay, even a question of minor importance raised by the Scriptures, whether women must wear veils, was eagerly discussed, both parties relying on Scriptural proofs.

When, in 1646, the General Court found it necessary to convoke a public assembly of the elders, they did so, protesting, however, that "their lawful power *by the word of God* to assemble the churches or their messengers upon occasion of counsel" is not to be questioned, and therefore the said assembly of elders, after having "discussed, disputed, and cleared up *by the word of God* such questions of church government and discipline ... as they shall think needful and meet," is to report to the General Court, "to the end that the same being found *agreeable to the word of God*, it may receive from the said General Court such approbation as is meet, that the Lord being thus acknowledged by church and state to be our Judge, our Lawgiver, and our King, he may be graciously pleased still to save us as hitherto he has done ... and so the churches in New England may be Jehovah's and he may be to us a God from generation to generation." It is remarkable that not only the church synod is to judge what is "agreeable to the holy Scriptures" but the civil government takes it as its own duty to make sure that the resolutions of the synod are really in accordance with the Scripture and only then to give their approbation. It is the secular power which feels bound to the Word of God and to superintend its strict observance. But in fact state and church are not to be distinguished in this period of New England history.

In 1641 the Rev. John Cotton, "teacher of the Boston church," published at London "An Abstract or the Laws of New England as they are now established." The first edition does not mention Cotton's name; this was added only after his death in a second edition, published in 1655 by his friend William Aspinwall. This Abstract by John Cotton does not represent, as its title seems to indicate, the actual law; it is a proposed code of laws for New England. But it has influenced to a great extent, if not the legislation of Massachusetts, at any rate the "Laws for Government, published for the use of New Haven Colony" in 1656. The remarkable feature is that Cotton gives marginal references to the Bible for each one of his rules, for instance: "All magistrates are to be chosen (1) by the free Burgesses—Deut. 1 : 13; (2) out of the free Burgesses—Deut. 17 : 15; (3) out of the ablest men and most approved amongst them—Ex. 18 : 21; (4) out of the rank of Noblemen or Gentlemen amongst them—Eccles. 10 : 17, Jer. 30 : 21," and so on. It is according to the Old Testament rule that the eldest son ought to inherit twice as much as his brothers; it is a true expression of the Old Testament meaning when punishment is extended even to animals which kill a man (cp. Ex. 21 : 28). The spirit of this legislation is almost as severe, not to say cruel, as the spirit of Charlemagne's Saxon law. Twenty-four kinds of trespassing are enumerated which are to be punished with death. It is evidently against the legislator's own view that an exemption is made for simple fornication, "not to be punished with death according to God's own law," as he adds by way of apology. In the second edition the Bible verses are printed at length in the text itself, the margin being devoted to learned remarks on different translations. The motto which expresses the character of this abstract is taken from Isaiah 33 : 22: "The Lord is our Judge, the Lord is our Lawgiver, the Lord is our King; He will save us."

The official Laws of Massachusetts, as established in 1658 and printed in 1660, have no Bible references in the margin; but in the restriction of flogging to the effect that no more than forty stripes should be applied, and in the requirement that sentence of death may be imposed only when two or three witnesses testify to the guilt, the Biblical rules given in Deut. 25 : 5 and 19 : 15 are seen to be at work. Sabbath-breaking is to be punished with a fine of ten shillings, the penalty being doubled in the second case. In 1630 a man had been whipped for shooting on the Sabbath.

In 1647 the General Court passed a law ordering that each township containing over fifty households should appoint a schoolmaster, and if there were more than a hundred families, a grammar-school was to be supported. This care for education is inspired by the desire of securing a true interpretation of the Bible, as is proved by the following statement of motives: "It being the chief project of that old deluder Satan to keep men from the knowledge of the Scriptures, as in former times by keeping them in an unknown tongue, so in these latter times by persuading from the use of tongues, that so at least the true sense and meaning of the original might be clouded by false glosses of saint-seeming deceivers; that learning may not be buried in the grave of our fathers in the church and commonwealth, therefore ordered," etc.

After the college had been founded in 1636, they chose in 1643 for its seal a shield containing three books with *Ve-ri-tas* written on them, two open and one seen from the back. Oxford has between three crowns one book with seven clasps. This book evidently is the Bible; it has *Dominus illuminatio mea* (Psalm 27 : 1) written on it. The seven clasps are said to indicate the seven liberal arts and the three crowns the three modes of philosophy. It is characteristic of the Puritan spirit that their shield had nothing but three Bibles. The meaning of *Veritas*, of course, is not (as it has been taken in recent times) that the aim of all research is truth. The Puritan fathers were not concerned with research; they believed in revelation, and it was by the revelation laid down in the Bible that truth was transmitted to mankind. The three Bibles may or may not be a symbol of the holy Trinity; the script on the front and on the back recalls the book written within and on the back in Rev. 5 : 1. They meant that the Bible was the fundamental source of all knowledge. Harvard College was founded to be a training-school for ministers, who should know the truth and its source. *Christo et ecclesiæ* became the second motto of the college. That it has developed into a university, containing, besides a college and the divinity school, schools for law, medicine, applied science, etc., is due to a total change of public opinion at a much later time. The Puritan use of the Bible has disappeared, but something of the Puritan spirit may still be seen in the inscription on the front of the modern building of the Harvard Law School, drawn from Ex. 18 : 20: "Thou shalt teach them ordinances and laws and shalt shew them the way wherein they must walk, and the work that they must do."

VIII

THE BIBLE BECOMES ONCE
MORE THE BOOK OF DEVOTION

Having made our way through the centuries, we now approach our own time, and at once we remark two facts: Never before had the Bible such a circulation as it has now gained. On the other hand, it seems to have lost most of its influence. We must look at these two facts before we raise the question what value the Bible has for the civilisation of to-day.

Printing greatly facilitated the circulation of the Bible and, as the result of the Reformation, it had become the book of the Christian family. And yet during the seventeenth and eighteenth centuries the circulation of the Bible was rather limited. The Bible might be a treasure of the household, but not the personal property of the individual. The first editions, as we have seen, scarcely exceeded one or two hundred copies. In contrast, one of the most assiduous and industrious promoters of Bible reading, Baron von Canstein, who settled at Halle in A. H. Francke's institute, published during the last nine years of his life (d. 1719) forty thousand Bibles and one hundred thousand New Testaments. To-day the British and Foreign Bible Society issues more than five million copies—one million Bibles, one and a half million New Testaments, and two and a half million parts of the Bible—yearly. The progress is due to the invention of the rotary press and other improvements in printing machinery.

Besides, the circulation of the Bible has received strong support through the foundation of Bible societies. The story is well known how Thomas Charles discovered the great desire for copies of the Bible among his Welsh countrymen, how, when he gathered some friends for the purpose of providing them with Bibles, the Baptist preacher Thomas Hughes put in the question, "And why not for other peoples, too?" and how on his motion the Society was started on March 7, 1804, as the British and Foreign Bible Society. It is wonderful to hear of the work done by this Society in the last hundred years. If one visits the Bible House in Queen Victoria Street in London he gets an impression of the extent and the importance of the work done there. The Society has its presses as well as its translators all over the world; it has its agents scattered through all the nations, and it has begun to do not only a publishers' business proper but scholarly work as well. A vast collection of Bible editions from all times and in all tongues has been gathered, and a valuable catalogue published which is of great importance for bibliography in general.

The greatest merit of the British and Foreign Bible Society, however, is the fact that it stimulated the foundation of other great Bible societies. There were some small beginnings in Germany and Switzerland. They suddenly became strong and influential in consequence of the report made concerning the British and Foreign Bible Society by its secretary, Doctor Steinkopf, and Basel and Stuttgart made a new start in 1804 and 1812. After the Napoleonic War in 1814, Mr. Pinkerton travelled through Germany with the result that Bible societies were started at Berlin, Dresden, Elberfeld, and Copenhagen, and in Holland, Norway, and even Russia. In 1808 Philadelphia joined the movement. The American Bible Society has twice canvassed the entire United States, finding that five hundred thousand families were without any Bible, and selling sixty million Bibles. It is remarkable that in the beginning Roman Catholics joined the Bible societies enthusiastically. A Bible society was founded at Regensburg in 1805, supported almost exclusively by the Roman Catholic clergy. But as early as 1817, soon after the restoration of the Jesuits by Pope Pius VII, these Bible societies were dissolved; the Roman Catholics were forbidden to be members of the other Bible societies, and in the syllabus of Pius IX, in 1864, the Bible societies are reckoned among the dangers of our time, together with Masonry and other secret societies.

By the help of the Bible societies it has become possible that Bibles should really spread among the people. In Germany each boy and girl who goes to school has his own Bible. Bibles and New Testaments are distributed among the soldiers. Most churches make a present of a Bible to each couple who are to be married. There is rather a superabundance of Bibles, which contrasts sharply with the estimation in which the Bible is held. As Spurgeon, in his drastic way, said in one of his stimulating sermons: "The Bible is in every house, but in many the dust on it is so thick that you might write on it: *Damnation*." It was a veteran Bible agent who, after thirty years' experience, said: "It is easy to give away dozens of Bibles, but only the one which you sell will be valued."

The circulation has been greatly enlarged by numbers of translations. We remember that the first translations of the Bible were connected with Christian missions; they were epoch-making for the languages, creating a written alphabet and a national literature. The translations of the sixteenth and seventeenth centuries were of a different character; they were the result of a religious reformation; they represented for the nation the culmination point in language and a remarkable stage in literature. Now again Christian missions revived, and started on a wonderful career all over the world, and they needed to have the Bible translated. The Bible societies did their best to provide as many translations as possible. From the eight languages of 600 A. D. and some twenty-four in the sixteenth century the number of languages into which the Bible has been translated has grown up to four hundred, and if we count the dialects separately we have over six hundred. The whole Bible has not been translated into all these languages and dialects, but in every case parts of it, sometimes the New Testament, sometimes only one Gospel, have been translated, and other parts will follow. It is interesting to hear the translators speak of the difficulties they have to overcome. One sees what influence the Bible has on civilisation. Often a language lacks some word which is indispensable for the translator; he has to adapt one or coin a new one. There is no idea more frequent in the Bible than the idea of God. The Chinese had no word which exactly corresponded, the usual words indicating either spirits or the sun or something of that sort. The Amshara lacks the idea of righteousness, the Bantu the idea of holiness. If the translator uses as an equivalent the word for separateness, his reader will get rather the notion of something split. Sometimes the translator will prefer to keep the Greek word, as in the case of *baptise*, but he must be careful, for *batisa* in Bantu means "treat some one badly." So the language has to be remodelled in order to become suitable for the purpose of translating the Bible. The Bible once again exercises a civilising influence on the languages of many peoples. With very few exceptions, such as a Malayan Bible of 1621 and a translation by John Eliot into the Massachusetts Indian dialect published in 1666, most of these translations originated in the nineteenth century and are due to the present missionary energy of Christianity. Here again it is mortifying to see how the Bible is spread among peoples who never had had civilisation before, while among the Christian nations, who, to a large extent, owe their civilisation to this very Bible, it is disregarded.

Besides the circulation we may also mention the enormous amount of mental energy spent on Bible studies by the scholars of this last century. Not only students of theology but also classical and Oriental scholars have joined to study the Bible, to comment upon it, and make everything in it understood. Specialisation in its inevitable course has caused a separation of Old Testament and New Testament studies. In order to understand and explain thoroughly the Old Testament one has to know several Oriental languages and follow up the daily increasing evidence for Oriental history, culture, and religion, whereas the New Testament scholar is bound to study the development of the Greek language and the whole civilisation of the Hellenistic period. Nay, even the Old and the New Testament departments are each specialising into the textual and the higher criticism, the theology or the religious history both of the Jewish people and of primitive Christianity. One scholar studies the life of Christ, another makes the apostolic age the topic of his special research; one is commenting upon the Gospels, another upon the letters of Saint Paul. The literature in these different departments has grown so rapidly that it is almost impossible to follow it and to survey the whole field. Nevertheless, we need a comprehensive view, and a large number of scientific journals, in German, English, French, some few also in other languages, are devoted to the summing up of results which have been attained by special research. There are dozens of dictionaries and encyclopedias dealing with Biblical matters either separately or in connection with other material. It is, indeed, wonderful what progress has been and is being made. One is astonished to find that every day brings new problems and new attempts at solution, and one cannot help admiring the energy and sagacity which are put into these studies.

But in spite of this circulation never attained before, and in spite of this active work of research, the fact remains indisputable that the Bible has lost its former position. There was a time, in the Middle Ages, when the Bible was at least one foundation of Christian civilisation, not to say the one foundation (as the men of that period would have said). Then there was a time, during recent centuries, when the Bible ruled daily life almost completely. Whether we regret the fact or approve of it, it remains a fact, and we have to face it, that those times are gone.

The Bible nowadays is one book among a thousand others. It is still revered by the majority of the people, but it is not so much read as it was in the time when it was the one book the people possessed. The enormous statistics for Bible circulation lose in effect if we compare the figures of the book-trade in general, the number of books published every year, and the numbers of editions and copies which some of the notable successes have attained.

The old problem, the Bible or the classics or a combination of both, is revived in a new form. There is a neopaganism in literature, and often it seems incompatible to read both the Bible and modern literature, and most people decide in favour of the latter. Once again the Bible has its rivals very numerous and strong.

The Bible in former times was held to be the divinely inspired text-book for all human knowledge. It was in the Bible that one had to look for information not only about God and God's will and everything connected with God, but also about philosophy, natural science, history, and so on. Now a secularisation of science has taken place by which all these departments of human knowledge are withdrawn from the ecclesiastical, theological, and Biblical authority.

The mediæval view of the world as taken from the Bible, or at least believed to be taken from it, had been utterly shattered by the great discoveries of the fifteenth and sixteenth centuries. When Columbus found the way to America and Vasco da Gama sailed around the Cape to India, and later others crossed the Pacific Ocean, the earth could no longer be considered as a round plane, it was proved to be a globe. Copernicus deciphered the mystery of heaven, the movement of the earth around the sun; Galileo Galilei followed in the same studies, and Kepler reached the climax of probability for the new theory. The church did not follow at once. It is remarkable that Copernicus did not win the assent of Luther. The great reformer, critical as he was, felt bound in this question to the authority of the Bible, and called the contradicting Copernicus a fool. It is well known how the Roman church by its inquisition treated Galileo until he withdrew his theory—formally, still holding it in his heart (*è pur si muove*, "and yet the earth does move"). Johannes Kepler, himself a Protestant and brought up with the fullest reverence for the Bible, found his own way out of the difficulty by distinguishing between the religious and the scientific aspect of the Bible, an anticipation of the modern solution. And if one is willing to maintain the modern scientific view of the universe as it has been established by the three men just named, and strengthened by their followers, he must renounce the Bible as authority in matters of science. It is a notable fact that even the Roman church, in 1817, withdrew the verdict against Galileo's theory and similar theses, thereby admitting that a Christian may safely deny the Biblical assumption that the sun moves round the earth.

The Bible in its first chapter tells us that the world was created in six days; geology now speaks of twenty million years and more. The Bible says that man was created on the sixth day by a special act of God; Darwin's theory is that the human race is the result of an evolution which eliminated numbers of former beings and developed ever higher species. The Bible tells of many miracles which can have no other meaning than that in certain cases the law of gravitation and other laws of nature are suspended; the scientist tells us that a law loses all meaning if it admits of exceptions. Of course, there are miracles and miracles: the healings of Jesus we may accept as historical without any hesitation, but the standing still of the sun in Josh. 10 : 12 is nothing but a poetical form of speech, and the floating axe-head is as legendary in the story of Elisha (II Kings 6 : 6) as it would be in any other legend.

In former times scholars wrote large volumes on the animals mentioned in the Bible and the flowers and the stones and so on; this they called sacred zoölogy and sacred botany and sacred mineralogy. It was not for their amusement: it was a serious study. The Bible was thought to be a text-book for every science, and it seemed to be much more valuable to get information of all kinds from the Bible than to collect real animals, flowers, or stones.

Likewise the human body was dealt with in the same scholastic way; it is a comparatively modern thing for physicians to be allowed to study the body and find out its real structure by dissection. Nowadays it is universally agreed that science and medicine are autonomous and are not dependent on the Bible.

The Bible was also the text-book for history, as we have seen. The history of mankind, according to this view, was limited to six thousand years. A great amount of mental energy was spent upon the question of Biblical chronology, which, however, proved to be hopelessly confused by the fact that various systems were used by the Biblical authors themselves. History was the history of the Jewish people, enriched by some glimpses of contemporaneous pagan history. Now, the discoveries in Egypt and Babylon and the deciphering of the Oriental inscriptions have illustrated the fact that the Jewish people was only one among others and one of the weakest of all these Oriental nations. Assyrian kingdoms were established as early as 6000 B. C. The famous code of Hammurabi is much older than the Mosaic law. If we compare them, we find that the former represents a high level of civilisation, while the latter establishes rules for nomadic life, a relation similar to that which exists between the Roman law and the national laws of the German tribes: though codified later, they represent, nevertheless, an earlier stage. The occupation of Canaan has come to be viewed in a new light through the exploration of Palestine. The history of the kings of Judah and Israel is now seen much more clearly than before to have been determined by politics; they are for ever steering between the influence of Egypt and that of Babylon. The accounts given in the Babylonian archives and the Egyptian inscriptions are to be compared with the Biblical account, and some may feel that the comparison is not always in favour of the latter. Even the social and religious position of the prophets is nowadays compared with contemporaneous facts in Greece, Persia, and India. The life of Jesus and the Acts of the Apostles have changed their aspect with the possibility of literary comparison. It is not so much the literary criticism of the Gospels and the Acts by themselves as it is this facility of comparison which contributes to shake the authority of the Bible. We find the same miracles told of Jesus and of the emperor Vespasian; some sayings of Jesus can be compared with utterances of Cæsar and Pompey. Many of his words have parallels in the Jewish literature as well as in the writings of the Stoa. I feel sure that the originality of Jesus will but gain by such comparison, but it is obvious that originality must be taken in a higher sense than is often the case; it is not the wording but the meaning attached to it which is new and original.

In this way everything which loomed so large when viewed standing by itself in the Bible has been reduced to its natural size; the earth has lost its central position; man is only one in a long line of similar beings; the history of Israel enters the large field of universal history; and even the personality of Jesus is subject to comparison and analogy.

This reduction is the necessary complement of the independence and autonomy attained for human science as the result of a long development. Already in the sixteenth century the humanists claimed for science the right to follow its own rules without being led and limited by the church's authoritative doctrine. They aimed at a civilisation free from ecclesiastical tutelage; going back to the classicism of pre-Christian times, they did not want the guardianship of the Christian church and its clergy. But the time was not yet ripe for this view. Even the reformers, Luther as well as Calvin, while they broke with the authority of mediæval scholasticism and of the Roman church, were not prepared to acknowledge the autonomy of science; they established the primacy of the Bible in an even stricter sense than it had borne in the Middle Ages. The Bible was to rule everything, and it was the Bible in its plain and simple meaning, without the mitigations which tradition and allegory had allowed in former times. To be sure, Luther occasionally granted some independence to secular science. He was furious when Aristotle was quoted as an authority in matters of religion, but would himself introduce him as an authority for civil government or for logic. He had a curious proof for this from the Bible itself. It was on the advice of his father-in-law, Jethro, a pagan, that Moses appointed the seventy elders to help him judge the people. Therefore for secular organisation one may take the counsel of the heathen, of the philosophers. But Luther was not consistent; as we have already seen, against Copernicus he insisted upon the authority of the Bible. He did not see that it was a question of astronomy without any relation to religion. In the seventeenth century the philosophers began to claim independence for the human reason, and soon they established reason as the highest authority, even in religious matters. It is very interesting to see the effect of this claim at the beginning. Even the most advanced liberals were so convinced of the infallible authority of the Bible that they tried by all means at their disposal to reconcile with the contents of the Bible the principles which the rational philosophy of Descartes or Spinoza had established. They started a new method of interpretation in order to make the Bible agree with reason. A long time had to pass before it became obvious to all competent minds that the Bible and reason were not to be reconciled by means of a makeshift harmony. It was only in the nineteenth century that the view forced itself upon all scholars that the Bible has to be understood in an historical way; that it does not give inspired information upon natural science and history, its revelation dealing with God and religion only.

By recent discoveries it is proved that the creation story in Gen. 1 is by no means a unique and original one; there is something similar in the Babylonian mythology; it may have been taken from there. The same holds true regarding the story of the deluge and others. So there is no reason for claiming for these stories the authority of revealed science; the Biblical author simply shares the ideas of his time. We are not bound to the scientific notions of a period two thousand years before Christ and four thousand years before our own time. And yet there is something unique in this creation story, as told in Gen. 1, for which one looks in vain in all the alleged parallels in Babylonian and other religions; it is the idea of the one God Almighty, who by his supreme will creates heaven and earth. That is the revelation conveyed to mankind by this chapter. We must not trouble about the specific description of creation; that belongs to the historical form. We cling with all our heart to the wonderful idea of the one creating God, and we realise that here revelation is given to us.

It is only by comparison that the real importance of a thing comes out. On a map of America, made on a small scale, the distances may seem short; comparing a map of Europe on the same scale one realises how long they are in fact. We are always in danger of taking some accidental feature for the main point. The frame does not make the worth of the painting.

As the Bible has lost its exclusive authority in the domain of science, so in the fine arts it has ceased to be the single source of inspiration. Since the Renaissance motifs taken from ancient mythology and poetry have come into competition with the Biblical scenes; the Dutch school cultivated the illustration of the life of the people and presented even the sacred story in this fashion—the mystery of sacredness has gone; it is purely human, not to say profane. The French liked landscapes and used Biblical subjects only as accessories. Pictures of battles, triumphs, apotheoses filled the galleries. Art to-day is anything but Biblical; modern painters have, most of them, no sense for sacred art. I venture to think they do better to keep away from it. For if a modern painter, when trying to illustrate the parable of the prodigal son in a triptychon, puts in the large middle field the man feeding the swine, giving only the left-hand corner to the return to the father, he has proved himself incapable of a religious understanding of the story, however finished a work of art his painting may be.

By all this process of secularisation the Bible has been drawn back from general civilisation and restricted to its own proper domain, religion. We must not insist on the fact that even here the Bible seems to have lost somewhat of its infallible authority. It is in the domain of theology as distinct from religion that this holds true. Strange as it may seem, it is a fact that the Bible is no more the text-book of theology. Theology, of course, can never do without the Bible, but here also the Bible is the source of historical information, not the authoritative proof for doctrine. Already in the period when the orthodox

Protestants vied with one another in asserting the inspiration of the Bible in the boldest terms and relied on the Bible for answers to every question, Samuel Werenfels (d. 1740), a professor at Basel, wrote the distich:

"Hic liber est in quo quærit sua dogmata quisque,
Invenit et pariter dogmata quisque sua."

"This is the book where each man seeketh his own ideas,
In it accordingly each findeth his own beliefs."

It was the support given by the Bible to every doctrine and every theory which made critical people doubt the propriety of proving truth by adducing proof-texts; and this not only for dogmatical questions but also for moral ones. It is well known how both parties in the controversy over slavery appealed to the authority of the Bible, and it would be difficult to say which party found the stronger support in the letter of the text. The same holds true regarding other questions of modern life; one can argue from the Bible pro and con regarding the use of wine. The Bible has been adduced in the question of polygamy. It can be quoted on both sides with reference to woman suffrage. It is indicative of the present attitude toward the Bible that this is so seldom done. The use of the Bible for the settling of modern social problems has brought upon many Christian minds a pitiful confusion. It has proved impossible to deduce from the Bible, even from the teaching of Jesus, rules for modern life. Times have changed and the conditions of life have altered.

All this prepared the way for the historical view of the Bible. Then the period of higher criticism began. It was to many a hard lesson; but we had to learn it. It was started—curious to say—by Roman Catholic scholars in France. Having the authority of the church behind them, they felt more free as regards the Bible than the Protestants did. Richard Simon made it evident that the transmission of the Bible excludes a mechanical view of inspiration. Astruc, a doctor, the physician of Louis XIV, discovered that in the Pentateuch two different sources were used. During the eighteenth century the theories of literary criticism were applied to all the books of the Old and the New Testament, and the scholarship of the nineteenth century has taken up the task, perfected the method, and reached in some questions a general agreement. To-day the principles of literary criticism in their application to the Bible are generally acknowledged. The books of the Bible are like other books; they are not to be treated as divine Scriptures but as human writings. One has to inquire in each instance about the author, his methods of writing, the sources of his information, his tendencies, and so on.

Criticism did not stop here; it overstepped the boundaries of purely literary criticism; it became historical criticism, too. The historicity of the facts reported in the Bible was called in question; recently the historicity of Jesus has been denied; and where his existence was admitted, still his teaching was criticised. Some people found it too ascetic, to others it was purely eschatological; in either case it could not be adapted to our own time. So even in its central points the Bible seemed to be attacked and its authority shaken. Instead of being restricted to the domain of religion, the Bible seemed to be denied even to the uses of devotion. But the present situation is not so desperate for the pious Bible reader as it looks.

We have once more to face the two facts: the circulation of the Bible has grown rapidly—immensely—and the estimation of the Bible has been reduced in nearly every field. Many a pious Christian, while rejoicing in the first fact, is greatly troubled by the second. Has the Bible ceased to be authoritative? Has it lost its infallibility? If the Bible is not true from cover to cover, then it seems to be not trustworthy at all. We had better put it aside and leave it to deserved oblivion. That is an argument frequently brought forward nowadays, both by people who disbelieve in the authority of the Bible and the truth of the Christian religion and by those who eagerly try to assert the old authority of the Bible as the inspired Word of God which reveals everything. They argue, and apparently not without plausibility, that if you destroy the authority of the Bible at any point, it is lost altogether; there is no limit to the destructive energy of our time. Therefore do not touch this question; leave the Bible as it stands—the sacred book, undisturbed by profane hands. It is the book by which our fathers were taught. Why should we disbelieve in it? Both these positions seem to be logically consistent: everything or nothing; infallible or no authority. But, in fact, the truth is never on one side. Hard as it may sound to our philosophers, the truth is very seldom logical. What seems to be consistency is, in fact, a confusion of two different aspects which ought to be kept separate. The Bible is not a text-book for any science—nay, not even for the science of theology. It is the book for Christian devotion. This was its original intention, and I venture to think that it is not a loss but a gain if the Bible is once more applied to its proper purpose.

As we have seen in the first chapter, the Bible proved itself to be an inexhaustible source of comfort and strength, of exhortation and inspiration to the Christians of the first period. They would not leave this book for any consideration—nay, they would even die for it. And so whenever the Bible was read by a pious Christian a new stream of life flowed through him and through the church. And this new life has always caused a strong desire for the Bible. There is a reciprocal influence between Bible and piety; the Bible creates piety, and piety demands the Bible. This is the experience of nineteen centuries; it is impossible that the twentieth century should alter it. As long as a pious Christian lives on earth, the Bible will exercise its influence upon him, and as long as there is such thing as the Bible there will be Christians. That is sure! It is not always easy to measure this private influence of the Bible on individual piety and devotion. People who read the Bible for edification usually do not talk much about it. In biographies it is not mentioned, either because the biographer took it for granted or because he did not care for it himself. Seldom do we have an opportunity, like the one given in Bismarck's letters to his wife, where he mentions frequently what Psalm or passage of the Bible he read before going to bed and discusses some points which have struck him. It is impossible to say how many people read the Bible privately for their own edification. Seeing how few know the Bible thoroughly, we might suppose that very few read it, but it is said that Bible reading among the boys in the English public schools is again increasing. And I feel sure that the time must come, and will come, when private reading of the Bible will again be a common practice among Christians.

But the Bible's task is not only to sustain individual piety; it has a second duty to perform. Christianity is not a mere aggregation of Christian individuals but a community—a church, if you will. It is necessary for any community to have a standard, for any church to have a creed. It is the Bible which has to supply this. Herein lies the danger of aberration, as we have seen in the second and the following chapters. The history of the church and of its doctrine gives ample proof of the fact that, taking the Bible as a rule for the church's dogma, Christianity not only missed the right path for the development of doctrine, but even lost the right use of the Bible. It is only by aiming at an historical orientation that the church can gain from the Bible the right direction for the setting forth of its doctrine. The doctrine of the church never can be, and never has been, identical with the doctrine of the Bible, because it is impossible to stop the development of history; besides, there are as many doctrines in the Bible itself as men who wrote the several books of the Bible, or even more. Saint Paul has not one doctrine of the atonement but half a dozen theories about it. The church has to formulate its own doctrine consistently with the Bible; that means a doctrine which keeps to the main line of religious development as testified to by the Bible; or, rather, to do justice to the variety of Biblical doctrines, permits a modern adaptation of the several modes in which religious experience is expressed. This seems vague, but it is the path which Christianity is bound to follow; and it promises success.

The modern view is that it is the religious experience of men, as testified to in the Bible, from which both the individual and the church take their start.

But Christians believe that through this human experience God himself is revealing his grace. Therefore it is still, as our fathers said, God's Word. And God will teach the church to formulate the common experience by the help of his Word. That is the present position.

———

The Interpet Manual of

KOI
HEALTH

Keith Holmes and Tony Pitham

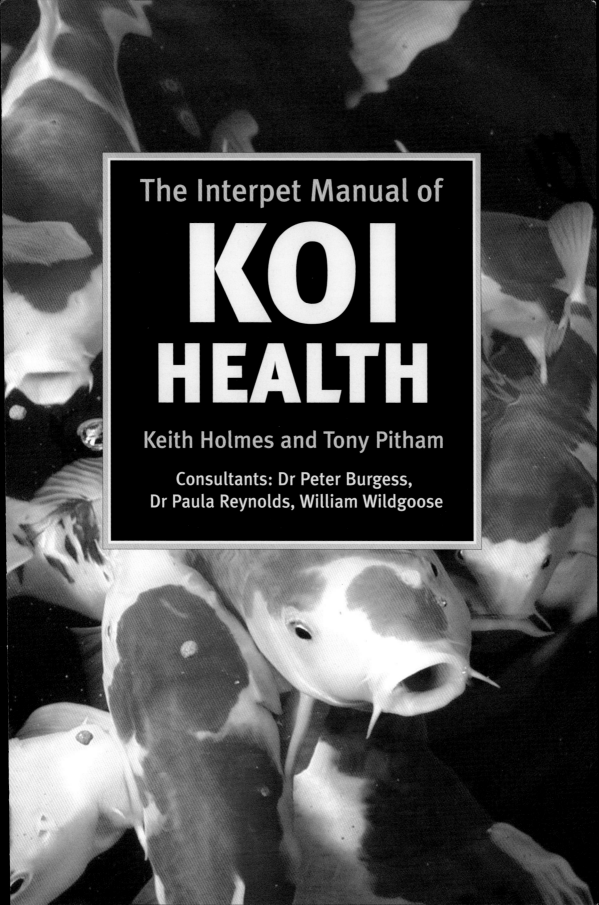

The Interpet Manual of
KOI
HEALTH

Keith Holmes and Tony Pitham

Consultants: Dr Peter Burgess,
Dr Paula Reynolds, William Wildgoose

The Authors

Keith Holmes is manager of Koi Water Barn, the premier koi company in the UK. He has worked there for nearly nine years – for the past four and a half of them as manager. Before joining Koi Water Barn, he was involved for four years in the general aquatic industry working with both tropical and coldwater species. Keith is a monthly contributor to numerous specialist aquatic magazines in the UK, and has had articles published around the world. Koi health has always been an area of particular interest for him and the practical experience learned at Koi Water Barn, combined with the advice and guidance of numerous experts, have helped make the writing of this book possible. Keith is co-author of the Interpet book *A Practical Guide to Building and Maintaining a Koi Pond*.

Tony Pitham is the owner of Koi Water Barn in Kent, and is one of the most respected koi dealers working in Japan. Koi Water Barn was established in 1984 by Tony's late father, John. Strong relationships built up over several years with many of Japan's leading breeders have led to a wealth of koi-related knowledge. He has judged and photographed the prestigious All Japan Shinkokai show, the top koi show in the world, and has supplied many show-winning koi. He has written for many of the top koi magazines worldwide and is co-author of *A Practical Guide to Building and Maintaining a Koi Pond*.

Published by Interpet Publishing,
Vincent Lane, Dorking,
Surrey RH4 3YX, England

© 2004 Interpet Publishing Ltd.
All rights reserved
This reprint 2008

ISBN 10 - 184286 099 2
ISBN 13 - 978 1 84286 099 1
Editor: Philip de Ste. Croix
Designer: Philip Clucas MSIAD
Studio photography: Neil Sutherland
Artwork: Phil Holmes and Stuart Watkinson
Production management: Consortium, Poslingford, Suffolk
Print production: Sino Publishing House Ltd, Hong Kong
Printed in China
This reprint 2005

The Consultants

Dr Peter Burgess is a fish health consultant and university lecturer, specializing in ornamental fish. He holds degrees in parasitology, microbiology and fish biology and was awarded a PhD from Plymouth University for research on whitespot disease in tropical marine fish. Dr Burgess writes regularly for several aquarium and koi magazines and contributes a regular feature on koi health problems to *Koi Ponds and Gardens*. He was a contributing author to *The Interpet Manual of Fish Health*.

Dr Paula Reynolds is an aquatic patho-biologist and proprietor of Lincolnshire Fish Health Laboratories and Research Centre. As well as offering a fish health service to veterinarians, koi dealers and hobbyists, her centre carries out health screening on koi from around the world. Epidemiology, the science of disease transmission, is one of her prime areas of research. She is well known to koi keepers in the UK for her association with many koi-keeping organizations and she writes regular articles on koi health for various koi-keeping publications.

William Wildgoose (adviser on pages 140-143 and 146-151) graduated from Glasgow Veterinary School in 1977 and has worked in general practice in London since then. He obtained his Certificate in Fish Health and Production from the Royal College of Veterinary Surgeons in 1997. He has provided professional fish health services to private hobbyists, retailers and importers and has been the veterinary advisor to the Ornamental Aquatic Trade Association for several years. He has written several scientific papers on fish health and many other articles for the scientific and hobby press. He was editor of the *Fish Veterinary Journal* for three years before contributing to and editing the BSAVA *Manual of Ornamental Fish* in 2001.

Authors' Acknowledgements

The authors would like to thank and express their appreciation of the following people and companies without whom this book would not have been possible – the late John Pitham, Sakai Fish Farm (Hiroshima), Narita Koi Farm (Nagoya), Ogawa fish farm, Nakamori and Co, Michel Capot (Koi Ichi Ban), Peter Burgess, Paula Reynolds (Lincolnshire Fish Health Consultancy), *Rinko* magazine, Martin Plows, the Koi Water Barn team, the Ornamental Aquatic Trade Association (OATA), Lisa Holmes for her patience during the writing of this book, and everyone else who has helped to make its publication possible.

CONTENTS

Foreword   page 6

 Part 1: Preventing Disease   page 8

 Part 2: Essential Skills   page 30

 Part 3: Koi Diseases   page 54

 Part 4: Treatments   page 130

Index   page 156

FOREWORD

by Dr Peter Burgess
Researcher and lecturer in ornamental fish health and husbandry

As with any pet, koi are susceptible to a variety of ailments that may crop up from time to time. Fortunately, many common health problems of koi can be successfully treated, provided the koi keeper has the basic knowledge to be able to diagnose and deal with the problem at an early stage. The aim of this book is to arm the koi keeper with this essential knowledge.

The Interpet Manual of Koi Health has been written specifically for koi keepers, whether they are novices with just a single pond in the back garden, or serious koi enthusiasts who are deeply involved in breeding or exhibiting their fish. In contrast to many textbooks on fish health, this manual presents technical information at a level that is readily understood by the non-scientist. It is primarily designed to be a practical guide, based largely on the authors' first-hand experiences gained over many years of working in the koi industry. As such, the information herein reflects current practices within the professional koi community and will be of interest to those employed in this field. The book is arranged in a logical sequence comprising four parts.

Part 1 addresses the all-important subject of disease prevention. The key to healthy koi-keeping lies in providing optimal environmental conditions and a well-balanced diet. With this aim, the reader is introduced to essential topics such as water chemistry and water quality, filtration systems, and koi nutrition. Maintaining a healthy koi pond is similar to looking after a car: various checks and services have to be performed at recommended intervals. These routine tasks are clearly laid out on pages 20-21. In terms of koi health, the old maxim "prevention is better than cure" is extremely apt, and for this reason it is recommended that Part 1 be read in its entirety.

Part 2 covers the "essential skills" that the koi keeper will need to acquire in order to monitor the health of his stock. This section begins with a simple overview of koi anatomy and biology, followed by practical tips on how to net and handle koi correctly, how to transport them safely, and how to use a microscope to check for parasites. Specialist procedures are also described, such as the taking of tissue samples for disease identification and laboratory investigations.

Part 3 comprises the major section of the book, dealing with commonly encountered koi health problems. When faced with a disease outbreak, the reader is recommended initially to study the various parasites and disease conditions that are illustrated on pages 58-61. These four pages serve as diagnostic guides to the various viral, bacterial, parasitic and other disease conditions that follow in A-Z order. Beginning with *Aeromonas* infections, each A-Z entry contains vital information regarding the disease, how to recognize it, and how to prevent and treat the condition. Where

chemical treatments are required, the authors suggest suitable medications and dose rates, plus other treatment information that will improve the chances of a successful cure. Each entry is lavishly illustrated with colour photographs depicting characteristic symptoms of the disease in question, thereby helping the koi keeper to arrive at a correct diagnosis. Where appropriate, there are close-up pictures of various parasites and easy-to-follow diagrams showing the often complex and fascinating life cycles that some of these parasites employ.

Part 4 describes various methods for administering treatments to koi, such as medicated baths and dips and the surface treatment of wounds. Here the reader will find additional information on chemical treatments in current usage. Some "advanced" techniques are also described, including methods for sedating koi, and the delivery of antibiotics by injection. It should be emphasized that these procedures (including skin scraping techniques described in Part 2) should not be performed without proper training. Ideally, they are best left to a veterinarian or suitably qualified koi health specialist.

Finally, it is important to mention that koi (and other fish) are capable of experiencing stress and there is mounting scientific evidence that they can perceive pain too. With this in mind, it is the responsibility of every koi keeper to ensure that his or her fish are given the same high level of care as is afforded to any other pet. The valuable information contained within this book will assist greatly in achieving this goal.

PREVENTING DISEASE

The best way of preventing disease is to control and limit the levels of stress to which your koi are exposed. Stress can be dramatically reduced if you have a basic understanding of water quality and realize how each different parameter will affect your fish. This allows you to recognize the signs of poor water quality quickly and to react to them in the appropriate way. This should be backed up by regular water testing and the various ways of doing this are described in this section. Steps to remedy poor water quality are also discussed here, and if this advice is followed, many disease problems can be stopped in their tracks by simply maintaining optimum water conditions. The old adage holds true: maintaining the water in a koi pond is like running a small-scale sewage works. If water is kept in optimum condition, other problems will be far less likely to occur.

Maintaining optimum water quality should go hand in hand with a good, regular programme of system maintenance and husbandry. A basic guide to the essential steps which you should observe is also provided in this section. Obviously every pond is different and your pond may require additional maintenance, but the points highlighted here should all be part of your overall maintenance programme. If your schedule and time allow, try to develop a routine whereby a set period of time can be dedicated to your pond every week just to attend to these basic jobs. If they are left undone, you could face potentially serious problems. The overall health of your pond can be further enhanced by the use of heating, specialist filtration equipment, such as ozone, and UV sterilization, and these are all examined here. These items are by no means essential to running and maintaining a healthy pond, but are all worthwhile additions if your system and budget will run to them. Heating, perhaps, is the exception as many koi keepers and koi professionals regard heating not as a luxury item, but as an essential part of a healthy koi pond.

Finally this section considers feeding, as this can have a significant effect on the health of your koi. It is vital that the correct foods are fed at the right time of the year – the reasons for this are

outlined, and the use of specialist foods described. Overfeeding can be one of the main causes of poor water quality and guidance will be found as to the correct feeding ratio for your koi. This advice should be integrated into your overall pond health and maintenance regime.

The practices described in this section alone are actually the first line of defence in preventing

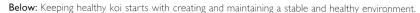

Below: Keeping healthy koi starts with creating and maintaining a stable and healthy environment.

many of the more serious health problems which are examined in section 3. If any adverse behavioural changes are noticed, water quality should always be the first port of call. If water quality proves to be acceptable, then the steps outlined in section 2 should be followed to allow you to test for the presence of many diseases. Section 3 will confirm the exact diagnosis and provides treatment advice. Finally section 4 explains how to carry out specific treatment methods which are referred to throughout this book. So in one compact, easy-to-follow volume you now have a complete health care manual incorporating advice on disease prevention, identification and diagnosis, and the most up-to-date treatment.

THE EFFECTS OF STRESS ON YOUR KOI

As you read this book it will quickly become clear that one of the most important things you can do as a responsible fishkeeper is to reduce the amount of stress to which your koi are exposed. This single precaution could be an absolutely critical factor in reducing the outbreak of health problems among your stock. The cause is simple – when a koi becomes stressed, its defences against disease are weakened and this makes infection more probable.

How can stress most effectively be reduced? The answer is to create a stable environment in which to keep your koi and, wherever possible, to avoid environmental change. However, this is easier said than done as there are numerous factors acting on a fish which all have the same end result of causing stress. Nevertheless, a few basic rules should be followed to help establish and maintain the most stress-free environment that you can. There are two key factors to observe – avoid overstocking and maintain optimum water quality. Poor water quality is one of the main causes of stress, and so regular, almost religious, water tests should be carried out; if identified sufficiently early, the necessary steps can be taken to rectify any problem with the water, and so limit the amount of stress to which your koi are exposed.

Other situations which may stress your koi include various basic fishkeeping tasks, such as netting a koi for inspection. This experience is highly stressful to a koi, and so excessive netting should be avoided. When your net enters the water, your koi will immediately start to produce a number of hormones, including adrenaline, which have an effect on the osmoregulation of the fish (see page 32). These hormones are produced to provide the fish with extra speed to avoid capture, much in the same way that when a person is in a dangerous situation, adrenaline production readies them for "fight or flight". Although released in an instant when a stressful situation arises, the physiological effects caused by the sudden production of these hormones may take very much longer to subside and return to normal. It is during such periods that fish become susceptible to infections. If a koi has to be inspected at close hand, the use of a suitable sedating agent can help to limit stress by calming the koi, preventing it from thrashing about violently and possibly damaging itself physically.

Environmental Changes

Even the process of purchasing a new koi for your pond is highly stressful for the fish as the whole business of netting, bagging and boxing, and the journey to its new home subjects the fish to high stress levels. When this is combined with the potential changes in water temperature, pH and hardness that the koi will experience when transferred to its new pond, a highly stressful situation results. When your koi have to cope with a situation like this during which dramatic environmental changes have occurred, they will naturally try to adjust to the new environmental conditions in which they find themselves.

Above: Transportation can be a highly stressful experience for koi and leave them vulnerable to infections.

However, this consumes a lot of the koi's reserves of energy as it struggles to adjust to these changes; as a result, other physical functions, including the immune system, may suffer during this period of acclimatization. Your koi have their guard down and are vulnerable to infection. These examples show how difficult it is to limit the effects of stress on your koi. Stress may (and probably will) occur while you are performing even the simplest of routine tasks.

So, what is the answer? To help combat the effects of stress on your koi and reduce the likelihood of opportunistic infections occurring, it is vital that a well-maintained system is kept, and that excellent husbandry skills are employed. Overstocking and unnecessary handling should also be avoided. Keeping a well-maintained pond and observing good husbandry should also speed up the recovery process when diseases do occur, particularly as the illnesses themselves actually add to the stress burden on the koi. Even the process of treating your koi with medications may prove stressful to the fish, and thus optimum environmental conditions are required throughout to aid quick recovery. Stress prevention should form an essential part of your healthcare regime. If stress levels can be kept to a minimum, the likelihood of diseases taking hold will also be diminished.

Above: Imported koi have to adjust to new water conditions which can take a toll on their immune systems.
Below: As a koi keeper, try to avoid excessive use of the net as it will have an effect on how stressed your fish feel.

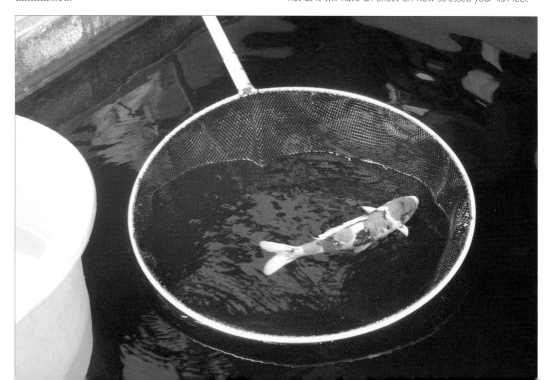

WATER QUALITY

To help to prevent outbreaks of disease in your pond, it is vital that water quality is maintained at the highest possible level. Most illnesses become more serious when koi are stressed, and poor water quality is one of the biggest stress factors which can occur within the pond. It is easy to test for the main water quality parameters – pH, ammonia, nitrite, nitrate, and carbonate hardness (KH) – and these can be easily rectified should a problem arise. In a pond with good filtration the process of nitrification which occurs in the biological filter will break down ammonia, which is both produced by koi as waste and released from decomposing organic matter, into nitrite. This is done by bacteria of the *Nitrosomonas* genus. The next stage involves nitrite being converted into nitrate by *Nitrobacter* bacteria. Nitrate is then taken up by plants in the pond as a natural fertilizer, and this is why many koi ponds incorporate some form of vegetable filter to aid in the breaking down of these nitrates.

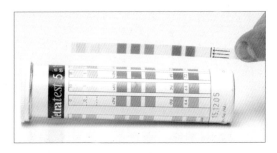

Above: Testing your water should be a key part of your koi healthcare regime. Test kits, like this strip which changes colour when dipped in the water, make this simple to do.

These processes all require the presence of oxygen and thus they are referred to as aerobic. However, if anaerobic conditions are found (i.e. oxygen is not present) – for example in a de-nitrification filter – further reduction of nitrate can occur, resulting eventually in nitrogen gas being produced. In a pond with a good filtration system, good water quality will be maintained by

How the nitrogen cycle works

Water returning to the pond from the last stage of the filtration system may still contain some nitrate. Nitrate is one of the nutrients responsible for promoting the growth of blanketweed.

Water changes are an important aspect of pond management, especially if ammonia or nitrite are polluting the pond. Regular water changes can also help to reduce nitrate concentration in the water.

By adding an oxygen atom into each molecule, aerobic bacteria (*Nitrobacter* spp.) convert nitrite into nitrate (NO_3). Nitrate is the final breakdown product of ammonia in the nitrogen cycle. It is far less toxic than ammonia or nitrite.

Protein present in food is used by koi for tissue repair and maintenance, growth and reproduction. Any excess protein cannot be stored and is excreted as ammonia. The protein in any uneaten food also ends up as ammonia.

By removing the hydrogen and adding oxygen into each molecule, aerobic bacteria (*Nitrosomonas* spp.) convert ammonia into nitrite (NO_2). Although not as harmful as ammonia, nitrite is still poisonous to koi.

Ammonia (NH_3) is released into the water via the fishes' gills. The small amount of urea voided in dilute urine also breaks down to form ammonia. Ammonia is very poisonous to koi.

the biological filtration system. However, it is important to observe a routine in which at least the levels of pH, ammonia, nitrite and nitrate are regularly tested as small changes in water temperature, an increase in stocking, or even a change in food can all have a detrimental effect on the efficiency of the biological filtration which ultimately will cause poor water quality.

There are many test kits available which make it easy for you to test your pond water. They come in many forms: liquid, tablet and even strips of testing paper which are simply dipped into the pond water and left for a period of time before the change in colour is compared against a chart. These tests are generally inexpensive, and should be used at least once a month, although weekly or fortnightly is better. For those who require more accurate reading, electronic testers are available, but generally at a much higher cost. In fact, although these give a more accurate result, the reading from tablet or liquid tests is generally a good enough indication for the average koi keeper. It is vital that any adverse readings should be acted upon immediately as failure to do so will only prolong the stress to your koi. Furthermore, long exposure to poor water quality can cause quite serious health problems on its own, as each parameter will affect your koi in a different way.

pH

This is the measure of relative acidity and alkalinity with 7 being neutral, below 7 acidic and above 7 alkaline. A pH measurement uses a logarithmic scale which means that a change from pH 7 to pH 8 is actually a tenfold increase. This is why even a small change in pH can have quite dramatic effects on your koi. Koi are happy in water with a pH anywhere between 7 to 8.5, as long as it remains constant. The pH level of the water in which your koi live ultimately has an effect on the pH value of their blood, and if the pH value of the pond water strays either to acidic or alkaline levels, and thus falls outside the acceptable range, your koi will start to show symptoms of acidosis or alkalosis. Acidosis occurs when the pH level drops below 5.5 and very acidic conditions result. If a rapid drop in pH occurs, your koi will start to behave erratically and try to escape from the pond by jumping. You will also observe increased gill movements, which result in your fish becoming very stressed,

Broad range pH testing

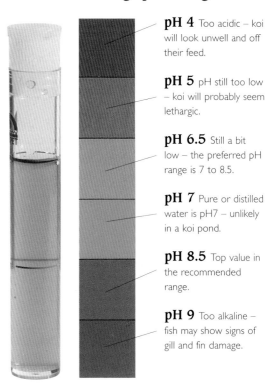

pH 4 Too acidic – koi will look unwell and off their feed.

pH 5 pH still too low – koi will probably seem lethargic.

pH 6.5 Still a bit low – the preferred pH range is 7 to 8.5.

pH 7 Pure or distilled water is pH7 – unlikely in a koi pond.

pH 8.5 Top value in the recommended range.

pH 9 Too alkaline – fish may show signs of gill and fin damage.

Above: It is vital to test the pH of water routinely as this affects the toxicity of ammonia.

leaving them susceptible to infection. If left untreated, losses may occur just from the change in pH level. If the pH change is much more gradual with the water becoming very acidic over a long period of time, you may not notice immediate changes in your koi's behaviour. Over time, however, the ability of the gills to extract oxygen from the water will decrease because colloidal iron is being deposited, and this will be indicated by gasping and irregular gill movements, as well as the production of excess mucus and the appearance of areas of redness on the skin. To reverse the effect of acidosis the pH needs to be brought back to an acceptable level, but avoid the temptation of doing this rapidly as a sudden increase back to correct levels can be just as stressful as doing nothing. To make the water more alkaline, crushed oyster shells placed in the filters are a good remedy. Alternatively you may wish to consider the use of a proprietary product designed to increase pH value.

Alkalosis occurs when the pH value rises above 9, and the water becomes too alkaline. Many of the symptoms associated with alkalosis are the same as those for acidosis, but your koi may also show signs of severe fin and gill damage if exposed to high pH levels for any prolonged period. To lower pH aquatic peat should be used in the filters. Alternatively you can use an off-the-shelf pH-lowering product. When changing pH value it is again vital that it is not done too quickly as this can be very stressful to your koi. Once the correct pH value is achieved, you must investigate further to establish why the pH value changed in the first place. Typical causes of high pH include the presence of lime in the water, which may have leached out from rocks or cement around the pond. Acidic conditions may be caused by algae blooms and excessive plant growth as these will remove carbon dioxide and nitrate, and so contribute to acidic conditions. Another cause of acidic conditions may be the build-up of carbon dioxide in the pond. Increased aeration will help prevent this from occurring by allowing carbon dioxide to gas off. Dirty pond conditions, causing the build-up of organic acids, may also lead to a decline in pH over time.

General Hardness (GH)

This is the total amount of salt and minerals present in a body of water. This quantity is basically made of temporary hardness which is removed by precipitation when water is boiled (it is otherwise known as carbonate hardness) with the remainder consisting of permanent hardness which comprise salts and minerals that will remain in solution after boiling. As most salts and minerals fall into the category of carbonate hardness (KH), koi keepers test for this category more frequently. Different countries use different scales to measure general hardness (English degrees, German degrees etc.) so it is vital to check which scale the test kit is using.

Carbonate Hardness (KH)

This is the measure of calcium and magnesium salts which are present in the water, especially if the water is alkaline. Soft water tends to be associated with acidic conditions while hard water is indicative of alkaline water. If pH fluctuations are being experienced, it is worth testing the pond water for hardness. If you are experiencing low levels of carbonate hardness, you may need

Carbonate hardness (KH) test

1: Add the KH reagent a drop at a time to a 5ml sample of pond water, and gently swirl the the tube to mix thoroughly.
2: Initially the sample turns blue.
3: As more reagent is added, the water sample turns yellow. Continue counting the drops added until the yellow colour is stable. Each drop added during the test represents 1°dH, which is equivalent to 17.5mg per litre of carbonate.

to add minerals to the pond as your koi need a certain amount of calcium and minerals for their good health. It will help to buffer the water which will help to maintain a constant pH level. This can be done by putting crushed oyster shells in the filters, or by adding a proprietary product designed for buffering the water in the pond. Certain medications also react differently in soft or hard water, so it is important to know about your water conditions should a problem arise. Generally in soft water chemicals become more toxic, while in hard water they become less so.

Ammonia (NH_3/NH_4)

This is released into the pond in the form of waste from your koi and from decomposing organic matter. Ammonia exists in two forms in water, free ammonia (NH_3) and ionized ammonia (NH_4). Free ammonia is the more harmful of the two and the effect it has on your koi increases with temperature and the pH of the water, with higher pH values making the ammonia more toxic. Salt used in your pond will have the opposite effect and decrease the toxicity of ammonia. Most commercial test kits just give one reading for total ammonia which includes free and ionized ammonia, but it does indicate

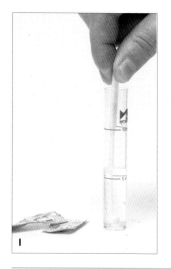

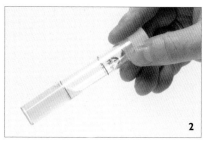

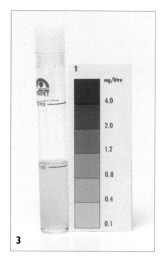

1: Here a tablet test for ammonia is being used and the tablets are being crushed.
2: Once the tablets are dissolved, the tube must be shaken to mix the contents.
3: After a set period of time, the water will change colour and this can be compared against the colour chart supplied with the kit.

whether an ammonia problem is present or not. If your koi are kept in water with high levels of ammonia numerous problems will be experienced. These include the build-up of cells on the surface

Ammonia toxicity and temperature

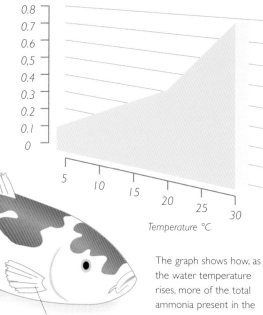

% free (toxic) ammonia in total ammonia

Temperature °C

High ammonia levels make koi susceptible to other conditions, such as fin rot.

The graph shows how, as the water temperature rises, more of the total ammonia present in the water changes into free ammonia which is very toxic to the koi in the pond.

of the gill lamellae, which reduces water flow over the gills and so the amount of oxygen which can be absorbed. This condition is known as hyperplasia. The mucus protecting the skin will also be damaged resulting in areas of redness. Internal organs may also start to fail if the level of ammonia remains high for a prolonged period. High ammonia levels will leave your koi highly susceptible to other infections, especially fin rot, dropsy and gill conditions.

To reduce high ammonia levels, regular water changes of around 10-20 per cent need to be carried out on a daily basis in extreme cases, and the use of filter-boosting products may be required to improve the performance of the biological filtration. These water changes should be done with purified tapwater or a dechlorinator should be used to remove chlorine and other harmful substances from the water. Zeolite can also be added to the filters – this is a rock which naturally absorbs ammonia over a period of time before it needs to be recharged with salt. Once the correct levels of ammonia are established, you must investigate why they rose so high. Common causes include the introduction of new stock, the filter not coping through becoming blocked with solid waste or failure of the pump, overstocking, overfeeding, and even over-zealous filter maintenance because if the filters are cleaned with tapwater, for example, this may kill some or all of the beneficial bacteria so impeding biological filtration. The other common cause is a new set-up where the filters have yet to mature.

Nitrite (NO$_2$)

Nitrite occurs naturally in a koi pond, as this is what ammonia is broken down into by bacterial action. Although not as toxic as ammonia, nitrite is poisonous to your koi if levels are allowed to become too high. In water with a high nitrite level, the koi may start to jump, or flick against the sides of the pond as if being irritated by something. This may appear to indicate a parasite or other infection, as these symptoms are common in many such diseases. However, first test for nitrites. Nitrite binds with the oxygen-carrying haemoglobin molecules in the koi's blood cells, forming methaemoglobin which does not carry oxygen. As a result the blood and gills take on a brown appearance. If left, high nitrite may result in losses of koi, although some koi do tolerate high nitrite levels better then others. Other symptoms of high nitrite include a weakening of the koi's immune system which leaves them susceptible to secondary infection, especially bacterial gill

Water Quality Criteria: Recommended Levels

The following table shows the recommended maximum/minimum levels for various chemicals present in water. Outside these levels, remedial action should be taken.

Dissolved oxygen	min 7-8mg/l
Free ammonia	max 0.02mg/l
Nitrite	max 0.2mg/l
Nitrate	max 50mg/l above ambient tapwater

disease. The addition of salt to a pond can help reduce the toxic effects of nitrite, but the best course of action is to follow the same procedure for reducing high ammonia. The reasons why the nitrite levels are high may well be the same as those causing high ammonia levels.

A vegetable filter

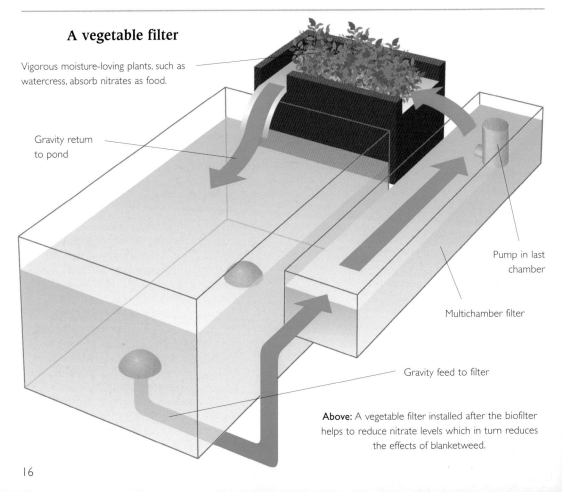

Vigorous moisture-loving plants, such as watercress, absorb nitrates as food.

Gravity return to pond

Pump in last chamber

Multichamber filter

Gravity feed to filter

Above: A vegetable filter installed after the biofilter helps to reduce nitrate levels which in turn reduces the effects of blanketweed.

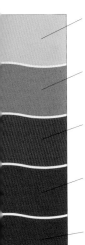

Less than 0.3mg/litre Fairly low, and not a threat to koi. If nitrite values rise, monitor regularly.

0.3mg/litre In soft water nitrite is more toxic and this level can affect koi health. Make partial water changes.

0.8mg/litre At this level nitrite is harmful to koi in both soft and hard water. Make regular partial water changes.

1.6mg/litre Nitrite combines with red blood pigment affecting ability of koi to use oxygen. Make daily water changes.

Over 3mg/litre Nitrite pollution now a serious problem and can kill fish. Water changes are essential.

Above: Nitrites are toxic to koi, so it is essential to use test kits to check the nitrite level in your water regularly.

Nitrate (NO$_3$)

This is produced as the last stage of the nitrific-ation process when nitrite is turned in nitrate. Nitrate can be tolerated in quite high levels by koi, and unless a very large vegetable filter or special purpose-made de-nitrification filter is used, it may be very hard to get levels down. Nitrate at very high levels may have an effect on the physio-logical condition of your koi and impair growth. High nitrate levels also encourage the growth of blanketweed, large amounts of which can have an effect on pH and oxygen levels. The presence of salt in the water will make nitrate more toxic, but even then, unless levels are excessively high, they should cause no real harm to your koi. The only exception to this are eggs which are sensitive to nitrate in the water, and koi fry which develop better in water which has a low nitrate reading.

Oxygen (O$_2$)

Oxygen enters the pond by the process of diffusion at the surface and at the same time carbon dioxide is released from the pond. If plants are present, the process of photosynthesis causes oxygen to be released into the water, although this is reversed at night when oxygen is absorbed by plants and carbon dioxide is given off. Oxygen levels are dramatically affected by temperature – the higher the temperature, the lower is the dissolved oxygen content of the water. This creates a Catch 22 situation as your koi most need oxygen in the hot summer months just when the water is least able to hold high levels of oxygen. As a guide a minimum level of 7-8mg/l of dissolved oxygen should be maintained if the temperature will allow, although at temperatures of 30°C (86°F) and above it may prove impossible to maintain these levels. It is important to make oxygen tests on site at the pond, otherwise a false reading may be produced.

How temperature affects oxygen levels

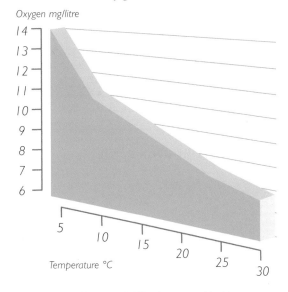

Above: Oxygen solubility decreases with rising temperature. Affected koi are initially lethargic but as oxygen levels fall, they rise to the surface gasping.

Gill cover flares as the koi tries to extract as much oxygen as possible from the water.

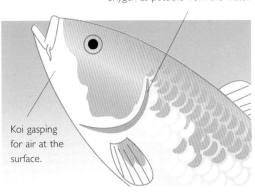

Koi gasping for air at the surface.

Above: Dissolved oxygen should be monitored, especially in hot weather: here an electronic DO tester is being used.

If oxygen levels become low you will soon see your koi starting to gasp at the surface, collecting around areas of water movement such as waterfalls or airstones, and displaying rapid gill movements. In such circumstances it is worth testing the oxygen levels by using a suitable test kit or electronic oxygen meter, then increasing the levels of oxygen in the pond by the addition of air-pumps, fountains, or anything which causes considerable surface disturbance and so increases the surface area available for diffusion. It is worth remembering that it is not just your koi which require oxygen, the bacteria in your biological filters do too, as do the many organisms which are found in the pond. Thus when low oxygen levels are experienced, it is vital that your koi are not fed to help decrease the levels of organic waste in the pond. Feeding should only resume when oxygen levels have risen. Water changes should be regularly carried out, and any waste or debris in the pond removed. Oxygen depletion may occur for numerous reasons, such as overstocking, insufficient aeration, poor system maintenance, excessive temperatures, and algae blooms. In exceptionally cold spells oxygen problems may

Oxygen in the pond – winter

Oxygen is readily soluble in cold water

The fish are producing less waste and the lower temperatures inhibit bacterial activity

The koi are inactive at low temperatures and their oxygen requirement is minimal.

Oxygen in the pond – summer

Blanketweed produces oxygen during the day, but consumes it at night.

Less oxygen is available in the water as the temperature increases.

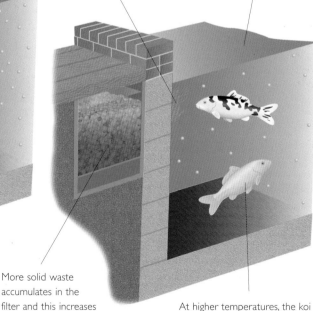

More solid waste accumulates in the filter and this increases the demand for oxygen by the aerobic bacteria.

At higher temperatures, the koi are increasingly active and need more oxygen.

also result if your pond is allowed to freeze over completely as it will seal the pond's surface from exposure to the air and prevent diffusion from occurring. Ideally your pond should be heated to prevent freezing (see pages 26-7 for more information on pond heating), or if this is not possible it should be at least covered to protect it from the elements, and a small floating heater installed which will keep an area free of ice.

Temperature

This has a dramatic effect on koi as the lower the temperature the slower their metabolism will function. At very low temperatures their immune system will also be affected. Koi are coldwater fish, but they do benefit from being kept in a heated pond with stable water temperatures. In unheated ponds temperature fluctuations cause stress, and koi are highly susceptible to disease over the autumn-winter-spring seasonal change. As the water temperatures falls below 14°C (58°F), a koi's immune system becomes less efficient, while at temperatures below 10°C (50°F) it is to a large extent shut down. This is a dangerous situation as many parasites and bacteria are still active at these temperatures, and matters are made worse because numerous medications do not work at lower temperatures. In addition, as the temperature drops so the koi's metabolism slows and its need for food decreases, resulting in the fish being far weaker than they are in the hot summer months.

If the water is allowed to cool, your koi may become dormant over the coldest months and this causes problems because if they are static on the bottom for any prolonged period they may develop pressure sores, which will require treatment and warm water to heal. Young koi under two years old may appear as if they are dead in cold water, and sometimes actually lie on the bottom of the pond or simply float in the water, and will only move if provoked with a net. This makes them highly susceptible to numerous infections. The condition is known as sleeping sickness, and is described on page 129.

These are the main water quality parameters which should be tested on a regular basis; however, it is worth mentioning that the presence of metals, chlorine, chloramines, pesticides, phosphates and other chemicals can also have an effect on your koi. These generally enter the pond when new tapwater is added, and they do not

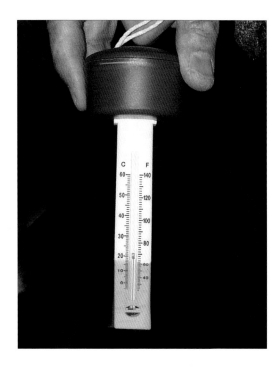

Above: There are several types of thermometer available that allow the koi keeper to monitor the water temperature routinely. This is a simple floating model.

need to be present in particularly high levels to cause a problem. It is vital that all tapwater should be conditioned before it enters the pond, either by the use of a chemical dechlorinator, or by passing it through a water purifier. These are available in numerous sizes, and can be purchased to remove more metals.

In order to determine if a specialist unit is required for metal removal, it is worth obtaining a water analysis which can normally be provided by your water supplier upon request. Metals may also enter the pond if any unsuitable metal pipework has been used, so it is vital to ensure that all equipment installed around the pond is suitable for use in an aquatic environment that will contain fish. Many garden ornaments and copper-based fountains are made of, or contain, harmful metals and so great care must be taken if you install such items in your pond.

One final warning – the use of chemicals in the garden, particularly insecticides and pesticides which can be carried on the wind, carries risk as they can be toxic to fish. Ideally garden organically if you keep koi.

GOOD HUSBANDRY & SYSTEM MAINTENANCE

In order to maintain optimum water quality it is vital that a proper maintenance regime is followed. One of the most significant factors contributing to outbreaks of disease is the build-up of waste and sediment within the pond. The removal of this is central to any good system maintenance programme. To ensure that all jobs are carried out when required, it is a good idea to develop a timetable which can be followed throughout the year. It should include the following tasks:

Daily tasks

- Check all koi for signs of behavioural change or physical damage. The ideal time to do this is when feeding, as when the fish are feeding from the surface you will not only be closer to the koi but you will also be able to see underneath the fish.
- Feed all koi, the frequency of this depends upon the time of year (see pages 22-5).
- Check pumps, air pumps, UV filters etc. to ensure that everything is functioning.
- In the summer months you should discharge your filter systems on a daily basis as your koi will be eating more heavily, and so larger volumes of waste will accumulate in the filters
- If your pond is a pump-fed system, it may be necessary to clean any pre-filters on the pump on a daily basis to ensure sufficient flow gets through to the filter.
- In the summer blanketweed may be a serious problem. Its growth can be so rapid that daily removal is required to prevent the pond from becoming clogged with weed, and so restricting water flow from either the bottom drain or pump.

Weekly tasks

- In a gravity-fed system, it is advisable to purge all bottom drain pipework at least once a week in the summer. This is done by shutting the valve to the first chamber of your filter (normally a 10cm/4in slide valve or ball valve), and allowing this chamber to empty by opening its discharge valve. When empty, the slide or ball valve can be re-opened; this will cause a massive surge of water to pass through the drain pipework and flush out any debris which has settled out in the pipework.
- If a skimmer is installed, it is important that it is checked at least once a week, and the collection basket emptied. At certain times of the year, particularly autumn, it may be necessary to do this daily to prevent the skimmer from clogging which will stop leaves from being removed and so allow them to decompose in the pond.
- On both pump-fed and gravity-fed systems, any mechanical filter media, such as brushes or foam, should be cleaned at least once a week to allow a good flow of water through the filter.
- Although not essential, it is certainly a good idea to set aside 30 minutes each week to test the water quality in the pond, and to take any remedial steps that may be necessary (see pages 12-17).
- Any koi which display physical damage or infections which require topical treatment should be netted and treated at least once a week. In some cases you may need to treat twice a week until enough improvement is seen for the frequency of treatment to be decreased.

Above: Skimmers remove surface debris, like food and leaves, from the pond; if not cleaned, they start to block.

Above: Be sure to clean your skimmer on a regular basis by simply washing it in a bucket of water or with a hose.

Monthly tasks

- If your pond is heated, it may be necessary at certain times of the year for you to adjust the heating system to raise or lower the water temperature. When doing this, only small changes of one or two degrees every few days should be made.
- As the seasons pass from autumn into winter, any aeration in the pond should be decreased to limit the effect of water chilling by reducing the amount of cold air which can diffuse into the pond. Also turn down (or off) any waterfalls and fountains for the same reason. When spring returns and starts to move into summer, you should recommission these as well as the air-pumps to increase oxygen levels in the pond as the water temperature starts to rise.
- Predominately a task for pump-fed systems, but one that may also be required in larger ponds where not all the sediment is pulled by the drains, is vacuuming the pond. The build-up of sediment on the bottom of the pond will not only harbour disease, but it will use up oxygen and create poor water quality. It is best removed.
- Check and clean filters as required. This is an ongoing job throughout the year and at least one major clean should carried out in the course of the year. Systems in which the discharge facilities from the filter chambers are limited will probably require more frequent cleaning; those that are discharged on a regular basis may only require looking at periodically. When cleaning any biological filter media, it is vital that pond water is used, as the chlorine in tapwater will destroy the beneficial bacteria found on the filter media.

Half-yearly tasks

- If running UV units, you should change the bulbs ideally every six months, or at the very least once a year. Although UV tubes will function for more than six months, after this time they do not operate at 100 per cent efficiency and so their ability to reduce green water is degraded.

Yearly tasks

- Any additional equipment associated with the pond, such as ozone units, requires yearly maintenance – the probe for the redox meter will need replacing, for instance. Make a note of

Pond sludge is discharged through this tube.

Extension tubes allow the suction nozzle to reach into deep water.

Above: Pond vacuum cleaners such as this can be used to remove sludge and debris from the pond floor or filter.

any special service requirements and ensure they are carried out at least once a year, or as otherwise suggested by the manufacturer.
- Make any major changes and modifications. Rather then disturbing your koi continually throughout the year, try to complete all major tasks at around the same time to limit stress to the fish. It is not ideal to move or disturb your koi, but if it has to be done, once is better than three or four times in the course of a single year.

By carrying out these tasks regularly, your pond will not only become a healthy and more stable environment for your koi, but it will also become more enjoyable for you. You should also have more time to enjoy your koi, as the number of health problems which will require your time and attention should now start to decrease.

WHAT AND HOW TO FEED YOUR KOI

What your koi are fed is an important decision, as ultimately it will have an effect on their overall well-being. It is vital that the correct foods are fed at the right times of year to avoid problems. Koi are omnivorous which means they will eat both meat and plant matter, and in most instances their nutrition comes in the form of a processed fish food which will be either in stick, pellet, or paste form. Floating sticks are a popular choice but they can prove expensive as each stick contains a lot of air. Pellets are a better food source as each one contains far more substance than a comparable food stick. Paste food is also a good choice, but many people are put off because it has to be prepared each day. Having said this, it is ideal as a treat or for feeding large individual fish as extra-large pellets can be formed from the paste. It is also important to ensure that the correct size of pellet is chosen for the size of fish in the pond. Many keepers now recommend that even large koi are better fed a medium-size pellet (6mm diameter) rather than large ones of 8mm and above.

Also consider feeding a certain amount of sinking food, as this not only encourages your koi to feed at different levels of the pond allowing more of the koi to get some food, but it also prevents damage from occurring when the koi

Above: Lettuce is a valuable source of vitamin C and other nutrients. Start by offering shredded leaves; in a short time koi will enjoy chasing a whole lettuce around the pond and tearing pieces off it.

1: To make paste food, measure out the required amount of powder.

2: Add water to the powder as directed by the mixing instructions.

3: Mix water with the paste until a dough-like consistency is achieved.

4: Roll and shape the paste in your hands to form large pellets of food.

5: Roll pellets to suit the size of koi in your pond. Remember that it will sink, which will encourage your fish to feed at different water levels.

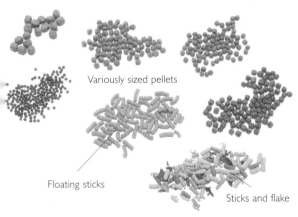

Variously sized pellets

Floating sticks

Sticks and flake

Above: Koi food is available in many different shapes and sizes. The type of food you give will partly depend on what time of year it is and how big your fish are.

come to the surface in a feeding frenzy and bump into one another. There are also health benefits to using sinking food as excess air is not taken in (see pages 118-9 for more information on swimbladder disorders). Whatever style of koi food is chosen, it will be made up of a number of constituents. Firstly there is protein which is important as it encourages growth and tissue repair. As proteins have to be used before they are excreted from the body as waste, it is important not to overfeed, and only to feed higher protein foods in warmer weather when your koi's metabolism is higher, so allowing more of the protein to be utilized. Secondly, fatty acids are also an important part of any koi food, as they provide an essential supply of energy. Lack of essential fatty acids results in serious health problems. Other main constituents of koi food include carbohydrates which are used for energy, vitamins which are essential for the well-being of your koi, and minerals like calcium, which is vital for bone structure, and sodium and potassium, which help to maintain the nervous system. The final constituent of any good quality food will be trace elements which include iron, manganese, zinc, iodine and others.

Right: Propolis can be added to your standard koi food by adding a measured amount to a weighed quantity of food.

Far right: Having added the propolis to the food, it should be thoroughly mixed, then allowed to dry before feeding to the fish.

What and When To Feed?

A koi's metabolic rate has a dramatic effect on its ability to process food. As temperature has a direct link to metabolism, the temperature of your pond will ultimately dictate what and how much your koi should be fed. If your pond is not heated, you will need to change your feed to a wheatgerm-based diet. This is generally lower in protein, and so is more easily processed by the fish. As a general guide, once water temperatures fall below 13°C (55°F) wheatgerm should be fed until the water temperature falls below 9°C (48°F) at which point feeding should be stopped altogether. Feeding should not be resumed until the water temperature has risen above 9°C (48°F), and wheatgerm should again be the choice of food. Once water temperatures are stable above 13°C (55°F), it is possible to opt for a standard staple diet, which will be suitable to

feed to your koi for the rest of the year, although in the summer months when water temperatures reach 18°C (65°F) and above, you may wish to supplement this with a high-protein growth food, or specialist foods to enhance colour.

If your pond is heated and is maintained at a minimum of 14-15°C (58-60°F) over the winter months, you can continue to feed throughout the year. However, it is still advisable to give your koi a month or two on wheatgerm even though the water temperature would allow a staple diet to be fed. This helps the koi to use up any excess reserves of fat, which in turn helps body shape and overall condition. Along with proprietary koi foods, you may wish to supplement your koi's diet with the occasional treat. The feeding of oranges, brown bread, lettuce, prawns and other shellfish is all permitted, as long as it is not overdone. It should just be an occasional treat.

Oranges A good source of vitamin C which helps to reduce stress and boosts the immune system.

Garlic Garlic is a real treat for koi which are attracted to any food coated in it. It can also be used to entice them to feed by hand.

Lettuce Some koi keepers feed whole lettuce to their koi which readily shred and eat this treat which is a rich source of valuable nutrients.

Brown bread This is a good source of wheatgerm and vitamins, but feed sparingly as it is rich in carbohydrate.

Prawns Koi thoroughly enjoy prawns, a good source of protein. Feed in the summer when water temperatures are higher.

Bloodworms It is best to use frozen bloodworms as live food carries the risk of introducing disease into your pond. Offer bloodworms in the summer.

Above: A good diet combined with good system husbandry and water quality will help to keep your koi healthy.

Some people also decide to add live food, such as bloodworm or tubifex, to their koi's diet. However, we consider that it is best to avoid the use of live food because of the associated risks of introducing disease to the pond. The better option is the freeze-dried alternative, as this is irradiated before packing and so is disease-free. No matter what you are feeding, you must ensure that the correct amount of food is given, as overfeeding will result in water pollution, while underfeeding will cause your koi to become malnourished. As a guide, during the summer months when water temperatures are above 18°C (65°F) your koi can consume up to two per cent of their body weight a day (very young koi and fry may eat five times this amount!), so if you have 100kg of koi in your pond, you would need to feed 2kg of food per day. This should not be done in one feeding session; it is better to feed your koi small amounts throughout the day. If this is difficult for you, automatic feeding equipment may be a better option. As a general guide, do not feed more food than can be finished completely in five minutes.

Proper storage of dry food is important, especially once the seal is broken. Food should be stored under dry and cool conditions in re-sealable containers so as to minimize the degradation of vitamins (notably vitamin C) and other unstable ingredients. It is also important to realize that it is not just the quantity of proteins etc. that makes a good koi food, but also the quality of the ingredients. So do not be tempted by cheap unlabelled foods – only buy from reputable fish food manufacturers. If a well formulated dry food is given, there should be no need to mix in extra vitamins and trace elements.

Additives

Many koi keepers now mix additives with their chosen brand of food. These include propolis for its health and immune system benefits, vitamins and trace elements, or spirulina to enhance red pigmentation. Whatever additive is used, it is generally necessary to hand-mix this with the feed. To maintain freshness this should be done either daily or every other day using only the volume of food that will be fed. Additives allow for specific ingredients to be mixed with the food, and of course they are much fresher than if they are included within the food at the time of processing.

SPECIALIST POND EQUIPMENT

In addition to the basic essentials needed to maintain a healthy koi pond, you may want to use additional equipment to help maintain a better environment for your koi, and so reduce the chances of disease.

Pond Heating

Many now considered this a must, rather than a specialist piece of equipment. However, there are still many koi ponds which are not heated. Heating your pond can be achieved by the use of an electric in-line heater or by a heat exchanger, which will either be in-line or of a design which is actually submerged into the pond or filter, and powered by natural gas, oil, or propane gas. Pond

Heat exchanger for gas-fired boiler

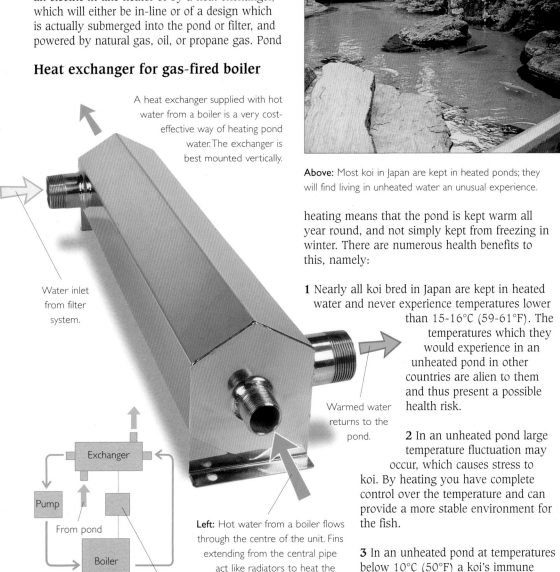

A heat exchanger supplied with hot water from a boiler is a very cost-effective way of heating pond water. The exchanger is best mounted vertically.

Above: Most koi in Japan are kept in heated ponds; they will find living in unheated water an unusual experience.

Water inlet from filter system.

Warmed water returns to the pond.

Exchanger

Pump

From pond

Boiler

Thermostat

Left: Hot water from a boiler flows through the centre of the unit. Fins extending from the central pipe act like radiators to heat the water flowing round them.

heating means that the pond is kept warm all year round, and not simply kept from freezing in winter. There are numerous health benefits to this, namely:

1 Nearly all koi bred in Japan are kept in heated water and never experience temperatures lower than 15-16°C (59-61°F). The temperatures which they would experience in an unheated pond in other countries are alien to them and thus present a possible health risk.

2 In an unheated pond large temperature fluctuation may occur, which causes stress to koi. By heating you have complete control over the temperature and can provide a more stable environment for the fish.

3 In an unheated pond at temperatures below 10°C (50°F) a koi's immune system will virtually shut down and

many medications cannot be used, despite the fact that numerous bacteria and parasites may still attack. By heating you can prevent your koi from being exposed to this risk.

4 In unheated ponds koi stop growing in very cold periods, and will not feed in the coldest months when water temperature drops below 9°C (48°F). Maintaining a higher temperature allows for all-year-round feeding which improves growth rates. You will also enjoy your fish more because they are not dormant for three or four months of the year.

If you do heat your pond it should be maintained at the following temperatures throughout the year: December, January, February = 15-16°C (59-61°F), March and November = 18°C (64°F), the rest of the year = 22-24°C (72-75°F). Changes in pond temperature should be made gradually at a rate of only a degree or two every few days. Many people are worried by how much it costs to run a pond heater. However, look at the budget this way – if you have a collection of fair-sized koi (40-50cm/16-20in and above) and one dies during the winter, the cost of replacing it would be far greater than the cost of heating the pond for the winter and possibly for the whole year!

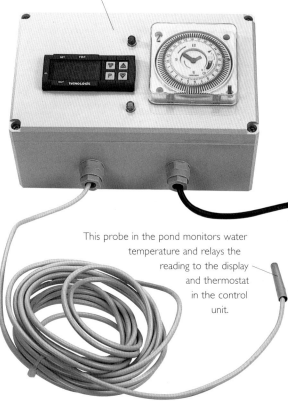

This is the control unit of the water heater; it houses the timer clock, the thermostat and a digital readout which displays the water temperature.

This probe in the pond monitors water temperature and relays the reading to the display and thermostat in the control unit.

In-line electric water heater

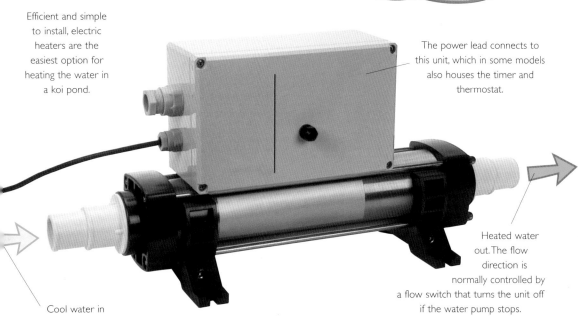

Efficient and simple to install, electric heaters are the easiest option for heating the water in a koi pond.

The power lead connects to this unit, which in some models also houses the timer and thermostat.

Heated water out. The flow direction is normally controlled by a flow switch that turns the unit off if the water pump stops.

Cool water in

Ozone Units

Ozone generators are commonly used by keepers of marine fish, and it is only recently that units have become available for pond use. They are still considered very specialist units and this is reflected in their generally high price. Ozone consists of an oxygen (O_2) molecule with an added oxygen atom, creating ozone (O_3). In simple terms ozone is very unstable and this third oxygen atom wants to disassociate itself from the other two. It does this by attaching itself to bacteria or protozoa which it destroys by burning through the cell wall. It may also attach itself to organic matter within the pond which then comes out of suspension and collects as foam on the pond surface so creating excellent water clarity. To reduce this foam build-up it is a good idea to operate a protein skimmer if running an ozone unit. Ozone can be quite harmful if used in a confined space, and may cause headaches and sickness if breathed in. The presence of ozone can easily be smelt; it has a similar smell to the one which you might experience after an electric shock. However, be aware that ozone can be harmful to humans at levels well below those detected by the nose. To avoid any problems it is vital that a unit be selected which either removes any excess ozone before it is released into the air, or else install the unit in a fully ventilated location. There are associated risks with the incorrect use of ozone, so it is vital that usage levels are controlled. This is generally done by using a redox potential meter which ensures a correct ozone dosage.

If too much ozone is used, it will create a sterile environment. Although this may sound like a good idea at first, it is not because if the koi are subsequently exposed to less sterile conditions they will quickly succumb to health problems. With ozone it is best to occupy the middle ground so that semi-sterile conditions are maintained. This means that micro-organisms are reduced, but not to the extent that the water becomes sterile. If used correctly, an ozone generator is an excellent addition to any pond as it will reduce the factors which are responsible for many health problems and improve water quality and clarity. It it advisable to run ozone in conjunction with your existing settlement and biological filter and treat it as an addition, rather then relying solely upon a settlement chamber, such as a vortex, and an ozone unit.

Ozone unit

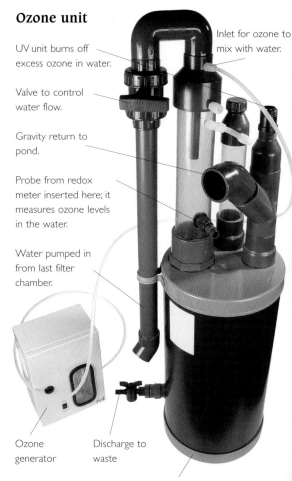

UV unit burns off excess ozone in water.

Inlet for ozone to mix with water.

Valve to control water flow.

Gravity return to pond.

Probe from redox meter inserted here; it measures ozone levels in the water.

Water pumped in from last filter chamber.

Ozone generator

Discharge to waste

Ozone gas gas reacts with pond water in this chamber.

Ultraviolet (UV) Clarifiers and Sterilizers

The UV systems used in most ponds are clarifiers. They help to prevent green water by killing the algae responsible for it as the water passes through the unit. It is possible, however, to use UV light to sterilize the water, and this is achieved by the use of UV sterilizers. These work by exposing the water from the pond to the UV light at much higher concentration, and this is achieved by only having a small distance between the bulb and the outside of the casing through which the water flows. Consequently, a much higher amount of UV light is required to sterilize a body of water effectively and this unfortunately makes UV sterilization of koi ponds impractical for most

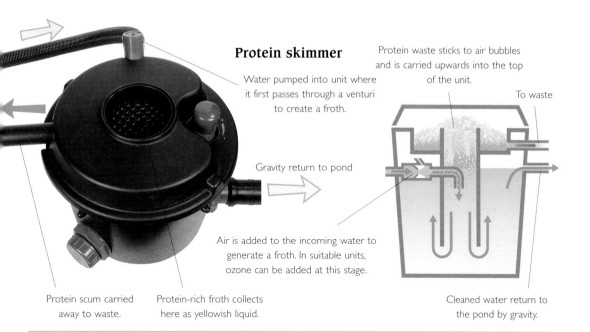

Protein skimmer

Water pumped into unit where it first passes through a venturi to create a froth.

Protein waste sticks to air bubbles and is carried upwards into the top of the unit.

To waste

Gravity return to pond

Air is added to the incoming water to generate a froth. In suitable units, ozone can be added at this stage.

Protein scum carried away to waste.

Protein-rich froth collects here as yellowish liquid.

Cleaned water return to the pond by gravity.

people because of the volume of water which they contain and the amount of UV light thus required. However, it is a viable proposition for smaller quarantine tanks. If you decide to buy such a unit, you will need to discuss your exact needs with your koi dealer or an equipment manufacturer to ensure that a UV sterilizer is purchased and not a standard UV clarifier as is normally the case.

UV clarifier

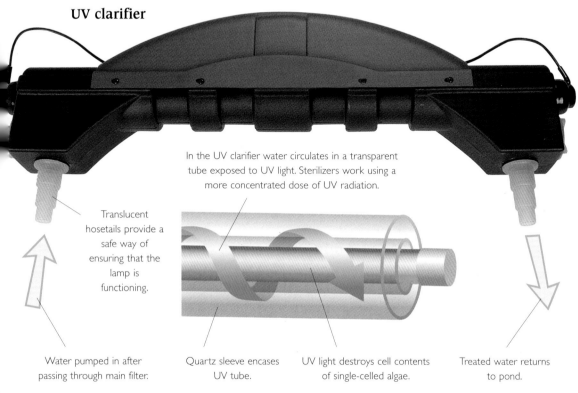

In the UV clarifier water circulates in a transparent tube exposed to UV light. Sterilizers work using a more concentrated dose of UV radiation.

Translucent hosetails provide a safe way of ensuring that the lamp is functioning.

Water pumped in after passing through main filter.

Quartz sleeve encases UV tube.

UV light destroys cell contents of single-celled algae.

Treated water returns to pond.

ESSENTIAL SKILLS

Having ruled out poor water quality as the cause of any problems, the next step in determining why your koi are not behaving as you would expect is to start looking for signs of disease and, if found, to identify exactly which disease it is. Too often people see their koi hanging in the water, flicking against the bottom, or gasping for air around airstones in the pond, and simply dose the water with an "anti-everything" treatment. Although this is better than doing nothing, it can create its own problems for many diseases require specific treatment and this scattergun approach generally will have no positive effect. Before any medications are added to a pond, it makes sense to know exactly what you are treating.

This section of book first looks at the anatomy of koi to give you an insight into how different parts of the fish's body function and what their physiological role is. This helps you to understand what effect a specific disease will have on the overall well-being of your koi, depending upon which part of the body is under attack. It will help you to appreciate the fish's external anatomy and where the internal organs are positioned and what their function is. This knowledge all contributes to your understanding of koi healthcare.

Next netting and inspecting koi is described. This is an important part of the process of disease identification; if it is done incorrectly, it can result in physical damage occurring which in turn may lead to other secondary infections. When netting koi you must use the correct equipment. If you do not own a viewing bowl, pan net and sock net already, they should be considered a vital addition to your koi first-aid kit.

Regular correct inspection of your koi is sensible as it often allows you to identify potential problems before they become serious. If you do spot a problem, it is a good idea to take a skin scrape or swab and these two topics are covered next. If taking a skin scrape, it is best to have your own microscope to examine the sample, and you will find a useful guide to buying and using a microscope in this section. A microscope is another piece of equipment that the serious koi keeper should not be without. Both

skin scrapes and swabs are simple procedures which can be carried out at home, and a detailed explanation of what is involved is given. However, the analysis of a swab is an involved process and it has to be sent away for testing to a suitable laboratory.

Finally in this section the procedures involved in transporting koi are examined. You may want to take your koi to a show, or need to get one to your local vet or koi dealer for examination, and it is vital that this is done correctly. Transporting koi incorrectly can be highly stressful and may cause opportunist diseases, such as those caused by parasites, to become a problem. One of the hardest things to guard against, but one which can cause the greatest stress to your koi, is temperature change. It is vital to try to regularize the temperature between the water into which the koi will be put and that in the transport bag. If your koi is not going into a new system, but is simply being taken for veterinary examination and then being returned, you must ensure that the temperature in the bag is not allowed to fall or rise too much. Tips on how to achieve this are given in this section.

If all these procedures are adopted and used on a regular basis as part of the routine maintenance of your pond, you will be far more likely to identify any problems early. You will also have absorbed the information needed to use section 3 of the book effectively. You will know which condition you are treating; as a result the correct course of treatment can be administered, thereby considerably increasing the chances of a rapid and full recovery.

Take Care!
While experienced hobbyists may feel comfortable carrying out the techniques described in this section, always consider the well-being of your fish first. If you are not an experienced fishkeeper, or are in doubt about any of the procedures, always consult a vet or koi health specialist first.

Right: It is important to learn the correct ways of handling koi to avoid causing them undue stress.

KOI ANATOMY

It is useful to have a basic understanding of the anatomy of your koi. Not only does this help in understanding how and why certain diseases cause the problems they do, but knowledge of what each part of the body does also helps in the identification and treatment of particular ailments which attack specific parts of the body.

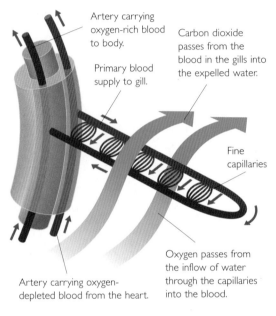

Artery carrying oxygen-rich blood to body.

Carbon dioxide passes from the blood in the gills into the expelled water.

Primary blood supply to gill.

Fine capillaries

Artery carrying oxygen-depleted blood from the heart.

Oxygen passes from the inflow of water through the capillaries into the blood.

Above: The drawing reveals how blood flow in the capillaries of the gill lamellae and water flow over the gill filaments allows gaseous exchange to take place.

The Skin, Scales and Lateral Line

A koi's skin is covered by a layer of mucus, which not only offers protection against disease but also helps streamline the fish to aid locomotion. This layer of mucus is continually being refreshed as the old mucus sloughs off into the water. Below the mucus lies the top layer of skin known as the epidermis. This is extremely thin and in fact lies above the scales. The epidermis is responsible for mucus production and assists wound repair by multiplying to cover areas of damage. Under the epidermis is the dermis and this is where the scales are formed. Scales make up a calcified flexible plate; they contain high levels of calcium and offer an extra line of defence. In times of nutrient depletion this calcium can also be used as an extra nutrient source. The scales tend to be uniform in shape

with the exception of those which form the lateral line. These have a tiny opening in them which appears to the naked eye as a line running along the length of the koi. The lateral line is a sensory organ used to detect vibrations in the water. Hair cells transmit any vibration via nerve fibres to the spinal cord which sends a signal to the brain. The dermis also contains chromatophores, which are responsible for coloration, as well as nerves, blood vessels and sense organs.

The Gills

The gills are made up of four bony arches which are the main support for the lamellae (or gill membranes) which lie in a V formation. These primary lamellae have a large surface area and contain many blood capillaries which allow oxygen to diffuse from the water into the blood. The gills are protected from damage by a bony cover known as the operculum. It is the flow of

Freshwater osmoregulation

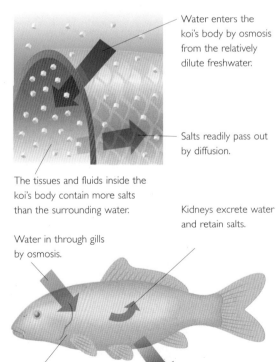

Water enters the koi's body by osmosis from the relatively dilute freshwater.

Salts readily pass out by diffusion.

The tissues and fluids inside the koi's body contain more salts than the surrounding water.

Kidneys excrete water and retain salts.

Water in through gills by osmosis.

Chloride cells in the gill lamellae actively take up salts as the gills are irrigated with water.

Copious amounts of dilute urine are produced.

Skin, scales and fins

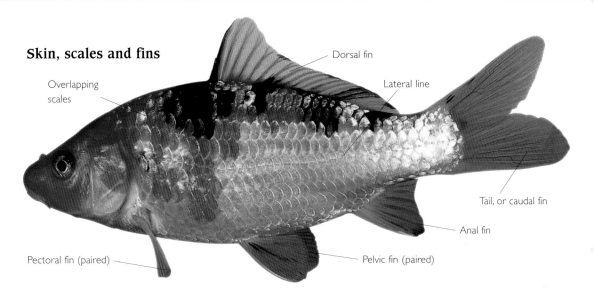

Dorsal fin

Lateral line

Overlapping scales

Tail, or caudal fin

Anal fin

Pectoral fin (paired)

Pelvic fin (paired)

water over the gills that enables koi to extract oxygen from the water for their survival. The process by which water is passed over the gills is known as the buccal pump; and it has two parts. First comes the water intake which is achieved by the fish opening its mouth while holding its operculum shut. Water collects in the mouth and the area under the mouth (known as the buccal cavity) which is now lowered. Then comes water expulsion when the fish closes its mouth while lifting its buccal cavity; this has the effect of forcing oxygen rich-water over the gills and out of the now open operculum. To optimize the diffusion of oxygen into the blood that flows through the membranes in the gills a countercurrent mechanism is employed. This means that the water flowing across the gills travels in the opposite direction to the blood. Consequently the blood to which the water is first exposed has a low oxygen content and so more oxygen can be extracted from the water, whereas at the end of the gills water which is low in oxygen is exposed to oxygen-rich blood and thus less diffusion is required. The main advantage of the process is that it allows for diffusion to take place along the whole length of the gill lamellae.

Osmoregulation (Gills, Kidneys, Skin)

This is the process by which koi control the balance between fluid and salt levels within their cells. As koi are freshwater fish their bodies have a higher salt concentration than the water around them, and consequently the salts in their cells

want to diffuse out into the surrounding water. Similarly, water enters the koi mainly through the gills and the skin, both of which are partially permeable. To help maintain the correct salt level within a fish, paired kidneys actually extract the required amount of salt, while producing urine as a waste product which is discharged via the vent. In addition koi control their gill movements so that their gills are exposed to the pond water for only a limited period of time, so reducing the levels of salts that diffuse out. Chloride cells located on the gills also help matters by taking up salts from the water that passes over them.

Swimbladder

This is an internal organ consisting of two chambers, and its purpose is to control buoyancy as well as to transmit sounds to the inner ear via a number of small bones known as the Weberian ossicles. The swimbladder in a koi is a gas-filled sac, and the level of inflation is generally controlled by blood vessels lying around it. Because the swimbladder is connected to the gut, koi can increase the level of gas within it simply by gulping air from the pond's surface.

Digestive Organs (Oesophagus, Liver and Intestine)

Koi do not have teeth – instead they have paired pharyngeal bones which are used to crush the food as it passes through the oesophagus into the intestine where it is digested and absorbed into the blood and carried to the liver. Any food which

Internal anatomy

The gills are the site of gas diffusion. Carbon dioxide is released into the water and oxygen is collected by red blood cells.

Sound waves are detected by the swimbladder and amplified by a series of backbones, linking them to the inner ear, enabling the fish to hear.

The trunk kidney conserves salts in the body and produces vast amounts of very dilute urine to remove water and maintain the correct osmotic balance.

The swimbladder is a gas-filled buoyancy organ that allows the fish to remain at any depth in the water with the minimum expenditure of energy.

Brain

Koi have very good eyesight

Backbone

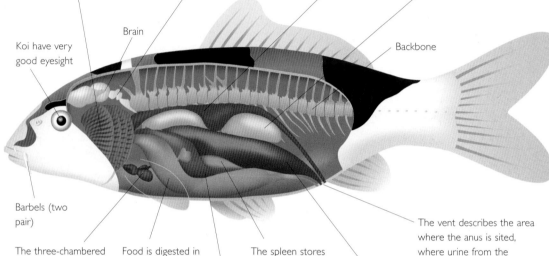

Barbels (two pair)

The three-chambered heart pumps deoxygenated blood to the gills. The muscular section of the heart (the ventricle) receives oxygen-rich blood from the coronary artery.

Food is digested in the intestine through the action of enzymes and absorbed by the blood supply.

The spleen stores immature red blood cells and produces cells of the immune system.

The vent describes the area where the anus is sited, where urine from the kidneys is released, and where eggs or sperm (milt) are shed into the water.

The liver stores or distributes digested food to the tissues, and breaks down unwanted proteins into waste.

The gonads are situated on either side of the body. The ovaries produce eggs while the testes produce sperm.

is not broken down by the digestive enzymes will be excreted via the vent as waste. Koi do not have stomachs – this is why the food goes straight from the oesophagus into the intestine. The liver in koi is large and usually deep red in colour, although if a vegetable-based diet has been fed it may have a brownish appearance. It deals with the distribution of nutrients, as well as with the breakdown of unwanted proteins which are turned into waste ammonia. The liver will also remove any toxins or poisons, as well as breaking down old red blood cells into bile.

Sight (Eyes)
Koi, like many other fish species, have excellent eyesight. Many experts think that they actually see things in a very similar way to humans, and are able to make out shapes and colours.

Fins
Koi have a number of fins. Some, like the pectoral fins, are paired while others are single, like the dorsal. These fins have various uses including providing propulsion, steering, and helping to maintain stability within the water.

The Heart and Circulation System
A koi's heart contains three chambers: the sinus venosus which receives blood from the veins, the atrium which pumps the blood into the ventricle which is the main pumping chamber sending blood through the aorta and arteries. Blood circulates from the heart to the gills, where it takes on oxygen, and then to tissue matter.

Above: When a koi comes to the surface to feed, it uses its fins to propel itself and to maintain its position in the water.

At this point it has a relatively high pressure. However, as this blood flows to the extremities of the body it becomes slower and the oxygen level decreases. Between 30 and 50 per cent of the blood is made up of blood cells. Most of these are red cells which carry oxygen around the body, and the remainder are white blood cells which are important to the koi's immune system. The rest of the blood consists of plasma which contains water, salts, glucose, plus any waste which is being transported around the body.

Reproductive Organs (Gonads)

These are located internally and are found on either side of the body. Female koi possess ovaries and these are responsible for the production of eggs. In some instances they can be very large (see pages 88-91 on egg retention). Testes are found in male koi and they are responsible for the production of milt (sperm). Both eggs and milt are released by a koi through its vent into the water.

The Immune System

The immune system comprises many elements. The first line of defence involves the sticky mucus layer which has anti-bacterial and anti-fungal properties and is continually renewing itself. Beneath the mucus are two skin layers which serve as physical barriers: the outer epidermis and the inner dermis within which the scales are rooted. Many infections take hold by entering through breaches in the skin. The acid conditions of the digestive tract are also unfriendly to pathogens that gain entry via ingested food or water.

If the koi's physical barriers are breached and an infection enters the tissues or blood, the next line of defence involves various white blood cells, antibodies and other substances involved in immunity. Several internal organs (notably the thymus, spleen, head-kidney, liver and lower intestine) play key roles in the koi's immune defences. One special element of the koi's immune system is the so-called "acquired immunity". If the fish has experienced the alien pathogen before, the fish's immune system will react quicker than if it has to combat a new intruder. The speed of reaction also depends upon the water temperature; lower temperatures lengthen the response time of the immune system, while levels of pathogen activity may still be high. This is why pond heating is so beneficial to koi healthcare.

NETTING AND HANDLING YOUR KOI

If you believe that your koi are suffering from any of the health problems which are discussed later in this book, you will probably need to take one or more fish out of the pond for closer inspection. This could be in order to take a skin scrape, a mucus swab, to move the fish into quarantine or simply to take a closer look at the fish before deciding on the next course of action. When moving or examining koi, you must do so in such a way as to cause the minimum stress or injury to the fish. Bad netting and handling can itself be a large stress factor which could lead to future health problems, and many physical injuries are caused by careless netting.

A sock net

A pan net

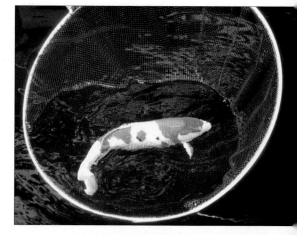

1: Catch the koi to be inspected in a suitably sized pan net.

2: Guide the koi to the bowl with the net, then use the edge of the net to tip one side of the bowl below water level.

Catching Your Koi

Before any attempt is made to catch a fish you must have the right equipment:
- a pan net suitable to accommodate the largest fish in the pond.
- a viewing bowl.
- a sock net.

A pan net is very shallow, as this reduces the risk of the fish becoming entangled in the netting. In fact this net should only be used as a guide and under no circumstances should you ever lift the net out of the water with the fish in it. You are basically trying to use it to shepherd the desired fish into a viewing bowl. Ideally get a helper at this point to submerge one side of the bowl so that the fish can simply swim from the net into the bowl. If you have to work on your own, float the viewing bowl and half fill it with water. Once the fish is caught, bring it to the surface and lift one side of the net so that it hooks over the lip of the

3: Gently tip the net to transfer the koi from net to bowl.

bowl. Then force one side of the bowl down into the water and simultaneously tip the fish from the net to the bowl. The viewing bowl used should be like the net: i.e. its diameter must be wide enough to accommodate your largest koi. It is advisable to opt for a floating bowl or else you may find you are spending more time lifting the bowl from the bottom of the pond than you are catching koi. When actually trying to catch a fish there are a few simple rules which should be followed. These will make it easier for you to catch the koi and reduce the risk of damage being caused to it.

1 Turn off all air pumps and water features, this will let you see what you are doing.

2 Move the net so that its edge slices through the water. This reduces drag and allows you to move the net much more quickly.

3 When bringing a captured fish to the surface avoid any underwater returns. The pressure of the water returning to the pond from these could force the koi into the net and cause it physical damage.

4 If you are trying to catch small koi or the pond is very large, you may find it hard to catch the fish with one net. Rather than chasing around your pond and risking accidentally bumping the fish with the net, try one of two tactics. Either ask someone to help you and give them another net so that they can keep the fish at one end while you try to catch it. If this is not possible, lower the water level to reduce the area in which the fish can swim.

5 If the pond is very large, netting a particular koi may prove too stressful to both yourself and the fish. If such a case it may be advisable to get a

1: If you have a helper, ask him to hold the bowl as shown.

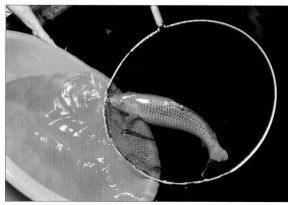

2: Move the net towards the submerged edge of the bowl.

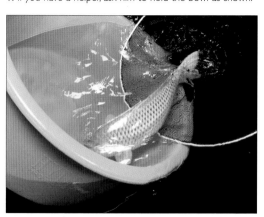

3: Gently tip the net so that the koi swims into the bowl.

4: To prevent jumping, keep the water level quite low.

1: Pull the sock net through the water to make it wet.

2: Coax the koi head-first into the sock net.

3: Hold each end of the net and lift it out of the water.

4: Pull the sock net through the water to release the koi.

custom-made seine net for your pond which allows all the koi to be caught easily without undue stress. Then the ones which need to be inspected can simply be removed and placed into a viewing bowl, before the others are allowed to return to the pond.

Once you have a fish in the viewing bowl, you may wish to move it or to inspect it more closely. There are four ways in which you can move fish without causing unnecessary stress and damage. They are:

1 Sock net

This is a net which is shaped very much like a table tennis bat with a long, open-ended, sock-like net trailing behind it. They are available in numerous sizes, and it is important to ensure that the one you are using has a large enough diameter for the fish in question, and that it will hold the full length of the fish in the sock. Before attempting to move the fish make sure that the whole of the sock is wet. Then hold the sock net in one hand under the water in the bowl and use your other hand to persuade the fish gently into the sock head first. Once fully in the sock, use one hand to hold the end of the sock while the other hand holds the handle. The sock net can then be lifted out of the water. Make sure that the net is kept as straight as possible. To release the fish from the sock simply immerse it in the water and let go of the end of the sock. Then lift the sock from the water by the handle, and if done correctly the fish will swim out.

2 Plastic bag

If a sock net is not available, a plastic bag can be used in much the same way. The only difference is that as the bag is sealed at one end, you will have to tip the fish from the bag.

3 Moving the bowl

If neither a plastic bag or sock net are available you can quite simply carry the viewing bowl to where you wish to move the fish. This may sound simple, but normally the bowl is heavy due to the volume of water it holds, and it may need two or more people to lift it. There is also a risk of the fish jumping in the bowl, and damaging itself. This method of moving fish is better suited to smaller koi less than 30cm (12in) in length.

4 Carrying the fish

This method should not be attempted unless you are confident at handling fish, and really it should

1: Put the plastic bag in the bowl, half-fill with water, then coax the koi into it.

2: Ensure enough water to cover koi.

3: Hold the top and one of the bottom corners of the bag.

4: You can now lift the bag and move the koi as desired.

not be considered if a sock net or plastic bag is available. The fish is quite simply picked up from the water and carried to its new location. When carrying a fish, one hand is normally placed under the pectoral fins while the other goes just behind the anal fin.

1: To move a fish by hand, position your hands as shown.

2: Ensure that your hands are comfortable, then lift the koi from the water. If the koi starts to move, do not tense – simply let your hands move with the fish.

The hard part is to know just how tight to hold the fish, and not to be nervous as this causes the fish to struggle. Really you should not grasp the fish but just let it rest in your hands. Some people say it is best not to look at the fish as this causes you to worry too much about what it is going to do. If the fish starts to struggle, you must stay relaxed and let your hands go with the movement of the fish. Once the fish relaxes, you can generally carry it without problems. The risk with hand-moving fish is that if one does panic you may drop it, and cause considerable damage and stress. This is more likely to happen with male fish which are more aggressive or Doitsu/leather varieties (no scales or a single line of scales) as they are more slippery.

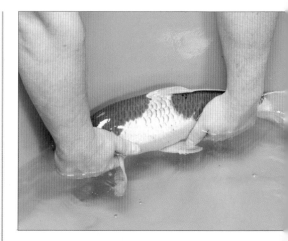

1: To tip a fish, hold it firmly against the side of the bowl.

2: Rotate the koi against the side until it is upside down.

3: It can be held against the bowl ready for inspection.

Once you have your koi bowled, you can inspect it for damage, parasites or take samples from it while it remains in the bowl. But if you want to inspect the underside of your koi for any problems, you have various options.

Hold the fish out of water
Follow the steps for carrying the fish, and lift it out of the water while someone else inspects underneath it.

Tip the fish in the bowl
If unsure about lifting the fish from the water, you can turn the fish upside-down in the bowl. You should push the fish against the side of the bowl – hold the fish quite firmly while doing this. Once you are happy with your grip on the fish, turn it over in your hands, so that it is upside-down in the water, but still against the side of the bowl. After inspection simply loosen your grip and the fish will return to an upright position.

Hold the fish in a plastic bag
An alternative approach is simply to bag it in a clear plastic bag and hold this up so that you can view the underside of the fish.

Use sedating agent
If unsure about the methods suggested, you can sedate (anaesthetize) the fish (see pages 132-4) and inspect it while it is under sedation. However, if you wish to take a skin scrape or swab, it is best to do this without the use of sedation as this may alter the results.

Spinning the fish
If you decide to use one of the handling methods, you may wish to employ a tactic called "spinning". You simply spin the fish gently with your hands while it is in the bowl for a minute or two. This causes the fish to become disoriented which in turn makes it easier to handle without the need for a sedating agent.

Do remember that if you have to net, inspect or move koi, if you try to do it in haste, with the wrong equipment or without correct planning, you could make a problem a lot worse or even create new ones. If you are ever unsure about the correct procedure, be sure to seek advice from your local koi specialist.

1: Using your hands, gently spin the koi with a circular motion.

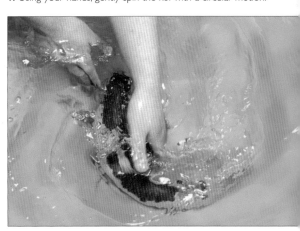
2: Continue doing this, working in the same direction.

3: After a minute or two the koi should be quite calm.

USING A MICROSCOPE

A microscope is an essential piece of equipment for the correct identification of diseases. It allows koi keepers to identify parasite infections. Many koi keepers cite the price of a good quality microscope as the reason they do not own one. But this is false economy. If you can identify parasites and treat them early, you can stop the spread of an infection before it becomes a real concern and leads to potential

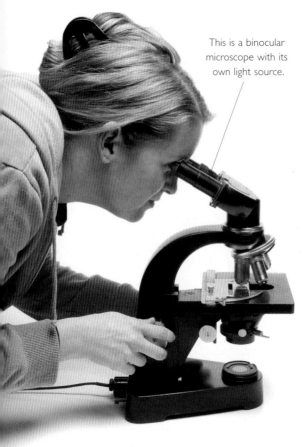

This is a binocular microscope with its own light source.

Above: A microscope is an essential tool for the koi keeper to aid in the identification of many diseases.

losses or physical damage to high quality koi. A good quality microscope is also a sound investment, and if the time comes when you no longer need it, as long as it has been well maintained you will easily be able to sell it again, and recoup some of your initial outlay. Various factors should be considered when deciding on the best unit for your budget and intended use.

Styles of Microscope

Firstly do you want a binocular (using two eye-pieces) or a monocular (single eye-piece) microscope? This choice is largely influenced by budget and personal preference. Another factor which is often influenced by budget is the decision whether you require a microscope with its own light source or not. A microscope with its own light source generally needs mains power to light a bulb in the base of the unit. The advantage of this is that the microscope can be set up in one location and used at any time simply by turning on the power supply, while the intensity of the light can normally be controlled allowing greater flexibility. The other – generally cheaper – option is to buy a microscope which does not have its own light source. Instead it has a mirror located in the base, which is turned to reflect rays of light onto the subject being examined. The disadvantage of this is that you are dependent upon an external light source, and the intensity of this light may not be controllable which can affect the brightness of the image.

Lenses

There are two lenses which you need to consider when purchasing a microscope: the eyepiece lens and the objective lens. Most microscopes feature more than one objective lens, commonly three will be found each with different powers of magnification. These lenses sit on a revolving turret so that the magnification can easily be changed by simply turning a dial which will move to the next lens. A microscope mainly intended for parasite identification should be equipped with lenses of the following power – 10x, 20x and 40x. The eyepiece lens is what you actually look down, and its magnification will affect the overall magnification of the image. These are easily interchangeable and thus allow for different levels of magnification to be achieved. The typical magnification of the eyepiece lens for parasitic identification is normally 10x or 15x. If a 10x eyepiece lens is used with an objective lens of 40x, a magnification of 400x can be achieved (10 x 40 = 400). Do not worry that you are limiting yourself by purchasing a microscope at this magnification. As long as you buy a reputable make, you will be able to buy other more powerful lenses later on.

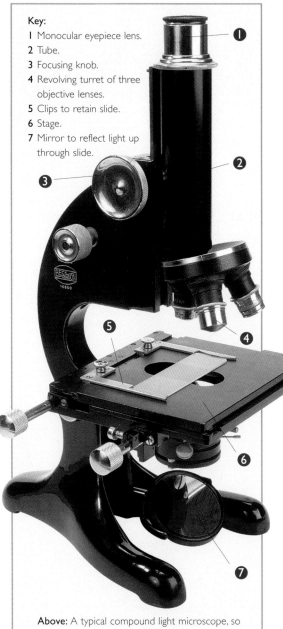

Key:
1 Monocular eyepiece lens.
2 Tube.
3 Focusing knob.
4 Revolving turret of three objective lenses.
5 Clips to retain slide.
6 Stage.
7 Mirror to reflect light up through slide.

Above: A typical compound light microscope, so called because the magnification is a compound of the lens power in the eyepiece and objective lenses.

Mounting A Slide

Having taken a slide for examination (see pages 44-5), it is essential that it is placed correctly on the microscope so that it can be viewed. The slide is placed is what is known as the stage, which

may either be fixed or move up and down. In some microscopes the stage moves up and down to bring the slide into focus, while others will work by moving the lens and eyepiece with a focus dial. The slide is held in place by a slide clamp. The sample on the slide is normally covered by a small square of thin glass called a cover slip.

Viewing The Slide

Once firmly in position the slide can be viewed. To prevent damage to the lens it is better to focus away from the slide. If you move the lens towards the slide you may over-focus and crash the lens onto it which can both break the slide, and more importantly damage or scratch the objective lens. There are typically two controls on a standard microscope for controlling the focus. The first of these should be used initially to allow an object to be found quickly and roughly focused. Then the second control allows for fine tuning of the focusing by moving either the tube or stage just a fraction each time the fine focus dial is turned.

Unless you known exactly what you are looking for and at what magnification it will be found, always start at the lowest magnification, then increase it once a full scan of the slide has been achieved. To ensure you see all of the slide, view it in a methodical manner making either left to right or front to back passes, before gently moving on to the next sector to be viewed. The slide is moved by use of controls situated underneath the stage. There may also be additional controls for finer movement which allows for exact positioning over a specific area.

Some microscopes may have additional parts, such as a condenser or an area which can hold special filters. They are not required for the simple identification of parasites, but they may have to be set up initially to allow the microscope to function correctly. You may find that once you have mastered the basic skills required to identify parasites that microscopy becomes a hobby in its own right. However, if you find the whole idea of using a microscope daunting, do not be afraid to speak to your local koi dealer and ask for guidance. Soon you will find that your microscope becomes a vital part of your koi healthcare arsenal.

HOW TO TAKE A SKIN SCRAPE

If your koi are not behaving in their normal way, but all water quality parameters including the oxygen level are acceptable, it is worth taking a skin scrape. This involves scraping a sterile blunt instrument, or (for the more experienced) a slide, over a fish's skin to collect some of the mucus which covers its body. The mucus sample can then be examined under a microscope, and any parasites present within the pond that may be affecting their behaviour identified. Typical behavioural changes include koi hanging in the water, swimming with fins clamped to the sides, rapid gill movements, fish congregating in areas of enriched oxygen such as water returns and airstones, fish that are isolated and not mixing with other koi in the pond, loss of appetite, and flicking or rubbing against any surfaces in the pond as if the fish were trying to relieve an irritation. If you do not own a microscope to examine the skin scrape, a nearby koi dealer can help, but they must be able to view the scrape quickly, ideally within 30-60 minutes of it having been taken. And you must be sure that the dealer has the right facilities and sufficient expertise to be able to make an accurate diagnosis.

To take a skin scrape you will need the sterile blunt instrument and some slides and cover slips to hand. If you are taking a sample from a large koi, it also helps to have someone to help you, as you cannot sedate the koi before taking the scrape. A sedating agent can have an effect on the results from the scrape, and so large koi must be physically held while one is taken.

Taking A Skin Scrape

1 Place the koi in a viewing bowl. Then tip out some water so just enough remains to cover the koi. When dealing with small koi you may be able to hold the fish in one hand while taking the scrape with the other. For larger koi it is far easier if you have an assistant who can hold the koi against the side of the bowl while you take the scrape. It is sometimes necessary to apply quite a bit of pressure to the koi while holding it to stop it from jumping about and damaging itself. To calm the koi down you can employ a tactic known as spinning (see page 41).

2 Once the koi is firmly held, take the blunt instrument or slide and run it along the fish's body. Do this from head to tail in the direction of the scales. **Never** take a skin scrape in the other

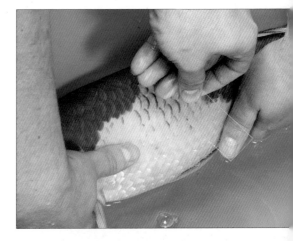

1: Take a blunt instrument or slide, as shown here.

2: Gently run it along the body in the direction of the scales.

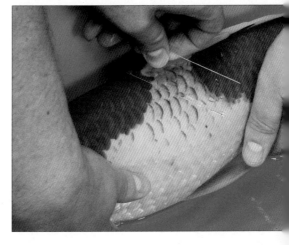

3: Body mucus will collect on the surface of the slide.

Right: Having taken your sample, it can now be examined. In order to prepare the slide, a cover slip has to be placed over the mucus. Then the slide can be positioned on the microscope ready for examination.

4: A collection of mucus will be deposited on the slide or blunt instrument used to take the scrape.

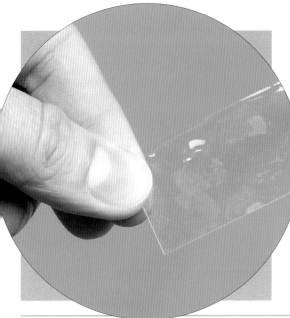

direction as this may result in scale damage. You may need to apply a little pressure while taking the scrape, and perhaps make more than one pass to get enough mucus for the sample. A skin scrape can be taken anywhere on the koi, but do take note of the symptoms which your koi are displaying. If, for example, it is gasping for air, take a scrape as close to the gills as you can. The amount of mucus required is quite small and as long as an area of the slide can be seen to have mucus on it, you will have enough to examine it successfully. If using a blunt instrument to take the scrape, the mucus should be transferred onto the slide once collected.

3 Once the scrape is taken you can put the koi back in the pond. Normally a scrape will not have any adverse side effect on the koi as long as it is done correctly.

4 You now prepare your slide for examination under the microscope by taking a cover slip, and using this to move the sample of mucus to the centre of the slide. Put a drop of pond water (**not** tapwater) on the slide to dilute the mucus sample, then drop the cover slip into position and gently ease it onto the slide allowing the mucus to spread out underneath it. If you do not have any cover slips, you can use another slide and sandwich the mucus between the two pieces of glass.

5 Now examine the slide under your microscope. If nothing is found, it pays to take scrapes from other koi in your pond.

Only consider taking scrapes when signs of parasite infection become obvious. Remember parasites will always be present but in low numbers; it is only when koi become stressed that these numbers increase and a problem results. As you learn how to view and interpret a scrape, you will be able to spot any increase in parasite levels and hopefully identify and treat the problem before it gets out of control.

HOW TO TAKE A SWAB

If water quality is fine, and a skin scrape has not revealed obvious causes of why your koi are looking off colour, perhaps with ulcers, sores and areas of infection appearing, it is worth taking a swab and sending it away for analysis to check if a bacterial infection is causing the problem. If your koi are already showing areas of ulceration or if previously damaged or diseased areas do not heal, consider taking a swab straight away as a bacterial problem is suggested by these symptoms. Also test the water quality and take a skin scrape to check for parasites.

Unlike a skin scrape which can be examined at home, a swab needs to be processed by a qualified laboratory. Your local koi specialist should be able to assist you to take a swab by supplying the necessary equipment and either sending it away for you or advising you on doing this yourself. The results may also be sent back to your local dealer or vet, and they can then advise on the correct course of treatment. Try to take and send swabs to a laboratory at the start of the week, unless otherwise advised by the laboratory itself, or by

your local dealer or vet. If you take swab on a Friday but the lab is closed over the weekend, work will not start on it until Monday at the earliest, and by this time the levels of bacteria on the swab may have decreased or increased to give a false reading.

Taking A Swab

1 Make sure that you have all the necessary items both for taking the swab and getting it in the post immediately. Generally you need the swab, a request form completed with your details and details of where and how the swab was taken, a pre-paid envelope, and a biohazard bag.

2 Now catch the koi and place it in a viewing bowl. As with taking a skin scrape it is better to avoid sedating (anaesthetizing) the koi as this can have an effect on the results when they are processed. Tip water from the viewing bowl until only enough is left to cover the chosen koi.

3 It is far easier to carry out this step with two people. One of you should hold the koi against the side of the viewing bowl so that any areas

1: Remove the swab from its protective sterile packaging and rub it over the area to be tested.

2: As soon as you have taken the sample satisfactorily, place the swab back into its sterile protective casing.

which look infected are easily visible. Some pressure may be required to hold the koi still but this will cause less harm than if the koi is simply left to thrash about in the bowl. If the koi is particularly lively, a technique known as spinning can be employed to calm it down (see page 41). Once the koi is held firmly in position, the other person can take the swab from areas of ulceration or sites of physical damage on the fish as it is these areas which give the most accurate diagnosis of what is actually present.

4 Only open the packing when ready to take the swab; the actual swab should not be taken from its container until the koi is secure in the bowl. This will reduce the risk of any airborne bacteria getting onto the swab and giving false readings. A swab is basically like a large cotton-wool bud, and to take a sample it is simply rolled back and forth over the area to be tested.

5 Once the sample is obtained, immediately place the swab back into its container, again to prevent any contamination. Write any necessary details on the container for identification purposes.

6 The koi can now be released back into the pond – it should suffer no adverse effects.

7 Once labelled, and with all required paperwork completed, the container can be placed in the biohazard bag. This goes into the addressed envelope which should be posted immediately, unless you have arranged to return it to your koi specialist or vet instead.

Make sure you use the quickest postal service available – many laboratories will supply pre-paid envelopes. The quicker the swab gets to the lab, the sooner you will have the results, and they will give a more accurate picture of what your problem is. As most of the work in processing the swab is done by a specialist laboratory there is usually a charge to pay. Do not let this put you off as the information which you will get back is priceless when treating your koi. However, avoid routine swab sampling in the absence of any health problems. There is a risk that routine swabbing might result in overuse of antibiotics which will only exacerbate existing problems of antibiotic resistance.

3: Immediately you have finished taking the swab, complete any paperwork which needs to go with it, and get it into the post.

THE RESULTS OF A SWAB

The results of a swab can normally be expected within four to five days. To process a swab the laboratory first smears the end of the sample over an agar plate, which is then placed in a special oven to encourage any bacteria present to grow. Once the bacteria have grown, the strain is identified and then a sensitivity test is carried out. This involves smearing a sample of the bacteria over another agar dish onto which discs are placed which contain different antibiotics. This dish is then put back into a oven and heated for a period before being examined. Any areas which reveal reduced bacterial growth indicate which antibiotics are effective against the bacteria, while any areas where there has been no change or even an increase in bacterial growth show antibiotics that are not effective.

A report is then drawn up by the laboratory and sent to your local koi specialist as they are normally the account holders for whom the lab works. Depending upon the level of reduction in

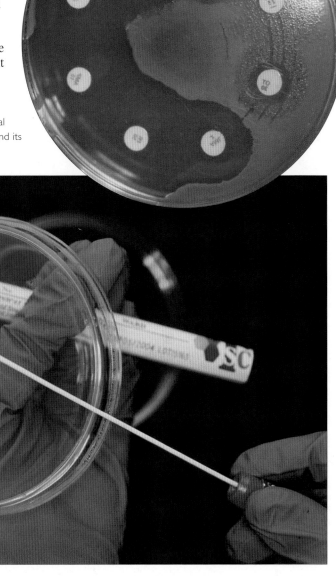

Below and right: An agar plate with eight discs containing different antibiotics (right). A bacterial sample is cultivated on an agar plate (below), and its reaction to the different antibiotics observed.

Above: A range of test kits and media used in the laboratory for the identification of bacterial disease. The cabinet is used for the cultivation of these bacteria.

the growth of bacteria, the relative sensitivity to particular antibiotics can be deduced. Although the report may show that a number of antibiotics are effective against the bacteria in question, always try the one which is most effective first. To speed up the whole process this information is generally faxed or emailed, while the original documents are sent in the post. Once the information is received, you will be contacted by your vet or local dealer to discuss the results. From the findings, you will be able to determine which species of bacteria is causing the problem, and at what level it is present. You will also be able to take advice on which antibiotic should be used to treat the problem. In the UK antibiotics can only be legally prescribed by a vet. In certain other countries, including the USA, some antibiotics are available over the counter without a prescription.

If a bacterial problem is present and the results show a high level of bacterial growth, it is usually necessary to administer antibiotics to all affected koi, and this is generally done via injection by a suitably qualified health specialist. The appropriate antibiotics can normally be purchased from your vet, but it may be necessary to show him the laboratory report in order to obtain the necessary drugs. If smaller koi are infected, it is important to tell both your local dealer and vet that this is the case, as it is not advisable to inject koi that are under 15cm (6in) in length. It may be that an antibiotic food should be used instead.

Remember that although testing water quality and taking a skin scrape should be the first steps taken to identify a disease, a swab should follow if these initial tests turn up nothing. Although many bacterial problems are easy to identify, such as ulceration or mouth rot, it is impossible to tell which species of bacteria is responsible and how it will react to a certain antibiotic. This is why swab analysis is vital as it allows not only the correct diagnosis but also the use of the correct medication. Prolonged use of the wrong antibiotic not only does nothing to help the condition to heal, but it may also lead to the bacteria developing resistance to the antibiotic so making that particular drug less effective in the future. As there are only a limited number of antibiotics available and licensed for use on koi, this is a situation which is to be avoided.

TRANSPORTING KOI

Sometimes you may need to transport your koi to your vet or a koi dealer for further examination to allow an exact identification of a disease to be made, or for extra treatment. While it is always better to treat a sick koi on site rather than putting it through the extra stress of being moved, this is not always possible. So there will inevitably be instances where you have to transport at least one, or maybe more, koi, in order to obtain expert advice or specialist treatment. In order to minimize the stress that this process will cause, it is vital that the koi should be handled and packaged in the correct manner.

Before attempting to transport any koi, make sure that you have the correct equipment needed to bag up your koi with the minimum of stress. You will need suitably sized bags for the koi to be moved, and it is best to have enough of these so that each bag can be doubled up, i.e. one bag placed inside another. This helps to prevent leaks occurring. A supply of air or oxygen will be required to inflate the bag once the koi is placed inside it. Ideally this should be oxygen, but most people do not possess an oxygen bottle. An alternative approach which can be used if the fish will not travel for longer than 60-90 minutes without the bag being opened and resealed, is to use a normal air pump to inflate the bag, and as this is a standard for most koi keepers, it proves a viable alternative. You will also need elastic bands to seal the bags, and a suitably sized box in which a bag can be placed.

Bagging Koi For Transportation

1 Once the koi in question are in the viewing bowl decide on the correct size of bag, and how many koi can be placed in each bag. Plastic koi bags are generally available from your local koi dealer and if you tell them the number and size of the koi that you are intending to move, they will be able to supply the correct size and quantity of bags. Expect to pay for these bags, however, as they are manufactured from thicker plastic, and generally have a double seal to make leaks less likely. These bags come in numerous sizes, but the most common are: 12in x 24in (suitable for small koi up to 5 to 6in), 16in x 30in (suitable for a number of small koi, or individual koi of 10 to 12in), 24in x 40in (suitable for a large number, say up to 30, small koi under 6in, or three to four koi of around 10in

1: Take a fish bag of a suitable size for the koi to be moved.

4: To prevent water from becoming trapped between the two bags, roll the tops of the bags down.

2: Decant a small amount of water into the bag.

3: "Double bag" putting one bag inside another.

5: Coax the koi into the bag adding water while doing so.
6: Having checked that the correct amount of water is in the bag, the top can be unrolled.
7: Hold the top of the bag and one of the bottom corners securely, and then lift it out of the viewing bowl.

to 12in, or individual large koi up to 28 to 30in). For larger koi than this you will require a bigger bag which your koi dealer may not carry as a stock item, and so it may need to be ordered.

2 Select the correct bag size, and add an inch or so of water to it. Then drop this bag inside another bag of the same size. This process is known as double bagging. Before continuing it is a good idea to roll the top of both bags over a

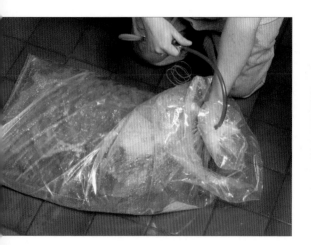

8: Hold the top tight while the air/oxygen hose is inserted.

9: Inflate the bag until only enough plastic is left to tie it off.

couple of times to prevent the gap between them filling with water. You are now ready to transfer your koi to the bag.

3 Lean over the bowl, take the bag in your hands and gently lower it into the water. Now coax the koi to be moved into the bag, you will find that the bag starts to fill with water at the same time. Once the koi is in the bag, lift it from the water, and see if it has the correct amount of water in it. For smaller koi the bag should contain about ⅓ water, allowing for ⅔rds air when inflated. However, for larger koi try and ensure that when the bag is laid on its side the water level is high enough to cover the gills.

4 When sufficient water is in the bag, use either an airline from your air pump to inflate the bag if only going a short distance, or if a longer distance is to be travelled use oxygen. Once the bag is inflated, it can be tied off using elastic bands. It is best to use two elastic bands just in case one should give. It is also vital that not just the inner bag be sealed in this manner, but the outer bag as well.

5 You can place the bagged koi inside a suitable box ready for transporting. The bag should be laid horizontally in the box, rather then stood up. This box should be a good fit for the bag to prevent it from rolling about. If the box is too big, pack the space out with something – spare plastic bags inflated with air are a good choice.

6 When placing the box in your car, position the box lengthways across the car. This prevents further damage from occurring to the fish if you have to brake suddenly as the koi will roll in the bag. If the box was positioned the other way, the koi would smash into the ends of the box. This is of extreme importance when larger koi are being transported. It is also an idea to place the box out of direct sunlight to avoid sudden changes in temperature.

7 If you are having to transport your koi over a longer distance, when moving house for example, you might want to consider using polystyrene boxes as these will help maintain a more stable temperature within the box. If it is very hot, you may wish to add ice packs inside the boxes to help maintain a cool temperature throughout the journey.

8 When releasing koi after transportation, check the temperatures of the bag water and the pond water. If they are significantly different, the bag should be allowed to float on the pond for 30 minutes to an hour out of direct sunlight before releasing the koi back into the water.

If you ever need to move a large number of koi it is worth discussing the situation with your local koi dealer, as they may have access to transportation tanks which can be filled with water and put on the back of a truck or trailer. They can also aerate the water in the tank with

10: Seal both bags separately with elastic bands.

11 and 12: Take a suitably sized box and place the bag in it; then seal the lid securely prior to transportation.

pure oxygen which is fed from an oxygen bottle on the vehicle via a special airstone in the tank. Koi moved this way can simply be sock-netted into the tank, then socked out when they arrive at their destination.

Below: Upon arriving at the final destination, you should float the bag on the pond for a period of 30 minutes or so to help stabilize any temperature differences. While doing this, ensure that the bag is kept out of direct sunlight.

KOI DISEASES

This his section of the book looks in detail at the various diseases which a koi keeper may encounter. Many of the diseases described here, such as tapeworm infestation or myxobolus, will probably never be experienced, but others, like *Trichodina*, whitespot and flukes, will undoubtedly cause a problem in your pond at some time in your koi-keeping hobby. This section is intended to allow readers to identify the problem by using the techniques described in section 2, and then to find the right treatment for that condition. In order to assist you, four pages of this section contain an illustrated guide to the diseases discussed. This should be your first place of reference, checking the symptoms displayed by your koi or on the microscope slide and relating them to the pictures on these pages. From here you can turn to the relevant entry that provides all the information required to make a more educated diagnosis, followed by a recommended course of treatment.

In order to get the best results from this book, and especially this section, it is vital that you should read section 2 closely and follow all the suggested steps to ensure that a correct identification of a disease is made, either by visual inspection, taking a skin scrape, or sending away a swab. If you do not take care doing this, an incorrect diagnosis may be made and the wrong treatment applied. This can be just as harmful – or even more harmful – than no treatment at all. That is why it is vital for a koi keeper to own a microscope, and to be prepared to send swabs away for processing when bacterial problems are suspected. Your local koi dealer or specialist will be able to help with this, although do not expect to get these services for free as they do cost money. However, this outlay is very small when compared to the cost of replacing an averagely stocked koi pond!

As well as making the correct identification, it is vital that you maintain a medicine chest containing appropriate treatments. Although it is impossible to keep stock of every treatment for every condition all the time, a few simple items will help with a vast number of the common conditions and complaints experienced by the typical koi keeper. Try and have the following to hand as a "just in case koi first aid kit" – sedating agents, malachite green, formalin, potassium permanganate, salt (this must be cooking salt, not table salt), Acriflavine, propolis or a similar wound sealer, cotton-wool buds or similar, a sharp pair of scissors, a scalpel and, of course, a good net and bowl in which to catch and handle the koi. Your local koi dealer should be able to supply these items, and may even sell an off-the-shelf first-aid kit containing most, or all, of them. These few items alone will stand you in good stead to combat a wide range of diseases, and respond quickly once an exact diagnosis has been made.

As you consult this section, it will soon become apparent that a few simple measures can help prevent the vast majority of the diseases featured. Good water quality, regular system maintenance, the use of a good quality food, pond heating, and a sensible low stocking level are the most effective measures to prevent disease from occurring in the first place. If you bear these precautions in mind and spend a bit of time each week ensuring that your system is maintained in optimum condition, there will be far fewer occasions when you will need to call upon this part of the book. However, when those times do arise, all the necessary information to progress from exact diagnosis to sensible treatment can easily be found and understood. This guidance allows you to pursue an educated treatment programme so as to return your pond to full health in the shortest possible time.

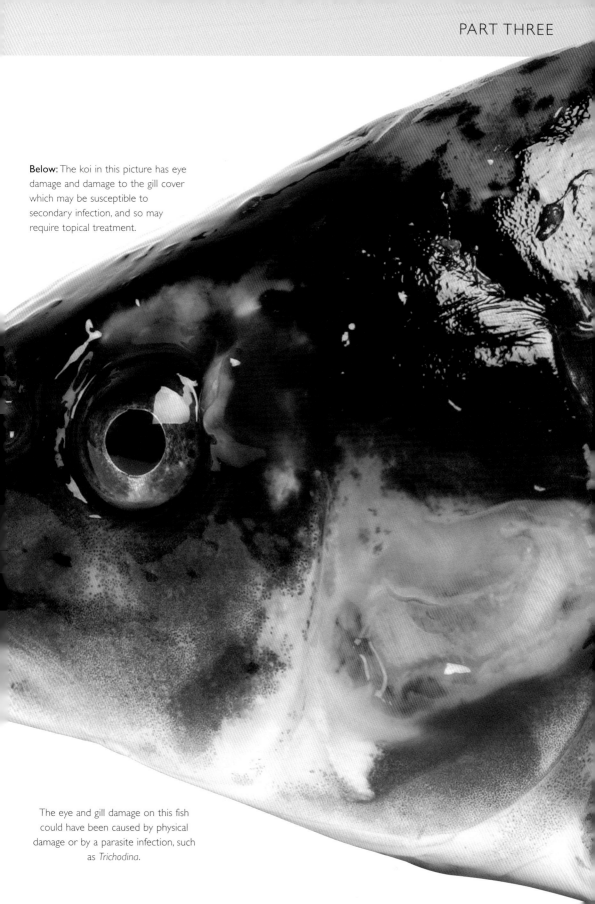

Below: The koi in this picture has eye damage and damage to the gill cover which may be susceptible to secondary infection, and so may require topical treatment.

The eye and gill damage on this fish could have been caused by physical damage or by a parasite infection, such as *Trichodina*.

PARASITES, VIRUSES, BACTERIA AND FUNGI

Parasites are creatures which require a host (i.e. your koi) in order to eat, reproduce, and survive. This host may be needed for long periods of time, as is the case with some parasitic infections, while others may only need a host for a limited time for a specific event, such as reproduction. External parasite infections in koi

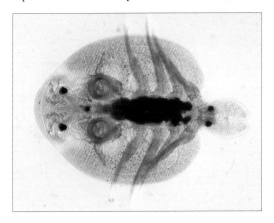

Above: A close-up of *Argulus* (a fish louse). This is one of the few parasites which can be seen with the naked eye.

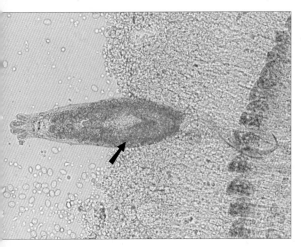

Above: *Dactylogyrus* is a fluke that attacks the gills. It is here seen under magnification through a microscope.

are commonplace and can generally be identified either by visible changes to the infected fish or by taking a skin scrape and making an exact identification under a microscope. Internal parasites are also often a problem, but they are much harder to identify because they live inside the fish. Generally most external parasitic infections can be treated easily once an accurate

diagnosis is made. It is quite normal to find one or two types of parasites present at any time in most ponds. It is only when your koi become stressed that their natural resistance drops and you will see the levels of parasites rise and start to cause a problem.

What Is A Virus?

A virus can only be seen by using a very powerful electron microscope which is a very expensive piece of equipment – so don't expect your vet or koi health expert to possess one! Viruses are extremely small. They can only live and reproduce by invading a living cell within a living creature. Having said this, viruses can also be very resistant to extreme temperatures and adverse conditions, and can survive outside the chosen host for extended periods of time. This makes treatment of viral infections very hard, as treatment leads to the affected cells, as well as the virus, being killed. The most effective way to combat viral infections is through vaccination to protect against infection, when a vaccine is available. For instance, a recently identified koi disease, koi herpes virus, is currently causing alarm. It is now being researched intensively in the hope that a vaccine can be produced in the near future. The only other approach is to provide optimum living conditions for the fish and allow their natural immune system to overcome the infection. This is much the same procedure as we adopt when we have a cold – we stay in bed, rest and wait until the body has overcome the virus and the cold disappears. Some viruses, however, can remain dormant in koi for months or even years, only becoming active again when the fish become stressed.

What Are Bacteria?

Bacteria come in many different shapes and sizes, but all are microscopic in size, and are single-celled organisms consisting of an outer cell wall which allows liquid and fluid to pass through. This is how they obtain nutrients. Most bacteria reproduce by a process of binary fission, i.e. one becomes two – two become four – and so on. This process can happen very quickly which means that extremely large populations of bacteria can appear in a very short space of time, as long as a viable food source is available. Bacteria are naturally present in a pond and they will survive in most conditions. In fact your koi will live

Above: A bacterial infection is shown here. This may have originally started as physical damage caused by flicking.

alongside the bacteria present in your pond quite happily until the environmental conditions become less favourable causing them to become stressed and so susceptible to infection. Alternatively if any areas on your koi become weakened – such as after a parasite infection or if physical damage has occurred – they will be attractive sites for the bacteria to attack. Many bacterial infections can be treated via topical treatment, the use of a medicated bath, or even a pond treatment. However, in very severe cases antibiotics may be required but this should only be as a last resort, and advice should be sought from a vet or a local koi specialist beforehand. If antibiotics are required, it is vital to ascertain which bacteria are causing the problem and which treatment will best help them. This information can be obtained by taking a swab and sending it for analysis. Once the results have been obtained, a course of treatment can be given to help clear up the infection. It is important, however, that a koi health specialist is consulted to get advice on the correct dose rate and how the treatment should be administered. Remember, not all bacteria are bad; in fact the filtration system at the heart of your pond works because beneficial bacteria convert

ammonia to nitrite, and then nitrite to nitrate and nitrogen gas.

What Is Fungus?
Although they are often thought of as plants, fungi do not contain chlorophyll nor do they go through the process of photosynthesis, and so they differ from plants. Instead some (called saprophytes) live on dead and decomposing organic matter, while others are parasitic and acquire their food from a living plant or animal. Fungi multiply via spores. Some species of fungus can reproduce asexually (without the need for both a male or a female to be present) while others require both sexes to be present. Many single-celled fungi can only be seen with a microscope, although others can easily be seen once they have reached an advanced stage of development. Common fungi include yeast, rust, mould and mushrooms. Not all fungi are bad, and in fact some help in breaking down organic waste and keeping the natural balance constant. Typical fungal infection in a koi pond is characterized by the presence of fluffy white tufts, similar to cotton wool, which will appear in areas which are susceptible to infection, i.e. sites of skin damage, or places weakened by other infections. Fungi rarely attack koi that are healthy, uninjured and unstressed.

DIAGNOSTIC GUIDE FOR CONDITIONS CAUSED BY PARASITES

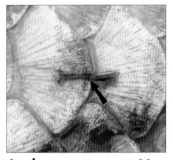

Anchor worm: *page 66*

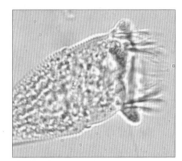

Apiosoma: *page 70*

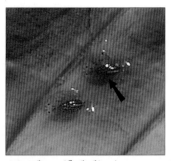

Argulus (fish lice): *page 72*

The gills and area around the eyes are susceptible to parasite infestation.

Parasite infections of the skin can lead to heavy mucus production.

Chilodonella: *page 76*

Some parasites, like tapeworms, live inside the fish and so are not visible externally.

Costia: *page 82*

Epistylis: *page 92*

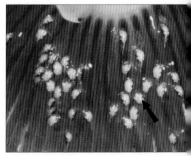

Gill maggots: *page 98*

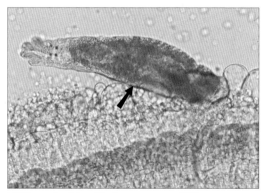

Gill and skin flukes: *page 102*

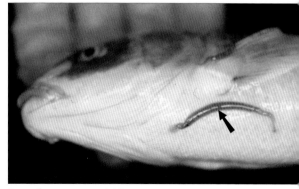

Leeches: *page 110*

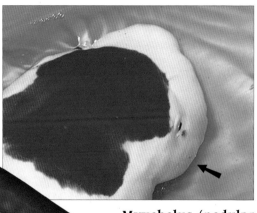

Myxobolus (nodular disease): *page 112*

Tapeworm: *page 120*

Many skin parasites may also be found on the fins.

Parasites like leeches and anchor worm may be seen attached to a fish's body.

Trichodina: *page 122*

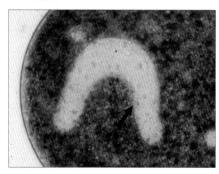

Whitespot: *page 124*

DIAGNOSTIC GUIDE FOR CONDITIONS CAUSED BY BACTERIA, VIRUSES, FUNGI AND OTHER EXTERNAL AND INTERNAL DISORDERS

Bubbles in the fins are an indication of gas bubble disease. Fins are also vulnerable to fungal rot.

Aeromonas: *page 62*

Columnaris: *page 78*

Curvature of the spine: *page 84*

Dropsy: *page 86*

Egg retention/Internal tumours: *page 88*

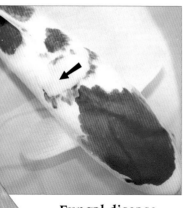

Gas bubble disease: *page 96*

Gill disorders: *page 98*

Fungal disease: *page 94*

Skin lesions are often the result of flicking to relieve the irritation caused by skin parasites.

Hi-kui: *page 106*

Conditions like dropsy cause external lifting of the fish's scales so that it resembles a pine cone.

KHV and SVC: *page 108*

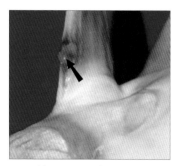

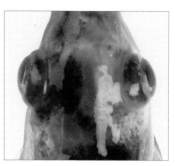

Papilloma and carp pox: *page 114*

Pop-eye: *page 116*

Swimbladder disorders: *page 118*

AEROMONAS INFECTION

Bacterial infection in a pond can be caused by numerous species of bacteria, but the most common is *Aeromonas hydrophila*. This is found in nearly all koi ponds, but as long as your koi are in good health, infection will generally not occur. It is only when your koi are stressed because of temperature fluctuation, overcrowding, poor water quality and other factors which have the effect of stressing the fish that the bacteria present can develop into a problem. If identified early, bacterial infections can be treated with the use of bactericides, but it is vital that it is caught early as advanced stages of infection may prove very difficult to treat. *Flavobacterium columnare* is another bacterium which may prove to be a problem for the koi keeper. Whatever bacteria are suspected, the most vital thing to do before any treatment is applied is to try and identify the exact organism you are dealing with.

Identification

The first course of action must be to take a swab from a koi showing symptoms. This has to be sent away for processing. The results will give you all the information required to treat the infection, as the exact bacterium will be known, plus which anti-bacterial will be effective against it. Symptoms of *Aeromonas hydrophila* include the build up of excessive mucus, and areas of reddening on the body which ultimately result in the lifting of the scales which in turn may result in the presence of ulcers. In some cases the scale lifting does not confine itself to a specific location on the body and the infected koi may take on a pine-cone appearance. Dropsy could then develop as well as other conditions such as pop-eye. Internal problems may also be developing along with the external symptoms. If losses do occur, internal examination may well indicate haemorrhagic septicaemia around the internal organs which is identified by a reddening of these plus the presence of excess amounts of fluids and blood.

If your koi start to develop numerous ulcers on the body and also around the head, gill cover (operculum) and mouth, it may be that "new hole" disease is the problem. This may be caused

Right: This koi has a severe case of *Aeromonas* which has resulted in lifting of the scales, which in turn may be an indication of bacterial dropsy.

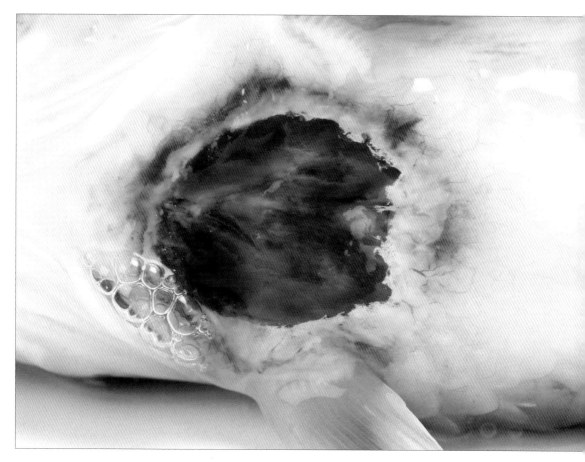

Above: An ulcer on the underside of a koi. This type of bacterial infection can be hard to spot until it has reached an advanced stage, due to its physical location.

by a variant strain of *Aeromonas salmonicida*. In extreme cases the mouth of the infected koi may simply appear to rot away. Areas of infection on the underside of the mouth are common and they are hard to notice until the disease is at an advanced stage, as this area is not easily seen by the koi keeper. New hole disease may cause high losses, especially in small koi. If new hole disease does take hold in a pond, the symptoms will develop quicker than with other similar infections. Because the symptoms are so disfiguring, with loss of scales and possible scarring, even if the infected koi is cured, the monetary value of the treated fish can be reduced dramatically. This once again means that taking a swab is vital as without this information the wrong medication may be used.

Prevention

The best way to prevent bacterial outbreaks is to run a clean pond. It is impossible to eliminate bacteria completely from the water, so it is vital to ensure that the environment in which your koi live is kept to the highest standard to ensure that levels of stress are kept to a minimum. This makes the chance of an outbreak far less likely. This can be achieved by keeping stocking levels to a minimum, only purchasing new healthy koi, and maintaining constant water temperatures without fluctuations. A good pond heating system really is essential in this respect. Other steps which can be taken to reduce the chances of a bacterial outbreak include the use of probiotics, as these may help to keep bacteria levels at a minimum. The use of ozone may be considered as not only will this help improve water quality and the overall pond environment, but it can also reduce bacterial levels in the water. Although not practical for every koi pond, it is worth mentioning the use of UV sterilizers. These differ from the typical UV clarifier used by most koi hobbyists in that they are not designed simply to stop green water, but work by exposing the pond water to a much higher concentration of UV light in order to kill waterborne pathogens.

Treatment

For any *Aeromonas* or other bacterial infections, treatment takes the form of anti-bacterial drugs which normally have to be obtained from a vet. However, for minor infections alternative approaches, such as herbal (*Melaleuca*) extracts to deal with small bacterial ulcers, may be considered along with the possible use of off-

Below: A koi with a bacterial infection on the caudal peduncle is shown. A number of scales have been lost, but the white tissue indicates that this area is starting to heal.

the-shelf proprietary bactericides which will be available from your local koi dealer.

When deciding which anti-bacterial to use, you must refer back to the results from the swab to see what is going to be effective. Generally for larger koi it will be necessary for each koi showing symptoms to be administered an antibiotic injection but advice should be sought from your local koi health specialist before any treatment is given. It is usually easier to do this if the koi is sedated (anaesthetized). At the same time it is important that any secondary infections like fungus be treated, along with any ulceration, by the application of topical treatments such as malachite green and propolis. When topically treating your koi, it may be necessary to remove lifted scales to help deal with the infection.

If a large number of smaller koi are infected, it

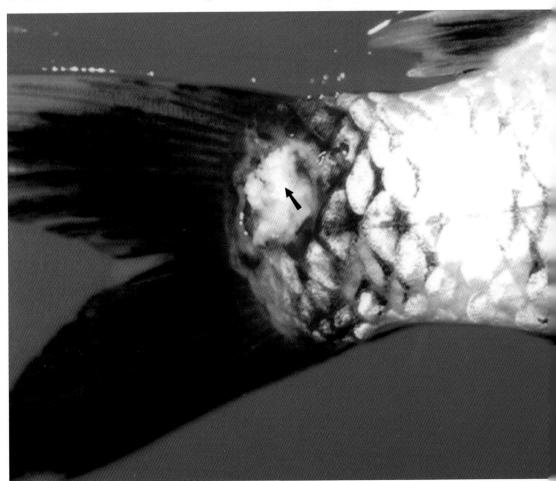

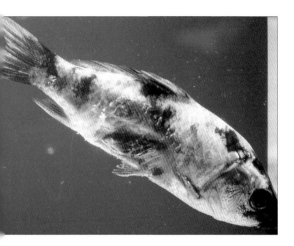

may be impossible to inject them all. In this case you can use anti-bacterials mixed with the feed, under the guidance of advice from your vet or local koi health specialist. Once again refer back to the swab results to determine which is the best treatment to use. If this is not an option, an off-the-shelf anti-bacterial medication may be added to the pond, or potassium permanganate may be used at the dose of 1.5g per 1000 litres (220 gallons), or Chloramine T at the minimum dose of 1g per 1000 litres (220 gallons). Along with these two medications, both Acriflavine and proflavin hemisulphate may also be considered as these too will also help lower the bacterial level present in the pond.

Above: *Aeromonas* infections may leave your koi open to secondary infections, such as fungus. As a result early identification and treatment is essential.

Below: When bacterial infections occur, scales may die. Unfortunately these may have to be removed to allow the infection to heal, and prevent it from spreading.

ANCHOR WORM (LERNAEA)

This is an infection caused by the parasite *Lernaea*. It is a crustacean but looks like a worm, hence its more common name – anchor worm. This infection is easily spotted with the naked eye once it has reached its more advanced stages, and you will normally see numerous thick, hair-like strands protruding from the koi's body. These can be anything from 5 to 12mm (0.2-0.5in) in length and can vary in colour from black to an off white. Anchor worms attach themselves to a koi with an attachment organ which can easily be seen under a magnifying glass or microscope. *Lernaea* reproduce by releasing eggs into the water which develop on the adult anchor worm in an egg sac. Once these eggs have hatched, they develop into a free-swimming stage, but a host koi must be found within a few days for full development to take place and further reproduction to occur.

Right: Dead anchor worms which have been removed from a fish. The larger end is what actually attaches to the koi.
Below: An anchor worm's attachment organ fixes itself by physically penetrating under the fish's scale.

Identification

Lernaea will attack a koi in many places but the most common sites for infection are the body (practically under the scales), the mouth, around the eyes, on the fins, the gills, and the joints of fins where they meet the body. In the very early stages of an anchor worm infection it is not possible to spot the typical anchor worm shape, and so infection may go unnoticed or be wrongly diagnosed, as it can look as if the koi has another

The life cycle of the anchor worm
(Lernaea)

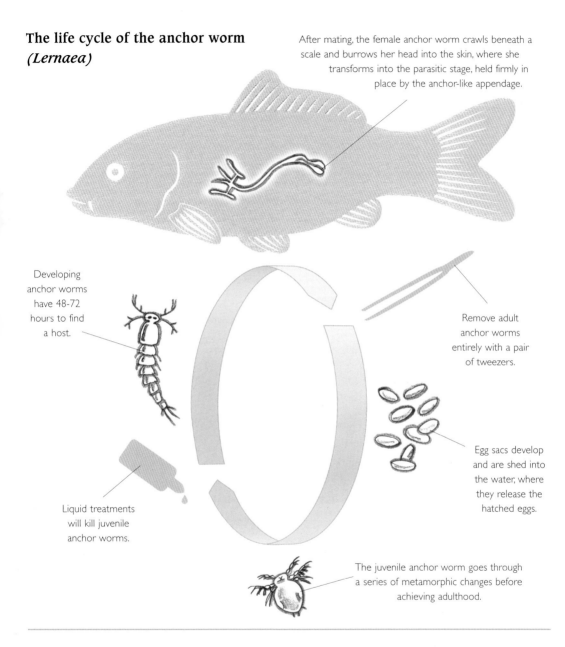

After mating, the female anchor worm crawls beneath a scale and burrows her head into the skin, where she transforms into the parasitic stage, held firmly in place by the anchor-like appendage.

Developing anchor worms have 48-72 hours to find a host.

Remove adult anchor worms entirely with a pair of tweezers.

Egg sacs develop and are shed into the water, where they release the hatched eggs.

Liquid treatments will kill juvenile anchor worms.

The juvenile anchor worm goes through a series of metamorphic changes before achieving adulthood.

parasite infection, such as whitespot, because of the presence of white dots on the body. These are in fact the young anchor worms. This is why it is vital to carry out a skin scrape when any disease is suspected to ensure that a correct identification is made and the right course of treatment is subsequently used. A koi infected with anchor worm may appear to move erratically and even rub or flick against any hard surfaces in the pond to try to relieve the skin irritation and dislodge any anchor worms attached to its body.

Anchor worm infections can reach quite high levels before they cause any real threat to the koi, except when the mouth or gills are being attacked as this may affect the koi's ability to breathe or eat. Another problem is that the attachment site normally becomes infected either by bacteria, fungus or even a virus. This happens because the anchor worm actually punctures the skin to feed on tissue fluid and cells which leaves an area prone to infection. Characteristic symptoms are scales lifting and the area around the anchor worm becoming red. In very extreme cases of infection you may notice your koi hanging in the water, and weight loss may also be observed. The life cycle of anchor worm is temperature-dependent and so it is not normally a problem in winter months in unheated ponds. At temperatures below 15°C (59°F) they become inactive. However, eggs and adult females may survive these colder months only to cause a problem when the water temperature rises above 15°C.

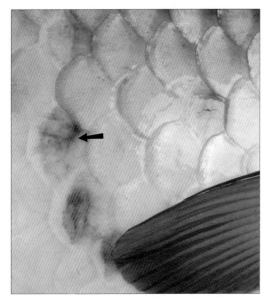

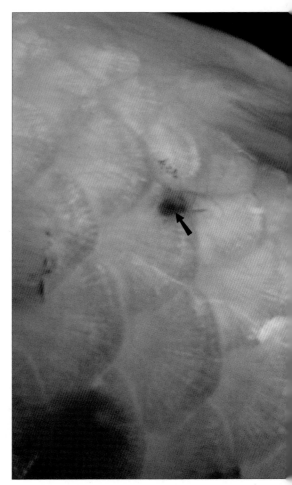

Above: Unfortunately removing the worm is not the end of the story. The attachment site often requires treatment. This is a typical example of anchor worm damage.

However, not only is this impractical in the summer months, it will also cause other problems, and so is not recommended.

Prevention

Anchor worm is a common problem on new imports of koi, especially when they have been recently harvested out of mud ponds in which they have spent the summer growing. It is quite common to find some anchor worm on new imports of koi, and most dealers will check for their presence and treat as a matter of course if any are found. Therefore, it is advisable to wait for at least a couple of weeks before taking delivery of koi which are newly imported to allow any treatment to take effect. The only other way of preventing anchor worm infections is to keep the water temperature below 15°C (59°F).

Treatment

If anchor worm is found, the first course of action should be to remove the adults physically from the koi. First sedate the fish, then gently pull the anchor worm from the koi with a sterilized pair of tweezers. Then apply a suitable topical treatment, such as malachite green and propolis or just propolis, to the attachment site. To get the full benefit from doing this, it is vital that all koi in the pond are inspected at the same time, and unfortunately this will need to be repeated after ten days or so to ensure that no new anchor worm have attached themselves or that others have been missed. While inspecting the koi for the presence of anchor worm, you should also

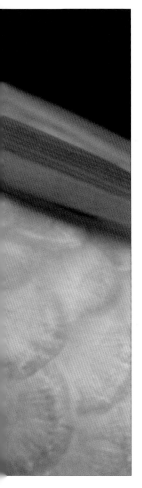

Above left: Although appearing very faint, a small anchor worm can be seen here attached to the underside of a koi close to its pelvic fins.

Above right: Here the anchor worm is being removed. If tweezers are not available, you can push the anchor worm out with your fingernail, but be sure that it comes out whole and that no part is left still attached to your koi.

check if any secondary bacterial infection has occurred and treat accordingly, seeking advice from your vet or local koi health specialist.

It is also vital to treat the pond to try and destroy the free-swimming stages of the *Lernaea* parasite and once again this will have to be done a number of times to ensure that complete eradication occurs as the adults and any eggs sacs are normally not affected by such treatment. Organophosphate-based treatments are effective in the eradication of anchor worm, but organophosphate-based medications have recently been banned in numerous countries including the UK. However, manufacturers of pond treatments are actively developing new products which claim to be effective against anchor worm. As improvements are made to them, it is to be hoped that these medicines will increase in availability and effectiveness.

If you live in a country where you can legally obtain an organophosphate-based chemical, be sure not to use it in a pond containing orfe or other species of fish which are highly susceptible to this type of medication. Of course moving these species to another pond or tank while treating the main pond can lead to further problems: it will only take one adult anchor worm to still be attached when the fish are reintroduced to the original pond and the infestation could start all over again!

APIOSOMA (PARASITIC GILL DISEASE)

*A*piosoma is an external parasite which will attack the gills, skin and fins of koi. If their numbers are allowed to escalate, they can result in fish losses. *Apiosoma* are ciliated protozoa, and are vase-shaped when viewed under a microscope. They have a large number of tiny hair-like parts which are used for controlling movement and in some cases even for feeding – these are known as cilia. These cilia are located in a circular arrangement at one end of the body. *Apiosoma* are very similar to *Trichodina* and *Chilodonella* and so many of the symptoms of this disease are similar to those infections. Thus a skin scrape must be taken and examined under a microscope for an exact identification to be made in order to allow correct treatment.

Identification

External signs of an *Apiosoma* infestation include the production of excess mucus which results in the skin looking opaque. In severe cases the actual skin colour may disappear as the mucus becomes so thick the body actually looks white. Infected fish may start to hang in the water with their fins clamped, and spend more time in areas of heavily oxygenated water, such as around water returns and airstones. This will especially be the case if the gills are attacked. If an extremely large quantity of *Apiosoma* are present, your koi may flick their heads from side

Above: One of the characteristic physical symptoms of *Apiosoma* is emaciation.

Above centre: *Apiosoma* is not visible to the naked eye and so a microscope is required to make an exact identification of this protozoan.

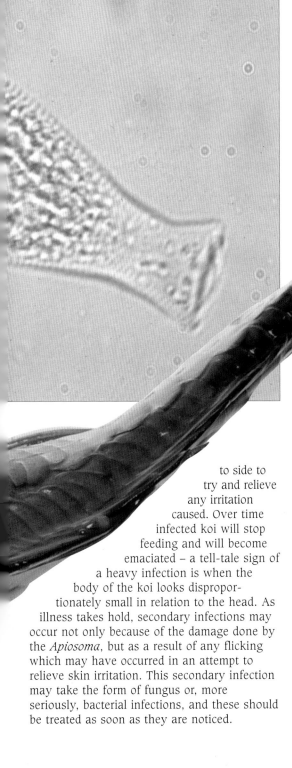

Prevention

As with many parasites, they are not a problem if a well-maintained system is kept. It is only when environmental conditions deteriorate that a problem arises. To avoid an outbreak of *Apiosoma*, good water quality should be maintained at all times, and regular maintenance should be carried out on filters to avoid the build up of sediment and mulm within the pond and filter system. When doing this, it is important that replacement water is conditioned as the use of untreated tapwater may result in more stress to the fish which could be a trigger for the problem itself. Also avoid large stocking levels as this parasite will thrive in heavily stocked ponds. Maintaining a constant water temperature will also prevent undue stress being caused to the fish as a result of temperature fluctuations, and so the use of a pond heating system is recommended to provide a regular and constant water temperature.

Treatment

Less severe cases of *Apiosoma* can easily be treated with a proprietary anti-parasite medication or the use of malachite green and formalin – the dose rate will depend upon the concentration of the mix. Alternatively the use of potassium permanganate maybe considered at a dose rate of 1.5g per 1000 litres (220 gallons) and this can be repeated every five to seven days over a period of three weeks (allowing you a maximum of three such treatments).

Salt can also be used as an effective treatment as either a bath or a pond treatment. If the infection has become severe, the chances are that there will be numerous sites of secondary infection on the fish and these will need to be topically treated with propolis. Although treatment will normally result in complete eradication of the parasites, a severe gill infestation may cause gill damage and so further losses of fish may take place even after the problem with the parasite has been eliminated.

to side to try and relieve any irritation caused. Over time infected koi will stop feeding and will become emaciated – a tell-tale sign of a heavy infection is when the body of the koi looks disproportionately small in relation to the head. As illness takes hold, secondary infections may occur not only because of the damage done by the *Apiosoma*, but as a result of any flicking which may have occurred in an attempt to relieve skin irritation. This secondary infection may take the form of fungus or, more seriously, bacterial infections, and these should be treated as soon as they are noticed.

ARGULUS (FISH LICE)

Fish lice are parasites which can attack a koi anywhere, but particularly around the fins and the mouth. Despite their name fish lice are not true lice, but rather a type of crustacean. They are more likely to be a problem in the summer months in warmer temperatures as their life cycle is much affected by temperature. As more and more koi keepers have heated ponds, they may be encountered at any time. They attach themselves to a koi by using suckers, and then puncture the skin to feed on the fish's blood and body fluids. When this occurs a toxin is released as the skin of the koi is punctured, and this toxin can be powerful enough to kill small fish, although it tends to have a lesser effect on larger koi. The area around this puncture site is liable to secondary infection and may be attacked

by fungus or bacteria. The toxin released by the fish lice may cause some koi to behave erratically as intense irritation may result from its effects.

Both female and male fish lice will attach themselves to a host koi and will feed from it before leaving to find another koi to attack. If a host is not found, fish lice can survive for up to three weeks without a host. They reproduce at night and after mating the female will leave the host to deposit the now fertilized eggs on the walls of the pond. Up to 500 eggs can be produced at each spawning and a typical female fish louse can spawn up to ten times in her life. These eggs take from 15 days at 25°C (77°F) to

Below: Here two *Argulus* (fish lice) can be seen attached to the dorsal fin of a koi.

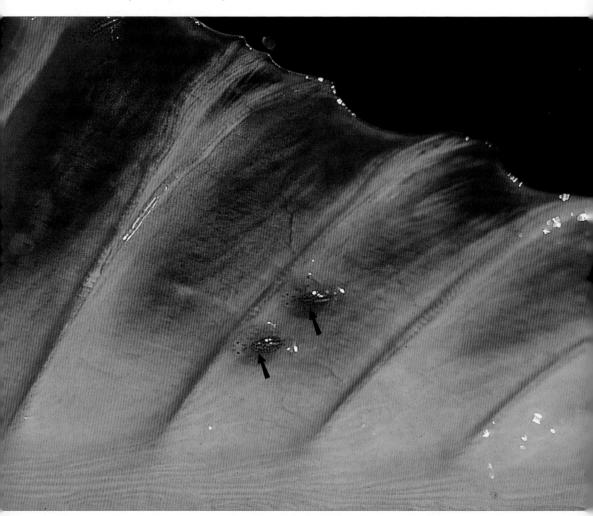

The life cycle of the fish louse (*Argulus*)

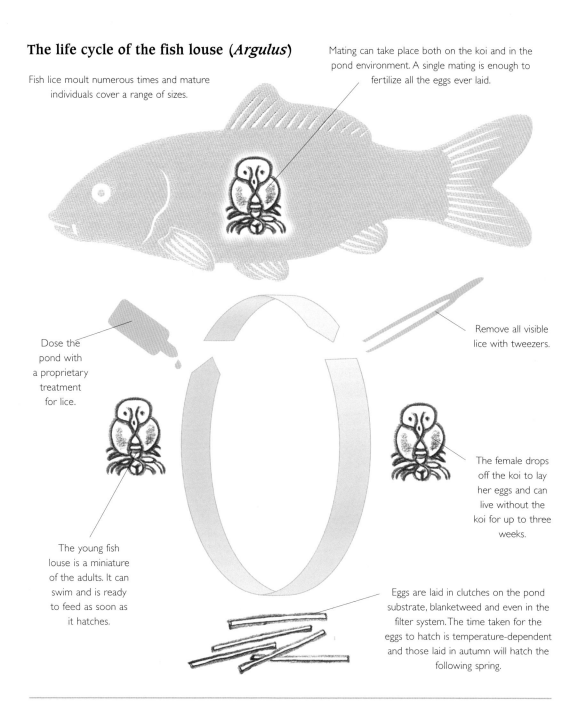

Fish lice moult numerous times and mature individuals cover a range of sizes.

Mating can take place both on the koi and in the pond environment. A single mating is enough to fertilize all the eggs ever laid.

Remove all visible lice with tweezers.

Dose the pond with a proprietary treatment for lice.

The female drops off the koi to lay her eggs and can live without the koi for up to three weeks.

The young fish louse is a miniature of the adults. It can swim and is ready to feed as soon as it hatches.

Eggs are laid in clutches on the pond substrate, blanketweed and even in the filter system. The time taken for the eggs to hatch is temperature-dependent and those laid in autumn will hatch the following spring.

24 days at 20°C (68°F) to hatch. Once hatched, the juvenile fish lice (which are less than 1mm in size) will quickly swim to find a koi to attach themselves to and use as a new host. Depending upon temperature these juvenile lice will reach sexual maturity within anything from 20 to 50 days, and then the whole cycle will start again.

Identification

Fish lice can easily be seen with the naked eye, and appear as semi-transparent discs swimming in the water or attached to a koi. They range in size generally from 3mm to 9mm (0.1-0.35in), although in some instances may be as large as 12mm (0.5in). A koi infected with lice will show a number of symptoms and in cases of heavy infestation it may be possible to actually see the fish lice attached to the koi. The classic behaviour

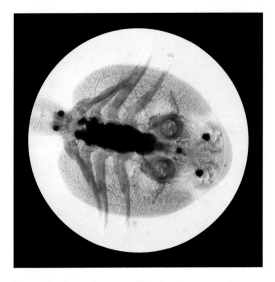

Above: *Argulus* can be seen without a microscope, either whizzing around in the water or on the fish themselves.

of a fish with fish lice is to start swimming erratically – this is not just a reaction to the toxin released into the koi, but also because the koi tries to scrape against objects in the pond in an attempt to rid itself of the lice. Unfortunately, although this behaviour may have the desired effect of ridding the koi of some of the attached lice, the rubbing causes new damage to the skin. If these lesions are not spotted quickly and treated, secondary problems such as fungus and bacterial infections may take hold. If a fish louse infestation is left untreated, the koi will eventually become very lethargic and will stop feeding. Smaller koi may start to die, and before this occurs they may be seen to be producing higher than normal levels of mucus.

Prevention
Fish lice have to be introduced to a pond, and can find their way in on new koi, plants, (very rarely) on visiting wildlife, and even live food. It is not just adult fish lice which may be introduced but eggs may be attached to a plant, for example. So when adding anything to the pond, time

should be taken to examine it for unwelcome visitors, and if any are found these should be removed. It is important that regular checks are made to ensure that infection has not occurred.

Treatment
If you spot a koi in your pond with fish lice, the chances are that a number of your koi will also be affected. It is important that all the koi are checked. When checking a koi for lice, you must remove any specimens that you find with a clean sterilized pair of tweezers. Once removed, you should topically treat the area from which the louse was removed as this will now be open to secondary infection. The use of propolis is ideal in this case and it should simply be sprayed onto the areas from which the lice were removed. This deals with the adult fish lice, but it does not address the problem of juveniles which have yet to find a host, and any eggs which may be present in the pond.

To get rid of the younger specimens, an organophosphate-based medication may be used, if you live in a country where such chemicals can be legally obtained. The treatment should be repeated possibly two or even three times at intervals of seven to ten days between each dose depending upon temperature. The repeated dose ensures that all juvenile fish lice will be killed. If during this time all the adults have also been removed, no new eggs will have been laid and so the cycle will be stopped. Many effective and safe proprietary treatments are available in countries where organophosphate-based medications have been banned, such as the UK, meaning that organophosphates do not have to be relied upon for eradicating fish lice. These products are readily available from your local koi dealer, and development of even newer products is continuing at a brisk pace.

If you are legally able to use an organophosphate-based treatment ensure that sensitive species such as golden orfe are removed from the pond before treating as they cannot tolerate this type of medication. Only return these fish to the pond after at least two or three weeks have elapsed after the last treatment.

Right: *Argulus* viewed under a microscope. As a koi keeper you would not see this detail when inspecting your pond, just small translucent discs with black dots inside them attached to your fish.

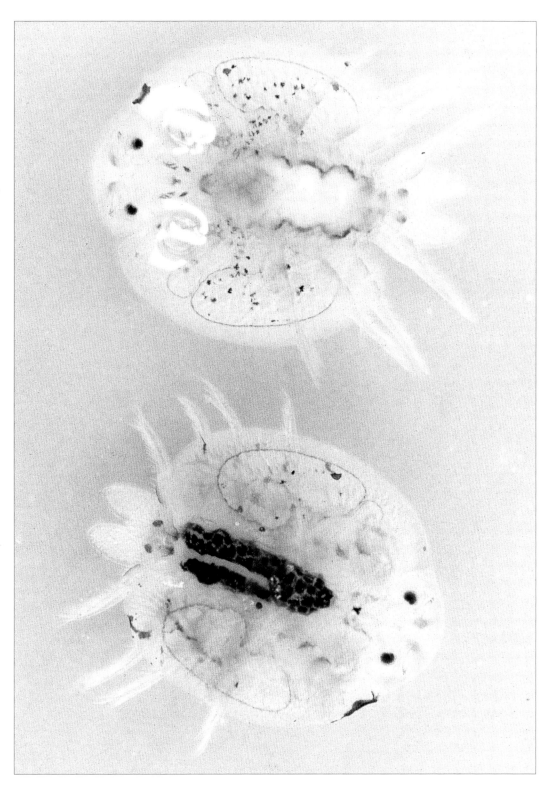

CHILODONELLA

Chilodonella cyprini attack the skin and gills of koi, and severe infections can result in rapid fish losses. *Chilodonella* is a ciliated protozoan, which has tiny hair-like parts called cilia that are used for controlling movement, and sometimes feeding. They cannot be seen with the naked eye and can only be identified with a microscope, which means a skin scrape must be taken. When viewed under a microscope *Chilodonella* will appear as a kind of heart-shaped parasite with rows of cilia running along its longer side. The parasite spreads through division and, as it can swim, infection from fish to fish can occur easily and very quickly in heavily stocked or poorly maintained systems. Infection can occur at all temperatures, although temperatures under 20°C (68°F) favour this parasite.

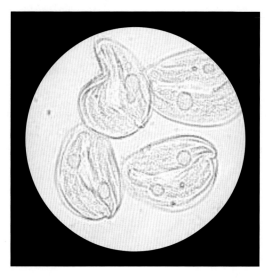

Above: For an exact identification of the protozoan *Chilodonella* to be made, a microscope must be used.

Identification

Koi infected with *Chilodonella* may display a number of symptoms which will differ depending upon whether the infection is limited to the body or also affects the gills. General symptoms of both types of infection include the koi appearing lifeless and hanging in the water with their fins clamped. You may also notice that the affected koi spend an increased amount of time in areas of heavily oxygenated water, such as by airstones or water returns. This is particularly the case when the gills are heavily infected. The fish may start to flick and rub against the sides of the pond or any objects located within the pond to try and relieve the irritation caused. This can result in physical damage which is then susceptible to secondary infection by fungus or bacteria. In cases where the skin is heavily infected, it may feel excessively slimy to touch due to the increased production of mucus. Areas of the skin may take on an opaque appearance and look stressed with blood vessels showing on the body.

If the gills become infected, the fish will show most or all of the symptoms described and it may also start to breathe more heavily as witnessed by erratic gill movements. If the infection is allowed to progress to an advanced stage, the gills may be damaged beyond repair, and the skin of the koi will eventually start to lose its protective mucus coating, and become very rough to the touch. This leaves the infected koi open to a number of secondary gill and skin infections. At this stage infected koi may lose their appetite which will lead to weight loss. When small koi are infected, after a while it may appear as if the head of the koi has outgrown its body. Even if treated and eradicated, the irreparable damage already done may result in prolonged fish losses. An important factor to consider when identifying *Chilodonella* is that many of the symptoms exhibited by your koi are the same for many other parasitic infections, so it is vital that a correct identification is made so that the right treatment can be administered. In some cases more than one species of parasite is present, and then a suitable treatment must be chosen to eradicate all identified parasites.

Prevention

As *Chilodonella* can swim, they may attach themselves to nets, live food, wildlife and even the hands of fishkeepers. Care must be taken to sterilize all equipment and you should wash your hands before handling food to avoid cross-contamination. If the pond is heavily stocked, rapid infection will also occur, so sensible stocking levels should be observed. Good water quality and system husbandry will also help in preventing an outbreak of this disease as it is only at times of stress that the parasite will be able to multiply at a rate quick enough to become a major concern. To help reduce stress the use of a pond heating system is also desirable to prevent fluctuations in temperature as this disease is more common in the spring and autumn when the

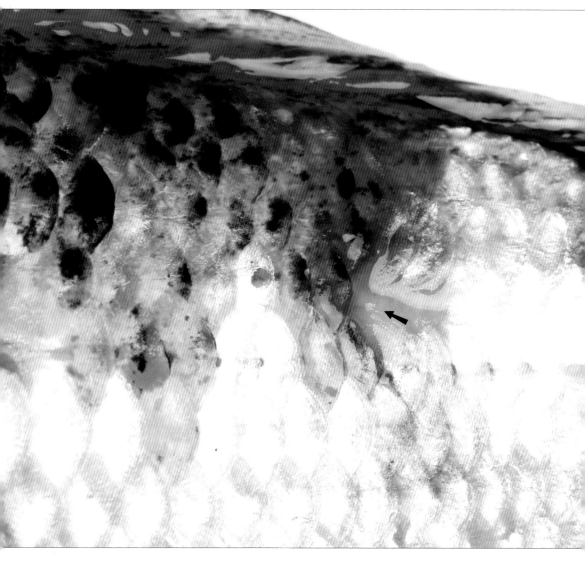

Above: *Chilodonella* causes infected fish to flick against the side of a pond, which may lead to physical damage like this.

water temperature warms after winter and then cools as winter approaches. *Chilodonella* is a greater threat at lower water temperatures of around 5-10°C (41-50°F). If the water temperature is kept above this, and good husbandry techniques are applied, the chances of a major outbreak are reduced.

Treatment

Chilodonella can be treated with a off-the-shelf parasite treatment, or alternatively with malachite green and formalin – the dose rates of which will depend upon the concentration of the solution. Alternatively potassium permanganate may be considered at a dose rate of 1.5g per 1000 litres (220 gallons). Salt can also be used to control *Chilodonella*, either as a pond treatment or a bath, the rate of which will depend upon the stage of infection. If opting to use salt as a pond treatment, be sure not to use medications such as formalin until the salt has been removed. It may also be necessary to treat any secondary infections and this can be done with topical treatment with propolis, or malachite green and propolis in more severe cases.

COLUMNARIS DISEASE (FIN ROT, GILL ROT, MOUTH ROT/COTTON WOOL AND SKIN COLUMNARIS)

*F*lavobacterium columnare (previously known as *Flexibacter columnaris*) is a bacterium which can cause a number of conditions in koi. It is generally associated with warmer pond temperatures of 15°C (59°F) and above. In warm temperatures it can result in rapid fish losses if not treated quickly. It is important not to confuse columnaris with a fungus infection as often the two can appear very similar, but a different course of treatment is required for each. If you have a powerful enough microscope, *Flavobacterium columnare* can be identified visually, but it does require some expertise and a real knowledge of what you are looking for. The easiest way to identify this bacterium is to take a swab from the affected area and send this away for analysis.

Identification of Fin Rot
A koi with fin rot will start to develop reddening of the fins which is followed by the development of small white areas on the ends of the fins. If these white areas are not treated quickly, the infection will start to eat away the fin, and eventually the whole fin may be consumed. If this happens, the infection may spread into the body of the koi, and at this point it may prove difficult to save the infected fish. A koi with fin rot may not show any adverse behavioural signs during the early stages of infection, and so close physical inspection is essential to catch the disease early before it can become a problem.

Treatment of Fin Rot
As soon as fin rot is suspected, the infected koi must be taken out of the pond and a suitable topical treatment be applied to the affected area. This may be malachite green, followed by the application of propolis. If the infection has become more established and the fin is actually being consumed and topical treatment has not halted this, it may be necessary to cut away the infected area of fin. This should be done with a sharp sterilized pair of scissors, and it may be necessary to sedate the koi before doing this. The fin should be cut away behind the area of redness, although before doing this advice should always be sought from a vet or koi health specialist. Once completed,

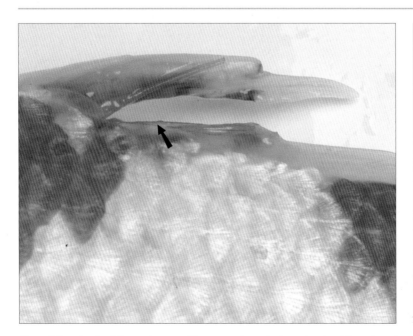
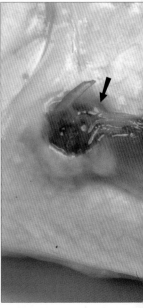

Above left and right: Advanced stages of fin rot are shown here on the dorsal fin and on the pectoral fin.

Above: Fin rot is shown here at an early stage, with the fin just starting to rot away. If caught at this stage, simple topical treatment may result in a full recovery.

topical treatment should be applied to the newly exposed fin to help prevent re-infection. If the fin has completely gone and the base of the infected fin is red and sore, it is possible that the infection has spread inside the koi and thus further treatment may be required and advice should be sought from your local vet or koi health specialist as to the best course of action. A swab should be done at this point to determine what infection you are treating and if the use of antibiotics is suggested by your koi specialist this will indicate which one should be used. It may also be advisable to add an anti-bacterial treatment to the pond to help lower bacterial levels.

Identification of Gill Rot

The signs of gill rot may not be noticed until the disease is quite advanced because the gills of your koi may not be readily inspected. So the disease may only be suspected when it has advanced to the stage that it affects the behaviour of your koi. A koi with severe gill rot may display some or all of the following symptoms: it may be lethargic and spend much of its time on either the bottom of the pond, or at the surface in areas of heavily oxygenated water, such as around airstones and water returns. Rapid or increased gill movement may be noticed. While hanging in these areas, the affected koi may appear to be struggling to maintain its balance in the water and list from side to side. You may also notice that infected fish swim erratically from time to time and may even crash into the side of the pond. In extremely severe cases (and often these prove fatal) the eyes of the koi will appear sunken. If any of these behavioural changes are noted, it is important to catch the fish in question and inspect the condition of their gills. In early stages of gill rot disease the gills may have small yellow or white spots on the filaments, and appear congested and stuck together due to excessive mucus production. The next stage will result in

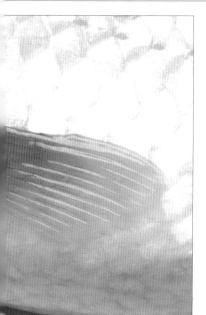

Above: Early stages of gill rot – small sections of the gill are missing.

the gills changing colour and becoming a dark red to black colour, while more filaments appear stuck together. Beyond this stage of infection the gills start to decompose and areas of the gills may turn grey; sections of the gill may even be missing in very severe cases. Once gill rot has reached this advanced stage, even if treatment is apparently successful, losses may be experienced for some time after the treatment has finished due to the severe damage to the gills.

Treatment of Gill Rot

In the early stages of gill rot caused by columnaris the use of a salt bath at the rate of 100g per 4.5 litres (1 gallon) of water for ten minutes may help the affected koi. In severe cases advice should be sought from your vet or local koi health specialist as to what additional treatment may be required. It may also be advisable to add an anti-bacterial treatment to the pond to help lower bacterial levels.

Identification of Mouth Rot (Cotton Wool)

This is sometimes confused with a fungus infection due to the similarities of the symptoms. At first a small white spot may appear on the nose of a koi. If not topically treated this will spread and result in an inflammation of the mouth, which in turn may result in a yellow or white discoloration of the skin. Because the skin is inflamed and may change colour, the disease is sometimes confused with fungus. A koi that is not treated will slowly lose its ability to eat and will start to look emaciated. It will also spend more time in areas of heavily oxygenated water, such as around airstones and water returns. The affected koi may also develop anti-social behaviour and spend a lot of its time apart from the other koi in the pond, appearing simply to hang in the water with its fins clamped. If not treated, the infected koi will starve because as the infection spreads it will not be able to eat.

Treatment of Mouth Rot

In the early stages simple tropical treatment with propolis may halt the progression of the disease. However, if it becomes more established it may prove necessary to seek advice from your local koi health specialist, who may advise that a swab should be taken from the mouth and sent away for analysis. The results of this determine which

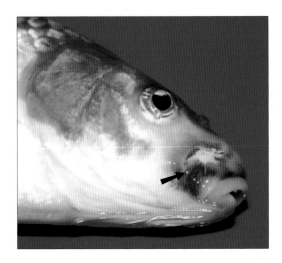

Above: This koi has mouth rot which has resulted in quite severe inflammation of the skin around the nose area.

antibiotic to administer if antibiotics are required. This will normally only be as a last resort after other possible treatments have failed. Antibiotics will be given as an injection, as it is more than likely that the koi in question will have lost its ability to eat. It may also be advisable to add an anti-bacterial treatment to the pond to help lower bacterial levels.

Skin Columnaris Disease

Flavobacterium columnare will attack the skin in areas of weakness such as may be present after a parasitic infection like whitespot or *Trichodina*, where the epidermal skin tissue is attacked leaving the koi open to secondary infection. Early stages of columnaris infection will be identified by the presence of small white or yellow areas on the koi; these will result in the production of excess mucus which may give the koi a hazy appearance. Along with the production of excess mucus, scales may lift and even fall out, and the mucus may appear to slough off the fish at this advanced stage. As this happens areas of redness may appear on the body of the koi, and it may start to rub against objects in the pond to relieve the irritation caused by this, which in turn exacerbates the problem. If the disease is not identified and treated, this behaviour will go on and the koi may start to swell and hang lifeless in the water with its fins clamped. If a koi gets to this stage of infection, the chances of recovery even with treatment are slim as the infection will have spread internally inside the fish.

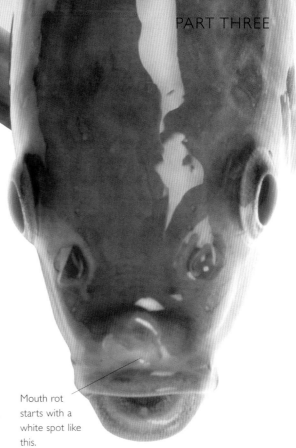

Treatment of Skin Columnaris

In its very early stages the application of a topical treatment such as propolis, or even malachite green and propolis, may prove sufficient to prevent further infection. However, once scale lifting or loss is experienced, you should seek further advice from an expert as the use of antibiotics, either via injection or in the feed, may be required as a last resort. A swab should be taken and the results of analysis followed regarding the anti-bacterial to use. While bactericides are administered, topical treatment should be maintained until the koi starts to show signs of recovery. Then the frequency of this can be reduced. If, however, the infected koi is heavily swollen and many scales are lifted, recovery is unlikely and the best course of action may be to humanely kill the koi in question to prevent any prolonged suffering. If numerous koi are showing symptoms, it may be necessary to administer a pond treatment to lower bacterial levels.

Mouth rot starts with a white spot like this.

General Pond Treatment

If a columnaris infection is suspected, it is a good idea to add an anti-bacterial treatment to the pond. This could take the form of Chloramine T used at a dose rate of 1g per 4500 litres (1000 gallons), although higher doses can be used but seek advice before administering. An alternative to this is potassium permanganate used at the dose rate of 1.5g per 1000 litres (220 gallons), or Acriflavine at a dose rate that will depend upon the concentration of the solution. Alternatively a good off-the-shelf anti-bacterial medication could be used, and these are readily available from numerous manufacturers.

Prevention

Flavobacterium columnare are bacteria which will attack areas of existing or previous damage. These could be physical injuries or damage left by other infections, such as parasites, so it is important that any vulnerable areas are kept clean and topically treated to induce quicker healing. Low levels of dissolved oxygen in the water, overstocking, and poor water quality (especially high levels of ammonia) may make an attack from columnaris more likely. Good husbandry and regular system maintenance will help in preventing an outbreak of columnaris bacteria. One factor which may make a columnaris

Above: Both koi have mouth rot. The top picture shows the early stages which can easily be treated topically. The bottom picture shows the advanced stages of the infection when specialist professional treatment is needed.

outbreak more likely is higher water temperatures. Unfortunately this puts the koi keeper in a Catch 22 situation as many other koi diseases are less likely to prove a problem in stable warmer water. This fact has resulted in a surge in the popularity of koi pond heating. So if you do heat your pond and maintain temperatures of over 15°C (59°F) all year round, keep an eye out for any of the symptoms of columnaris infection.

COSTIA

Costia, or *Ichthyobodo necator* as it is known scientifically, is an external parasite which is active in a vast range of temperatures from 2°C up to 29°C (36° to 84°F). It is a parasite which can survive both as free-swimming organism or attached to a host. When viewed under a microscope on a skin scrape, costia looks like a misshapen circle. However when viewed in its free-swimming stage, it simply appears as a small spot moving quite vigorously. At this stage it may be extremely hard to identify because of its very small size, and the fact that it has a short life span of just a matter of hours.

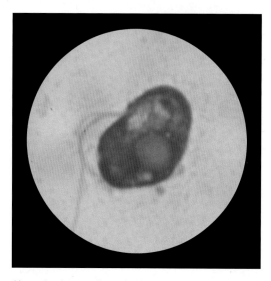

Above: It takes a well-practised eye to spot the shape of the costia parasite under the microscope.

Identification

Costia cannot be seen with the naked eye so exact identification can only be achieved by taking a skin scrape and viewing under a microscope. Physical symptoms of costia are similar to other external parasites and these include excess mucus production, which is a common diagnostic sign of costia on koi. In severe cases reddening of the skin and open wounds may also be present. Often the head will appear as if it has white film over it, and you may also find that the fins of infected koi become reddened. Along with this the infected koi may become lifeless and hang in the water while clamping their fins.

If spotted early, costia can easily be eradicated, but on young koi it will develop quickly and can

result in losses. If heavy losses are being experienced, costia should be investigated early on as one of the possible causes. In severe cases fish may also go off their food and become emaciated. You may also notice that your koi suffer from difficulties in breathing and show erratic gill movements while spending long periods of time near the surface in areas of highly oxygenated water, such as near airstones and water returns. Finally your koi may be seen to rub and flick against the side of the pond to try and relieve the irritation caused by this parasite, which in turn can lead to secondary fungal or bacterial infections on skin abrasions.

Prevention

Costia is a condition which mostly becomes a problem when your koi are under stress. This is normally caused by environmental factors such as poor water quality, changes in temperature, and poor system maintenance. Thus it is vital that good husbandry techniques are employed, such as regular water changes, filter discharges, and water testing. It is also beneficial to install some form of heating system to prevent temperature fluctuations because this disease is most likely to occur in colder water, or at times when temperature changes are more likely, e.g. autumn going into winter and winter going into spring. Care should also be taken when purchasing new koi to avoid any showing symptoms, and if in doubt a salt bath can be given to the koi before introduction to the pond as salt is very effective against this disease. Salt baths can be given at varying strengths for differing amounts of time but a good guide is 100g of salt per 4.5 litres (1 gallon) of water for ten minutes.

Treatment

Because costia has a short life span when not attached to a host koi, a one-off treatment will normally be sufficient to get rid of the infection. A general off-the-shelf anti-parasite treatment may well prove to be sufficient against costia, and these types of treatments are readily available from numerous manufacturers. An alternative approach is to use malachite green and formalin at a dose rate that depends upon the concentration of the mix used. Malachite and formalin are effective while the pond temperature is above 11°C (52°F). If this is not the case, salt

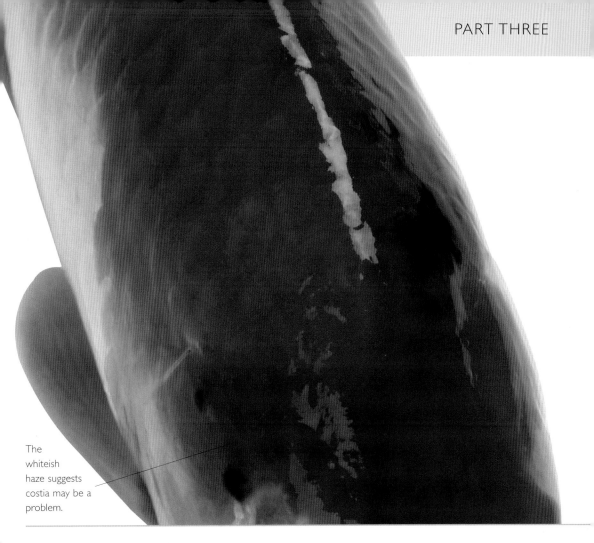

The whiteish haze suggests costia may be a problem.

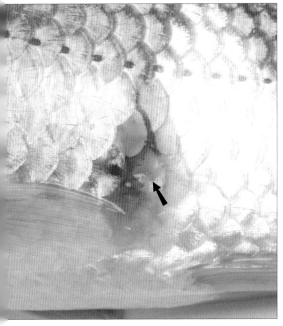

Above: A tell-tale sign that costia may be present is the presence of a milky haze over the skin, most noticeably on the head and shoulder region of the koi.

Left: As with most parasite infections, flicking will occur when costia is present which may result in physical damage occurring to the skin of the fish, as can be seen here.

can be used and is generally an effective treatment for costia at all temperatures, although if you do this please ensure that formalin is not used until the salt is removed from the pond via water changes. If using salt it should be added at a dose rate of around 7 to 14g per 4.5 litres (0.25-0.5oz per gallon). Another approach against costia is simply to increase the water temperature, but as this has to be raised to at least 30°C (86°F) it is not an ideal proposition for the koi keeper or for the koi! After treating for costia be sure also to treat any secondary infections which may have occurred. This can be done topically by applying propolis in conjunction with a suitable fungicide or bactericide.

83

CURVATURE OF THE SPINE

This is not a disease but a physical problem which is experienced by many koi keepers, especially those with a pond that is not stocked exclusively with koi but also contains varieties such as orfe. Orfe are susceptible to spinal problems following use of certain anti-parasite chemicals. This may also be a problem for the koi breeder and one not exclusively limited to curvature of the spine – other deformities, such as deformed eyes, missing fins, part or missing gill plates etc., may also become apparent. When breeding koi it is vital that the correct brood stock is selected; avoid the selection of closely related koi, such as brother and sister or parent and offspring. The environmental conditions in which the eggs are kept during development are also critical to the proper development of the young – if these are not ideal, developmental problems may occur, especially if critical factors such as water quality are not correct.

Identification

This is an easy condition to spot as your koi will appear as if it has a kink or bend in its spine, normally between the dorsal fin and the tail. In extreme cases it may not be limited to just one kink or bend – your koi may have a number of these creating a Z-shaped appearance.

Prevention

Usually this condition occurs in mature koi for the following reasons: overdose of medication or use of a particular medication, electric shock, lightning strike, and malnutrition. We shall consider each in turn. Certain medications, namely organophosphate-based treatments, work by attacking the central nervous system of parasites such as anchor worm and fish lice. If used at the correct dose rate, they pose no threat to the health or condition of your koi. However, if your pond contains other species, such as orfe, these are more susceptible to this type of medication and often the orfe develop a kink or bend in their spines. If this type of treatment is used for koi and the exact capacity of the pond to be treated is not known, an accidental overdose may occur resulting in some or all of the koi develop a kinked spine. It is vital that the exact

Right: Curvature of the spine as shown here may be caused by numerous factors, such as electric shock, lightning strikes, malnutrition, or overdosing with certain medications.

volume of your pond is known before any medication is added. The best way of determining this is to use a flow meter when filling the pond and these can be purchased or hired from your local koi outlet.

Problems with electrical items within the pond, such as pumps or UV units for example, can also cause curvature of the spine, as an electric shock may affect the fishes' central nervous system resulting in kinking or bending. The best way to avoid this is to run all electrical items from an RCD (residual-current device) as this will cause them to be switched off as soon as a fault occurs. Nowadays it is normal to run all outdoor electrical items from an RCD, particularly when using equipment in conjunction with water. Unlike a normal fuse an RCD causes the electrical supply to switch off within milliseconds of a fault or short circuit occurring. Another factor which may cause curvature of the spine is lightning strikes which cause koi to flex violently, risking spinal damage as a result.

Physical deformities such as curvature may also be caused by malnutrition and the use of an incorrect feed, especially in the case of newly hatched fry and juvenile koi. It is important that a suitable high quality feed is fed at all time, and that mineral and vitamin additives are used appropriately. If the food is of a suitable standard, the use of additives is not necessary. Bad handling techniques may also lead to a koi being dropped and injuring its spine. Certain internal bacterial infections have been linked with spinal damage, but these are relatively rare.

Treatment

Once a koi exhibits a bent or kinked spine, there is very little that can be done to correct the condition. A koi with a bent spine may live a normal life without any adverse effects except aesthetic ones as its appearance is affected. In some severe cases, however, an affected koi may start to lose the ability to swim correctly which can result in it not being able to feed. In these circumstances, or if the affected koi appears to be in distress, it may be necessary to consider euthanasia to prevent prolonged suffering.

Right: Even if a koi has quite severe curvature of the spine, it is quite often the case that it will continue to live a normal happy life. As there is no treatment for this condition, in such cases the fish should just be left alone.

DROPSY

When encountered in a koi pond, dropsy is normally confined to one koi at any one time and it is usually caused by an internal bacterial problem, i.e. organ failure caused by bacterial infection. Dropsy can, however, be induced by a viral infection, although this is seldom seen by the hobbyist, but when this does happen a number of koi will start to show the symptoms of dropsy at the same time. Dropsy can also be caused by a parasite which attacks the kidneys; this results in them enlarging and losing their ability to function – eventually kidney failure will result. In some cases dropsy can simply be due to fluid retention, and if this is the case the use of salt as described later can normally cause the build-up of fluid to be released, and the koi saved. However, if this is to work, the diagnosis of fluid build-up must be made early and the necessary treatment applied before any bacterial infections occur.

Identification

Early signs of dropsy include swelling of the body and protrusion of the eyes. Following these early symptoms the body continues to swell, and this results in the scales on the infected koi lifting, causing the fish to take on a pine-cone appearance. In these advanced stages the koi may also lose its ability to maintain correct balance in the water because its swimbladder is under abnormal pressure caused by the accumulation of fluids within its body cavity. If you suspect dropsy, you may also notice a decrease in appetite plus a tendency for the affected koi to remain at the water surface and stay close to areas of high oxygen, such as water returns and outlets from the pond.

Prevention

You may have the most advanced, well maintained pond but still experience dropsy, for it is hard to completely prevent this disease. The only obvious precautions to take against dropsy are to ensure that a well balanced and healthy diet is fed at all times, water quality is good, the water is heated, and all basic husbandry procedures are maintained to the highest level. When purchasing new koi avoid any which exhibit any of the early symptoms of dropsy Unfortunately even this may not prevent dropsy from occurring as sometimes it just strikes without any explanation – organ failure due to old age, for example.

Treatment

When the symptoms of dropsy are spotted, you should isolate the affected fish. However, the practicalities of doing this depend on the size of the koi, and also the size of the quarantine facilities which you have available. It is pointless isolating a 60cm (24in) koi in a 100cm (40in) tank as the stress this will cause will outweigh any advantage obtained by moving the infected koi in the first place. The first treatment for dropsy should be the introduction of salt, and this should be applied at the level of around 5 to 6kg per 1000 litres (11 to 13lb per 220 gallons) of water for at least three to five days, or until improvement is seen. However, it is sensible to isolate the affected fish in a temporary holding pond to avoid subjecting all your fish to salt and thermal stress, especially as many types of dropsy are very hard to cure. The water temperature in the treatment pond should also be slowly increased to over 25°C (77°F) and perhaps even as high as 30°C (86°F). This should be done at the rate of 1°C every day or two.

To this salt treatment you may wish to add a good anti-bacterial medication which is safe to use with salt, e.g. Acriflavine. Whatever medication is chosen, follow the directions and complete a course of treatment before reassessing the situation. One of the most distressing things about dropsy is that although it can sometimes be cured, in most cases it proves fatal. This is generally because by the time external symptoms are spotted, irreparable internal damage and/or infections have occurred, mainly to the kidneys, and they are beyond treatment. For this reason treatment should be assessed constantly and if the symptoms seem to be worsening after five days or so it may be kinder to consider euthanasia.

Below and right: Dropsy is easily spotted by the swelling of the body. In advanced stages your koi may take on a "pine-cone" appearance and have bulging eyes.

In advanced stages of bacterial dropsy reddish areas may appear on the body.

Above: The raised "pine-cone" scales and protruding eyes exhibited by this fish are typical symptoms of dropsy.

EGG RETENTION/SWOLLEN ABDOMEN/TUMOURS

Occasionally a koi may develop an unusual physical characteristic, such as a swollen abdominal area or a growth on a fin. These can be caused by a number of factors: some are hereditary, others are induced by changes in the environment or the presence of a bacterial or viral infection. If a tumour is found, nine times out of ten it will prove to be harmless. If it is internal, little can be done other than careful monitoring of the affected koi. If the growth is external, it may be possible for a vet to remove it surgically but the chances are that it may return once removed, and there is also a risk that the area from which it is removed may becoming infected. So generally the best approach is to leave suspected tumours alone and just monitor the affected fish. The only time action should be considered is if the koi appears in distress and loses its ability to eat. Then euthanasia should be considered as the humane option.

If the swelling is in the abdominal area of a female koi, it is possible that the fish is egg-bound. Other possibilities – although they are very unlikely – include the presence of worms or the initial stages of dropsy. Some internal growths and egg retention can put pressure on the swimbladder which results in the koi losing its ability to stay upright in the water.

Identification

If you suspect that a koi is egg-bound, first confirm that the affected fish is female. A koi needs to be around 30cm (12in) or longer to sex. It is possible to identify a female koi by comparing body shape and fin size – female koi tend to be broader across the shoulders and fuller bodied with a cigar shape, while male koi tend to be more slender with a torpedo shape, and the fins on a male koi may be larger and less rounded at the ends. However, the most reliable method of sexing is to inspect the vent area to determine if the koi is female or not. A female koi will have a line running from head to tail in the vent area crossed at one end with another line running from side to side to give the appearance of a T. A male koi will simply have a line running from head to tail. Having determined that the koi is female, gently feel the swollen area; if it is soft to the touch but is not too fluid, it could possibly be unreleased eggs. If the area feels hard, it could

Below: A dissected koi which is egg-bound. The eggs have started to develop bacterial infection, while their sheer volume has resulted in damage to the internal organs.

Right: This koi has an internal tumour (the arrow shows the abnormal bulge). It may be of the ovaries, although only a post-mortem will allow an exact identification to be made.

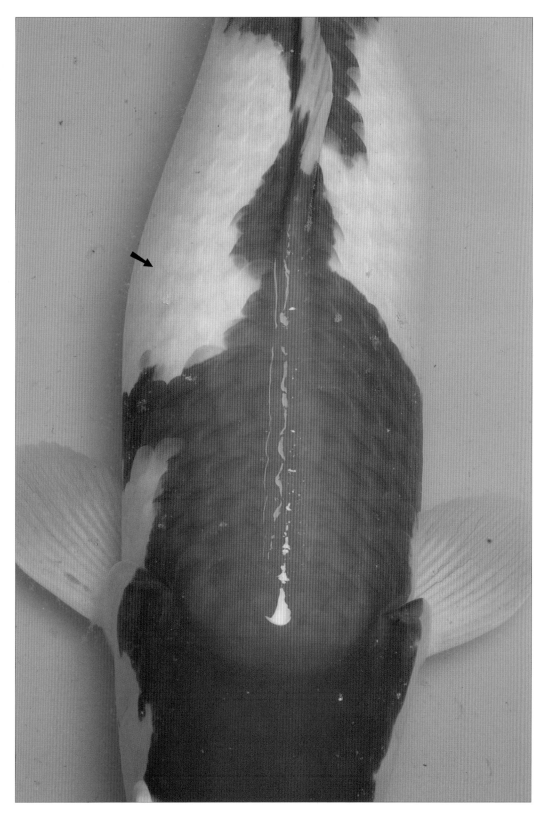

Determining The Sex Of A Fish

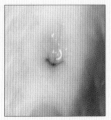 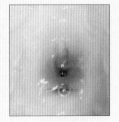

Male **Female**

One possible way to sex a koi is by examining the shape of the vent. Female koi have a line running from head to tail which has another line running across it at the tail end. Male koi do not have this cross-piece. Instead they just have a simple line running from head to tail. However, this difference is not easy for a non-expert to distinguish – you need a very experienced eye to do it accurately.

still be eggs but is more likely to be a tumour. However, without invasive surgery which is normally ineffective it is impossible to make an exact diagnosis.

Prevention

Just because you have a pond containing male and female koi, it does not mean that the females will spawn. Generally, however, if the environmental and dietary conditions are right, female koi will produce and store eggs each year. They are generally released during spawning which takes place when the water temperature hits 20°C (68°F) or higher. If spawning does not occur, these eggs are usually reabsorbed by the koi. However, sometimes this does not happen and a koi becomes egg-bound. Many keepers believe that the increased prevalence of pond heating and the fact that mature female koi do not experience a cold spell is making these cases more common. Unless you are a koi breeder, it is best to maintain a constant temperature throughout the winter of around 16°C (61°C). However, if you have female koi which are to be used for spawning, these should be allowed a

Left: This koi has a suspected tumour of the reproductive organs. In some cases it can be difficult to determine if a koi has a tumour or another condition such as dropsy, which can cause similar physical symptoms.

colder spell for around two months. This lets these koi use up excess reserves, i.e. unused eggs, and get into condition for the following season, making the chances of a koi becoming egg-bound less likely.

Treatment

Having determined that the koi in question is actually egg-bound, a number of approaches can be considered. You may want to separate the female koi in one tank, and a number of male koi in a separate tank. The water temperature in these tanks should be maintained at around 18°C (65°F), then after a week or so of separation the female and male koi can be reintroduced and the temperature raised to over 20°C (68°F). This should induce spawning. If this does not result in the koi spawning, it may nevertheless have the result of getting the females into spawning condition which can be seen if the vent appears to be distended. If this is the case, it may be worth considering hand spawning (hand stripping) the koi. This should only be done by someone who has experience of this procedure.

If this proves to no avail, the final step is to consider the use of hormones to induce spawning. These can prove expensive and are not guaranteed to work, and specialist advice should always be sought before their use. There is also a risk that the koi may not respond well to these treatments and further problems can result from the use of hormone injections, which may even result in death. Thus the risks of this procedure need to be considered before any decision is made.

If you do decide to go ahead with the use of hormones, you must seek professional advice as it is vital that the correct dose rates are used at the correct times. If after this your koi is still showing signs of swelling and looks egg-bound, it may be worth considering giving the koi in question a couple of months in cooler water – say 4°C cooler than the main pond – over the winter period. This of course only applies if the main pond is heated. If it is unheated, winter will cool the water naturally. Now it is best to leave well alone and simply keep a watchful eye on the koi in question, and monitor the situation on a daily basis, only taking further action – humane killing by leaving the fish in a sedating agent for a prolonged period – if the koi looks as if it is in distress.

EPISTYLIS

Epistylis is a ciliate protozoan which is not visible to the naked eye and so exact identification must be via a skin scrape examined under a microscope. When viewed like this *Epistylis* looks bell-shaped with a long "handle" connected to it. Tiny hair-like cilia on the end of the bell shape may be seen. Cilia are used for controlling movement, and in the case of *Epistylis* are also used to feed on waterborne bacteria. *Epistylis* may also be seen in its contracted form and in this instance it will simply look circular.

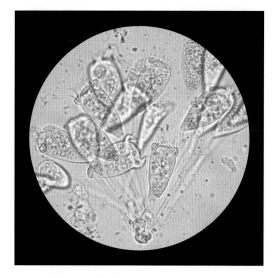

Above: The long bell-like shape of the protozoan *Epistylis* is visible under the microscope, but it takes a practised eye to make an accurate identification.

Identification

In the early stages of infection no external visible signs may be seen on the infected koi, but behavioural changes such as flicking or hanging in the water may be observed. At this point microscope examination of a skin scrape is the only way to make an exact diagnosis. As the infection worsens, small white patches may appear on the skin which can develop in size up to 5mm (0.2in) or so. At first these may be limited in number, but as they become larger they will spread and more will become apparent on the body of the infected koi, as well as on the gills. As these small white patches spread, the skin will become redder and this eventually leads to scales lifting and (if not treated) falling out. This leaves the affected area susceptible to secondary infections from bacteria or fungus.

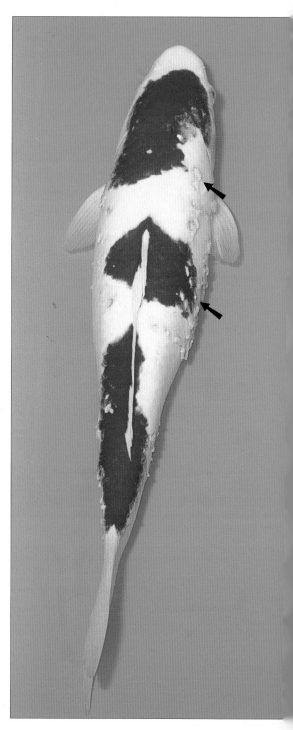

Above: This koi is in the later stages of an *Epistylis* infection. The white patches on the skin are turning into areas of redness, and scales may be lost as the infection develops.

Above: This fish exhibits the early stages of *Epistylis*. If treated at this stage, the loss of scales may be prevented.

At this stage of infection it is vital to check regularly for other parasites as these will quickly take advantage of the situation and worsen the problem. As the *Epistylis* infection spreads, it is quite common to see ulceration caused by bacteria attacking areas from where scales have fallen. As the situation worsens, badly infected fish will stop eating and start to look emaciated, and spells of inactivity will be seen as the koi simply hang in the water with their fins sometimes clamped to the sides of their bodies. At this stage losses can be expected. Even if the fish survive they may be disfigured, and so although they may recover full health, they will not have the same financial value as before the infection occurred. *Epistylis* infections are very unlikely to occur when the pond temperature is below 12°C (54°F), but as the temperature rises the level of infection will increase. Water temperatures of over 20°C (68°F) lead to high levels of parasite activity.

Prevention

As with most diseases improved husbandry and system maintenance can reduce the likelihood of infection and *Epistylis* is no exception to this. Lower stress levels also make the occurrence of this disease less likely and the use of a pond heating system will help reduce harmful fluctuations in water temperature. But if you do have a pond heater, be sure to pay extra attention for the presence of *Epistylis* as the protozoa will be encouraged by higher temperatures. If spotted early *Epistylis* should not cause a major problem, but if allowed to get to an advanced stage it will leave the infected koi highly susceptible to other infections. If *Epistylis* is experienced, take extra care to check for the presence of any other infections which might move in and create a whole new set of problems.

Treatment

Epistylis can be treated with an off-the-shelf parasite treatment, or alternatively with malachite green alone. Dose rates will depend upon the concentration of the solution. Alternatively salt can also be used to control *Epistylis* effectively. It should be used as a bath, at the dose of 100g of salt per 4.5 litres (3.5oz per gallon) for 10 minutes, which should be accurately timed. This can be repeated for three consecutive days. Unless the infection is halted early, secondary infection may well occur and this will generally need specific treatment. This can be done via topical treatment with either propolis alone, or malachite green and propolis in more severe cases. Fungus is also common and in most instances this will need to be treated topically with malachite green and/or propolis.

FUNGAL DISEASE (COTTON WOOL)

Fungal disease in a pond may be caused by a number of fungi which are naturally present in most bodies of water, for example the aquatic fungus *Saprolegnia*. These fungi will not prove a problem to healthy koi in a well maintained pond, and in fact their presence helps to maintain a balanced ecosystem as they live on decomposing and decaying matter. These fungi will only attack damaged areas of skin or decomposing waste. So fungal disease is a secondary infection as it requires a koi to be already damaged, for example by a parasite. Only then will fungus attack the weakened area of skin, fin or mouth. Fungus will also attack dead eggs, so during spawning it is important to remove any eggs which become infected with fungus. The tell-tale sign of this is that the egg will turn white and then a furry growth appears around it. If these infected eggs are not removed, the fungus may spread to healthy eggs nearby. Infected eggs can easily be removed with the use of a pipette.

Identification

Developed fungal infections are easily visible to the naked eye, as the infected area will have a white tufty growth covering it. In some instances this may resemble cotton wool, though it is not always white – instead it may have a brown, black, or grey appearance. In early stages of fungal infections it is not always possible to spot an attack without taking the koi out of the pond and inspecting susceptible areas. To begin with only one or two small white strands may be noticed, but these build up over time to become the cotton-wool-like tufts typical of a fungus infection. It is important that fungal infections are spotted early as this both enables the infection to be removed quite easily, and it also reduces the chances of death occurring from the fungus attack. In a severe fungus infection, when large areas of the body are covered with a cotton-wool-like fur, the chances of survival are dramatically reduced as the fungus will start to attack the koi internally, which leads to irreparable damage to the internal organs.

Be aware that there is a condition known as mouth rot or cotton wool mouth which looks like a fungus infection. In fact it is not caused by fungus but by the bacterium *Flavobacterium columnare*, and so it requires a different course of treatment.

Prevention

Fungus is a secondary infection and will only become a problem after something has damaged the protective mucus coating of your koi. This could be due to a parasite infection, bacterial infection, netting damage, poor water quality, spawning or poor diet. In fact any stress factor could leave your koi susceptible to a parasite infection, for example, and thus potentially a secondary fungal infection. So the secret to preventing fungus is to provide a stress-free environment for your koi. This

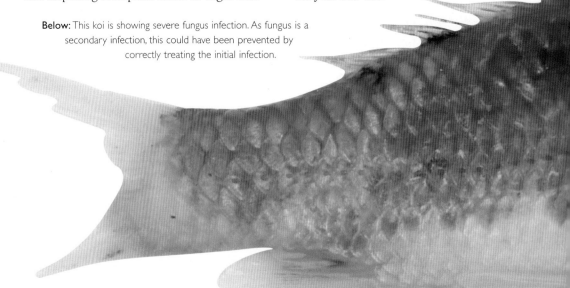

Below: This koi is showing severe fungus infection. As fungus is a secondary infection, this could have been prevented by correctly treating the initial infection.

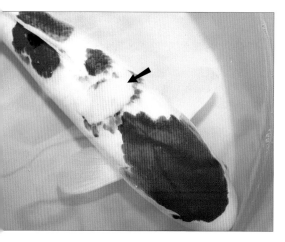

Above: This koi has an area of fungus in front of the dorsal fin. The most probable cause of this is physical damage which has gone unnoticed, and caused the fish to succumb to a secondary fungus infection.

can be achieved by regular system maintenance, water testing, and pond heating to prevent fluctuations in water temperature.

Treatment

Before attempting to treat fungus you must identify what has allowed the fungus to become a problem and treat this first. If this is not done, you will be fighting a losing battle in trying to get rid of the fungus. A large number of proprietary fungal remedies are available which can be used as a bath or pond treatment with differing levels of success. The best approach in the case of fungal infections is to topically treat infected koi individually. If you are dealing with only a light infection, this can be done in the pond. However, in severe cases where large areas of the koi are covered, it may be preferable to treat the koi in a quarantine tank. This will help reduce the number of fungus spores that are released into the water to a minimum.

Topical treatment should be applied to the areas affected with fungus, and it may be easier to do this if the koi is sedated first. Alternatively the koi can be held while being treated. Before applying topical treatment the fungus should be removed with a cotton-wool bud, then malachite green should be applied to the area, before the whole area is finally sprayed with propolis. Then the treated koi can be returned to the pond. If, when the fungus is removed, it looks like a bacterial infection has occurred, i.e. there are large areas of ulceration, it may be necessary to take additional steps and these should be discussed with your local koi health specialist. Fungus will attack dead eggs, so if you are spawning your koi, it is a good precaution to apply a suitable anti-fungal remedy to the pond once spawning has finished, e.g. methylene blue. However, take care to maintain optimum conditions when using methylene blue as it can destroy the nitrifying bacteria in your filter.

GAS BUBBLE DISEASE

This condition is very similar to the "bends" which divers experience when they rise to the surface too quickly – the rapid change in pressure results in tiny bubbles forming in the blood. In a koi pond gas bubble disease can occur when both nitrogen and oxygen reach levels of super-saturation – 120 per cent for nitrogen and over 200 per cent for oxygen. Supersaturation occurs for a number of reasons, and is generally encountered at lower water temperatures when water will hold higher levels of oxygen. One

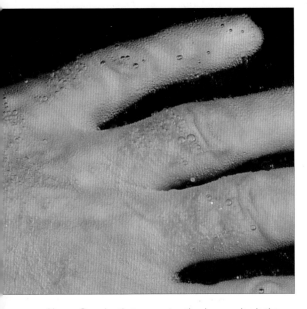

Above: One sign that supersaturation is occurring is the formation of tiny bubbles on the pond wall. This condition is illustrated here by the presence of very small bubbles coating the surface of a hand immersed in the water.

factor which may cause supersaturation are algae blooms, as during the process of photosynthesis high levels of oxygen are released into the water. Water that is drawn from a natural underground spring or well may contain nitrogen at supersaturated levels, although this is a problem which is more likely to be encountered by the fish farmer rather than the hobbyist who is using conditioned tapwater. Finally use of pressurized equipment, such as sand filters, may result in any trapped air in the unit being forced into solution in the water causing supersaturation. Gas bubble disease can be fatal, but if the signs are spotted soon enough steps can be taken to alleviate the problem.

Identification

As a koi takes water in over its gills, the gases which it contains are diffused into the blood. When water which is supersaturated with nitrogen and oxygen passes over the gills, higher levels of these gases enter the blood. Once they are in the koi's bloodstream, changes in pressure which occur within the circulation system result in the excess levels of nitrogen and oxygen coming out of solution and forming tiny bubbles in the blood. These bubbles are known as embolisms and it is the nitrogen bubbles which pose the greatest threat to your koi. Nitrogen bubbles in the blood can block blood vessels and affect the circulation. In severe cases they may result in abnormal behaviour, unstable swimming and even death. Oxygen bubbles in the blood seldom block blood vessels. External signs of gas bubble disease include small gas bubbles that are visible on the fins, around the eyes, and on the gills. Nitrogen bubbles may even cause the eyes to swell and pop-eye to develop. If air bubbles become trapped between the two outer layers of skin, you may notice that the skin starts to lift, and as more bubbles collect in this area the more pronounced the lifting will appear.

Below: Gas bubble disease is very seldom experienced and can be very hard to identify. Here the presence of small bubbles in a fish's dorsal fin can just be seen.

Prevention

Gas bubble disease occurs when the water becomes supersaturated, so the best prevention is to stop this from occurring. One of the main causes is an algae bloom so good maintenance and regular algae removal will help prevent this. The use of an ultra-violet filter will also help to keep algae blooms to a minimum. If blanketweed and other algae which are not controlled by UV light become a problem, the use of an appropriate pond treatment may be a good idea. Gas bubble disease can also occur when gases become trapped in pressurized filtration equipment, such as sand filters, so it is a good idea to bleed off any excess air build-up in the unit when using such items. Good aeration also reduces the chances of this disease occurring as it will dispel the excess gas from the water. So if levels of dissolved gases climb over 100 per cent they will be able to diffuse back into the atmosphere.

Above: The pectoral fin of a koi suffering from gas bubble disease. Here the bubbles can be seen radiating out along the fin away from the body of the koi.

Treatment

The first thing you should do is start to exchange large amounts of the water for water which is not supersaturated as this will help bring the levels of dissolved gases back to normal. When doing this ensure that dechlorinated and conditioned water is used to avoid causing excessive levels of stress. You should also try to create as much surface disturbance as possible as this will encourage the excess gas levels in the water to diffuse back into the air. Normally if these steps are taken, no further treatment will be needed and the koi should return to health. If, however, nitrogen bubbles have formed in the blood, there is a chance that blood vessels may have become blocked, and so sudden losses may still occur.

GILL DISORDERS (STICKY GILLS, GILL MAGGOTS AND GILL ROT)

Gill problems can be caused by numerous factors including parasites, many of which are described elsewhere in this section. Other factors which can cause gill problems are gill maggots, poor water quality which can result in sticky gills, and the fungus *Branchiomyces* which will cause gill rot. Bacterial disorders may also result in gill damage and again these pathogens are examined elsewhere in this section.

The problem with gill diseases is the fact that they are not easy to spot in the early stages of infection because the gills are covered by the operculum. The problem is only normally apparent once your koi show other symptoms, such as gasping, hanging in areas of heavily oxygenated water, such as waterfalls and airstones, and even going off their food. When these symptoms are noticed, the koi in question should be taken out of the pond, and the gill cover gently lifted for closer examination of the gill. The problem this causes is that although the majority of gill complaints can be easily treated, the survival rate will depend largely upon the extent of the damage already done to the gills. In some cases losses may continue to be experienced for a number of weeks or months, even after the infection has been treated successfully.

Above and below: Here are two tell-tale signs that a potential gill problem may be occurring. The top image shows very pale gills, while the bottom picture shows gill filaments which are sticky.

Sticky Gills

This condition is normally caused by poor water quality or low oxygen levels resulting from lack of aeration. As the name suggests, this complaint is easily identified because the gill filaments will be clumped together, and they may appear to be

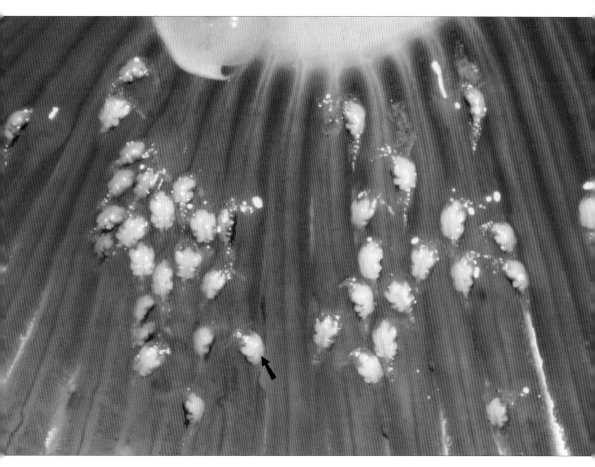

Above: A section of a gill which is infected with gill maggots. This is seldom experienced by the hobbyist; however, if you think that this may be a problem, seek specialist advice.

covered in mucus. The first thing to do is to test the water quality within the pond, and establish levels of dissolved oxygen (DO). If these prove to be low, steps should be taken to correct them as quickly as possible, i.e. make small (10 to 20 per cent) water changes with dechlorinated water and increase aeration, if possible. It is important to check for the presence of other diseases. An indication that these might be present will be if any of the gills are grey in colour or if any of the filaments look as if they are being eaten away or rotting. If any of these signs are spotted, it may signify the start of something more serious so a skin scrape should be taken from the koi in question starting as close to the gills as possible. If a bacterial infection is suspected, a swab should also be taken from around the gills. Having ruled out the presence of anything more sinister, and if water quality tests have identified the underlying

problem, the best course of action is to give the infected koi a salt bath once a day for three consecutive days. This should be done at a dose rate of 100g of salt per 4.5 litres (3.5oz of salt per gallon) for ten minutes, remembering to add plenty of aeration to the water being used in the bath. This, combined with correction of the water quality in the pond, should lead to a rapid improvement and full recovery, as this is not a particularly serious condition.

Gill Maggots (*Ergasilus*)

Gill maggots are parasitic crustaceans which, if left untreated, can cause major gill damage, and result in large fish losses. These parasites are found on the gills, gill covers, and the mouths of infected koi. When spotted, steps should be taken not only to eradicate the adults that are seen on the koi, but also any juvenile stages present in the water. The life cycle of the gill maggot starts when the females attack the gills of a chosen host koi. These females produce egg sacs which give this parasite its name because of their uncanny resemblance to a maggot. Once these egg sacs have released their eggs into the pond, a free-swimming juvenile stage hatches within a few days, which will then continue to develop until a suitable host is found. At this stage mating will take place after which the males will die, while the female takes root in the gills of the new host, where the cycle can start again.

The adult female can survive for a considerable time on the host if left untreated. One course of treatment is to use a suitable organophosphate-based formulation. However, such chemicals have recently been banned in a number of countries, including the UK. As a substitute new proprietary off-the-shelf treatments are becoming available which can be used as an alternative to organophosphates and these will be readily available at your local koi dealers. If you live in a country where organophosphates are legally available, you must realize that the treatment will only be effective against the adults, so further treatments will be required to eradicate the juvenile stages as they develop into adults. When using any organophosphate-based treatment be sure that species like orfe are not present as they will not tolerate this sort of medication.

Branchiomyces – Gill Rot

This condition is generally only a problem for koi which are housed in poorly maintained ponds, or ponds which are plagued by excessively high

The life cycle of the gill maggot *(Ergasilus)*

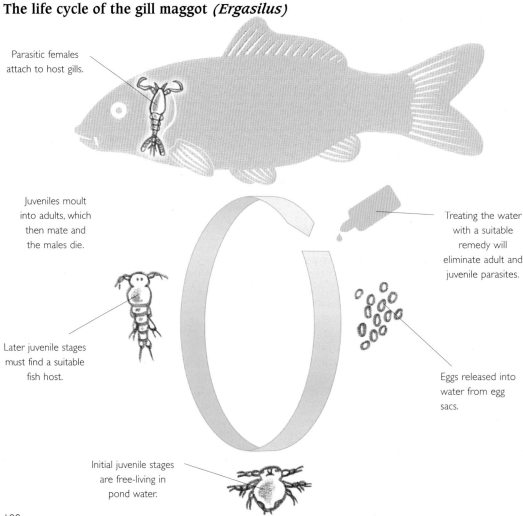

Parasitic females attach to host gills.

Juveniles moult into adults, which then mate and the males die.

Treating the water with a suitable remedy will eliminate adult and juvenile parasites.

Later juvenile stages must find a suitable fish host.

Eggs released into water from egg sacs.

Initial juvenile stages are free-living in pond water.

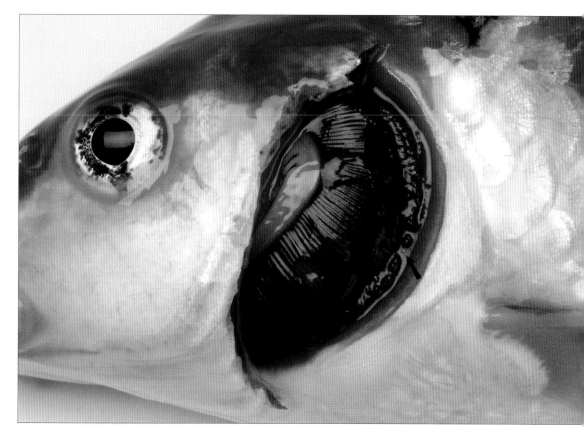

Above: In the more advanced stages of gill disorders, the actual filaments of the gills may start to rot away or physically disintegrate, as seen here.

levels of algae, such as green water or blanketweed. It is a rare condition in the UK so is unlikely to be encountered by the koi hobbyist. Koi infected with this fungus will start to show many of the symptoms of sticky gill. However, this will get progressively worse and result in the actual gill starting to rot away, and this stage can be characterized by areas of grey or brown discoloration on the gill filaments, as well as visible holes on the gills where actual filaments have rotted. The only way that exact identification of this fungal problem can be made is to examine some of the infected gill filaments under a microscope. Because of the dangers involved when taking samples from the gills, this procedure should only be attempted by a suitably qualified person. Even with a gill sample, it may prove incredibly difficult to make an exact identification.

It is very difficult to treat infections of *Branchiomyces* and the best approach is to work on prevention by ensuring optimum conditions at all times, and so hopefully avoiding an outbreak. If an outbreak does occur, you should consider the use of salt baths for the infected koi while at the same time improving the environment in which they are housed by regular water changes, and the introduction of commercially available chemicals to improve water conditions and assist the performance of the filters. Salt can be used as a bath at 85 to 100g per 4.5 litres (3 to 3.5oz per gallon) for ten minutes once a day for three consecutive days. Remember to provide added aeration in the bath.

Alternatively a proprietary gill medication may be applied to the pond, or treatment with Chloramine T could be considered at a minimum dose of 1g per 1000 litres (220 gallons). The problem with this disease is that not only is it hard to eradicate, but it also causes physical damage, from which the gill may not regenerate. Consequently losses may occur for some time.

GYRODACTYLUS (SKIN FLUKES) AND DACTYLOGYRUS (GILL FLUKES)

These are the two most common types of worm infection which will be encountered by the koi keeper. If identified early, they can normally be easily eradicated. Both *Gyrodactylus* spp. and *Dactylogyrus* spp. are external parasites which attack koi by means of their specialist attachment organs. *Gyrodactylus* – more commonly known as skin flukes – are worm-shaped and have a set of hooks for fastening on to a koi located at the rear of their bodies. When viewing skin flukes through a microscope (they are not visible to the naked eye), up to four developing flukes can be seen within the adult, each one located within the next. Skin flukes give birth to live young, but only one at a time, and the reproduction rate is normally low, unless the koi are stressed which is when an outbreak will occur. Once a skin fluke is attached to the host koi, it will live on mucus, skin and blood. However, even if a skin fluke loses its host, it can still survive for up to five days.

Dactylogyrus – or gill flukes – attack the gills of koi. They also have hooks to attach to the host koi located at the rear of their bodies, but these are surrounded by a number of smaller hooks. Unlike skin flukes, gill flukes do not bear live young, and in fact they are hermaphrodites. So each worm can produce and fertilize a single egg at a time. Once this egg is laid, it may well fall away from the gills, and will develop over a number of days into a free-swimming larva. Development at this stage is rapid but a host must be quickly found for continued survival. If a host is not found, larvae will only survive for a number of hours. Once a host is found, the larva will reach maturity in around a week and then start reproducing.

Below: Here a gill fluke can be seen under a microscope. A skin scrape must be taken for a definite identification of flukes to be made. When taking the scrape, try to take the mucus sample as close to the gills as possible.

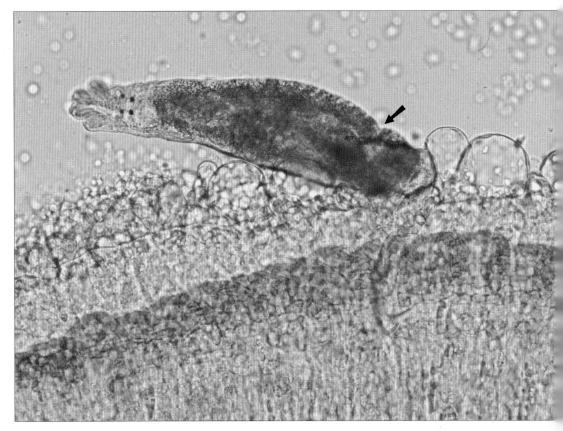

The life cycle of the gill fluke *(Dactylogyrus)*

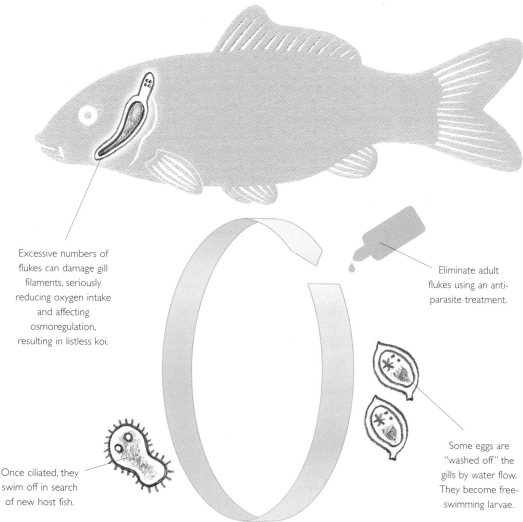

Excessive numbers of flukes can damage gill filaments, seriously reducing oxygen intake and affecting osmoregulation, resulting in listless koi.

Eliminate adult flukes using an anti-parasite treatment.

Once ciliated, they swim off in search of new host fish.

Some eggs are "washed off" the gills by water flow. They become free-swimming larvae.

Identification

Neither *Gyrodactylus* nor *Dactylogyrus* is visible to the naked eye and thus a skin scrape must be viewed under a microscope for a positive identification. A skin scrape from the body is sufficient to identify both types of flukes, as gill flukes will normally attach themselves to the body of a koi and make their way towards the gills over a number of days. Both types of worm may appear to move over the slide by a process of expansion and contraction. When a koi is infected with skin flukes, it may start to produce large amounts of mucus, and if the infection

becomes severe, secondary infections such as fungus or bacterial problems may arise. If gill flukes are the problem, the gills will show the signs of infection, and this will be characterized by discolouration of the gills and the presence of large amounts of mucus causing the gill filaments to stick together. If this mucus builds up, the operculum (gill cover) may appear lifted because it is unable to shut, and the affected koi may hang in the water close to heavily oxygenated water, i.e. near airstones and water returns.

You may also notice that food is not taken as readily as normal and over time the koi may

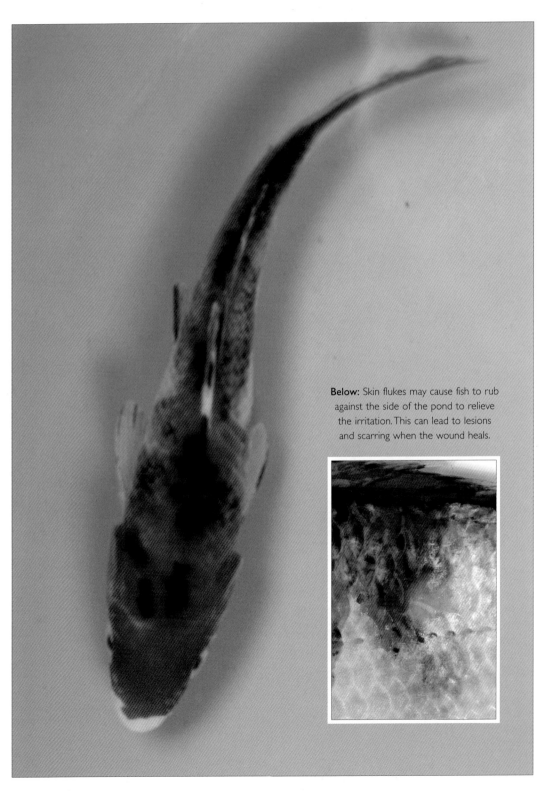

Below: Skin flukes may cause fish to rub against the side of the pond to relieve the irritation. This can lead to lesions and scarring when the wound heals.

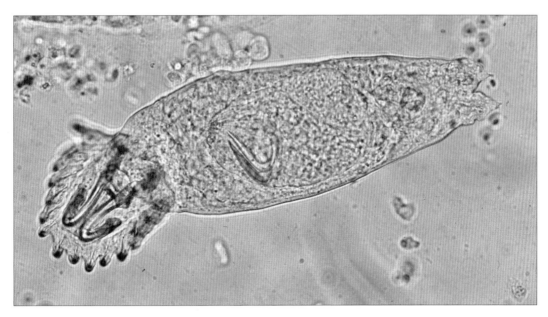

Above: A skin fluke is shown. Closer examination shows that inside the adult fluke a baby fluke is developing.
Left: A small koi with a heavy fluke infestation. As the infection takes hold, your fish may become emaciated and exhibit a milky colour due to excess mucus production.

become emaciated. Unfortunately if skin and gill flukes are not identified early on, secondary problems will occur. In the case of gill flukes if sufficient damage is done to the gills before the disease is spotted, losses may occur. You may also see your koi flicking and rubbing against the side of the pond to try and relieve the irritation caused by these parasites and this in turn can cause physical lesions which may become infected.

Prevention
You can expect to find the odd fluke on a koi, but it is when the environment in which the koi are kept deteriorates significantly that flukes start to reproduce at a fast enough rate to cause a problem. It is therefore important to maintain optimum water quality and prevent rapid temperature changes; the installation of a pond heating system is beneficial in this respect. Also maintain optimum oxygen levels and carry out regular system maintenance, including regular small water changes, to help to prevent these diseases from occurring. When buying koi, avoid any fish showing signs of excess mucus production and irregular gill movement.

Treatment
When treating skin flukes it is normally only necessary to apply one treatment as the flukes can only survive for a few hours without a host, whereas with gill flukes it may be necessary to perform a course of treatments because of the period over which the eggs hatch and develop. The eggs themselves are impervious to chemical attack. There are numerous proprietary medications which are designed to treat flukes, all with varying results. An alternative to these is to use malachite green and formalin at a dose rate that will depend upon the strength of the solution. If opting to use this, ensure that the water temperature is above 11°C (52°F). If water temperatures are lower than this but still above 7°C (45°F), it may be worth considering the use of potassium permanganate at a dose rate of 1.5g per 1000 litres (220 gallons), which can be repeated, if required, every five to seven days for a period of three weeks.

A final possibility is to employ an organophosphate-based medication. This, however, is not a universal option as such chemicals are banned in a number of countries, including the UK. In parallel with treating and eradicating the fluke infestation, it may also be necessary to treat any secondary infections which have occurred. This can normally be done by applying propolis topically in combination with an appropriate bactericide.

HI-KUI

Hi-kui is a disease which only attacks the skin of koi with red pigmentation, especially Go Sanke varieties, i.e. Kohaku, Showa and Sanke. The term Hi-kui is composed of two elements – hi means red and kui translates as eaten, so Hi-kui can simply be described as a disease which eats the red areas of pigmentation on koi. Hi-kui is widely used to describe a number of conditions, although the actual cause could in fact be a number of things. Hi-kui may be used to describe complaints such as localized, minor skin conditions which can normally be easily treated using the methods described below. At the other extreme it may be used to describe complaints such as skin cancer which require examination by your vet or koi health specialist who will advise on a suitable treatment regime. It must be said that skin cancer in koi is not something which is widely experienced, although if in doubt specialist advice should always be sought. Hi-kui only tends to affect good quality koi with stable areas of red pigmentation – lower quality koi whose red pigmentation may be unstable are seldom affected.

Identification

Hi-kui disease may show itself in a numbers of ways. First you may notice a small discoloration of an area of red pigmentation, causing the red pigment to look faded compared to the rest of the red on the koi. This area may also look matt and sunken and lack the same sheen as the rest of the fish. Secondly an area of red pigmentation may take on a brown haze, and look raised compared to the surrounding area. Thirdly small dark brown areas may appear with a diameter ranging from a pinhead up to the size of a small coin.

Whatever symptoms your koi exhibit, the problem is caused by a thickening of the overlying epidermal tissue which may be triggered by a number of factors, the most likely being overexposure to sunlight resulting in sunburn. Excessive sunlight can trigger tumours of red pigment cells by damaging the cells' DNA. Poor husbandry and system maintenance may make attacks of Hi-kui worse, as dirt and waste within the system can attract anaerobic bacteria which will view these affected areas as an ideal site for secondary infection.

Prevention

As overexposure to sunlight is one of the main causes of Hi-kui disease, shading the pond is a good idea. For this reason many keepers believe that koi kept in green water are less likely to get Hi-kui, although this is not an attractive solution for the typical hobbyist who wants to view their koi in a clear water. Good system maintenance and regular discharges of collected waste will all

Right: This fish is showing advanced stages of Hi-kui – the red pigmentation and skin tissue is breaking down.
Below: Hi-kui disease generally only affects higher grade koi, which have red pigmentation, such as Go Sanke varieties.

help. They do not necessarily stop Hi-kui from occurring, but they do help to prevent other infections taking hold. It is also essential to ensure that optimum oxygen levels are maintained at all times, especially in high temperatures which usually coincide with high exposure to sunlight. Despite these precautions it may be impossible to stop an outbreak of Hi-kui as it can simply appear through no fault of your own. Unfortunately it tends to occur more readily on high quality koi with strong and stable hi (red), and if your collection contains fish which fall into this category, be warned that it might just happen!

Treatment

Hi-kui is not contagious and in real terms it has no effect on the overall health of the koi, as long as the system in which they are kept is of a suitable standard and is well maintained. The main effect of Hi-kui is cosmetic – it degrades the appearance of your fish, and in the case of high value koi, it may devalue them. Whether you decide to treat or not is a matter of personal choice. If you do decide to seek treatment, the koi in question will need to be sedated before any surgical treatment can be carried out. Having sedated the fish, a vet or koi health specialist will scrape away the area of Hi-kui with a clean sterilized scalpel until the raised parts of Hi-kui are gone, or at least reduced in size if a large area is affected. Then a suitable topical treatment may be applied to the area to stop secondary infections, such as fungus. Propolis is a good treatment to apply although malachite green or similar will do.

The koi can then be returned to the pond, but the treated area of skin must be monitored on a regular basis to ensure that no secondary infections occur. It may be necessary to repeat the topical treatment on a regular basis until the area is healed. An alternative, less drastic treatment is to apply a steroid-based cream to the affected area for a number of weeks, with the cream being applied several times during the day. This approach is generally preferable as a first step before having the area of Hi-kui surgically removed and possibly leaving your koi open to secondary infections.

KOI HERPES VIRUS (KHV) AND SPRING VIRAEMIA OF CARP (SVC)

KHV is a disease which until recently was seldom mentioned, but as more cases of this virus are identified it has become a condition which is feared by all koi keepers. Koi which have KHV may show symptoms similar to many other diseases, such as severe gill damage and disintegration of the gill filaments, the production of vast amounts of excess mucus, loss of colour, and severe internal problems due to the way in which this pathogen liquifies the internal organs.

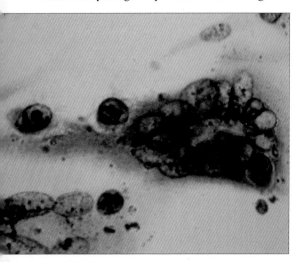

Above: The koi herpes virus seen under an electron microscope; the chemical process of preparing the slide creates the discoloration which can be seen here.

KHV is a virus and although steps are being taken to develop a vaccine to protect koi from it, at present there is no cure. Only preventative measures can be suggested.

Koi which have been exposed to the koi herpes virus may well die, and losses of over 80 per cent of stock can be anticipated by the hobbyist, especially if an exact diagnosis of KHV is not made early on. Currently the only way that KHV can be tested for accurately is by a PCR (polymerase chain reaction) test, and for this a koi will have to be sacrificed and sent away to a specialist laboratory for analysis. This virus is affected by temperature and so keeping your koi at certain temperatures can limit the effect of this disease. In low water temperatures (around 7°C/mid-40s°F or lower) the koi herpes virus will become dormant and losses should be reduced.

However, as the water temperature warms the virus will become active again, until temperatures of over 27°C (80°F) are reached which are not tolerated by the KHV virus. However, this does not mean that koi already infected with KHV are free from the disease; it is simply that they are being kept at temperatures levels where the disease will not develop.

As temperature plays such an important role in the spread of KHV through the pond, those times of the year when temperature changes occur are the most likely periods for an outbreak of KHV. Winter going into spring and autumn going into winter are typically the worst times for this disease. As KHV will only cause fatalities in a limited band of temperatures, and because the virus can lie dormant within a fish for a period of time, there is no way of being 100 per cent certain that a koi is free from KHV.

So what is the answer? Once KHV is positively identified, should you take drastic action and kill all your stock and disinfect everything? This may seem like the logical action and to some people it will be the right thing to do. However, when you re-stock there is nothing to prevent you from inadvertently introducing more koi with the KHV virus. So an alternative approach is to raise the pond temperature to around 25°C (77°F) and see if the virus breaks out. If it does, let it run its course, removing dead koi as they succumb. Generally not all the koi will die and those which survive may have developed their own immunity against the virus. However, these koi will probably carry the virus, so any new koi introduced during the active temperature range may develop KHV, while any subsequent stress will reduce your koi's immunity, thus risking a "reawakening" of the virus. The other problem with this approach is that you will limit movements from your pond as no fish can be moved because of the danger of spreading KHV. Other than keeping the pond very cold – around 7°C/mid-40s°F or lower – or very warm – 27°C (80°F) or higher – there is no real answer for dealing KHV at this present time.

In fact, although it may seem drastic, the best possible course of action to take once KHV is positively identified is probably to sacrifice your stock and start again, keeping your fingers crossed that none of the new purchases has KHV.

As more and more people learn about KHV, it is to be hoped that koi breeders, dealers and retailers will take proper steps to have stocks tested for the virus. As more becomes known about KHV, when quarantining stocks many dealers will actually raise the temperature to the range in which KHV outbreaks will occur, in order to rule out the presence of this disease.

SVC – Spring Viraemia of Carp (*Rhabdovirus carpio*)

This is a disease which you really hope you will never experience as it is a notifiable condition. This means that once it is identified, you must inform the relevant authorities who may well take the step of killing your stocks and disinfecting your whole system. SVC is a virus and thus can only be accurately identified by sacrificing a koi and sending it away for testing by a laboratory with the facilities to check for this condition. SVC should not be a concern for koi keepers as long as they do not introduce stocks from the wild, especially if they live in a country where SVC is present. In fact it is illegal in most instances to take and move wild stocks without

first discussing your intentions with the appropriate authority. It is also wise to avoid importing koi from a region or country which is known to have SVC. That is why strict licensing is in place in countries where SVC is not currently a problem.

SVC will cause symptoms of ulceration on the skin of your koi, as well as areas of reddening as the virus progresses. Sometimes these are accompanied by swelling of the belly area, and a loss of colour in the gills. Surprisingly SVC will not result in heavy loses of adult koi, but if small young koi are infected losses of 100 per cent may be expected. If you are unfortunate enough to encounter this disease in your fish, it is vital that the correct authorities are notified. In most cases the laboratory carrying out the testing will do this as a matter of course. Although the subsequent culling may be hard to bear, try to remember that it is not only in your best interests but also those of the whole koi industry.

Below: One of the many symptoms of KHV is the occurrence of severe gill damage and disintegration of the gill filaments, as pictured here.

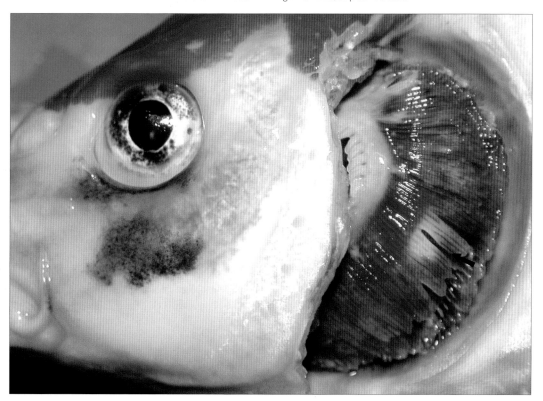

LEECHES

These can be a problem in a koi pond, especially if it is a planted one. They normally find their way into a pond on plants, live food, newly introduced koi or visiting wildlife. There are many species of leech, but the most common fish-parasitic leech is *Piscicola geometra*. This leech can grow up to 8cm (3in) in length. Leeches attach themselves to a host koi with their sucking mouthparts. These are used to draw blood as a food source from the host koi. In the process leeches can transmit other infections to the host koi. Leeches can also live without a host for a considerable time and will leave the host koi to reproduce. They lay numerous eggs which are

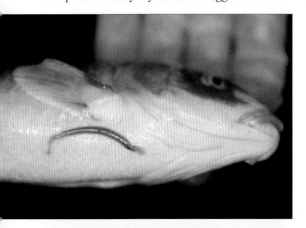

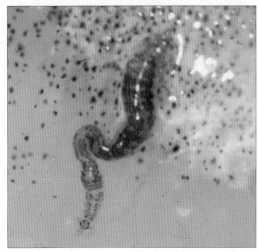

Above top: A leech can be seen attached to the underside of a koi. This should be carefully removed ensuring that the attachment organs are not left embedded in the fish.
Above: Leeches should not pose a particular threat unless they are found physically attached to your koi.

wrapped in a cocoon which is normally dark brown or grey colour. It may be found attached to plants, rocks, or even the filter media if the leeches manage to make their way into the filter system. Once these eggs hatch, the new leeches find a fresh host and feed on this for a time before leaving the host koi to digest their meal.

Identification

Leeches may be present in a pond for some time and go unnoticed if not actually observed on a host koi. Most species of aquatic leeches are harmless to fish and do not attach to or feed on koi. However, if one is seen on a koi, it is unmistakable – large in size and worm-like in appearance. Leeches attach themselves anywhere on the body of the koi, and a tell-tale sign of a leech infection is the presence of red lesions on the skin, which are caused by the leech attaching itself and drawing blood. If a leech infestation is suspected, it is important to check the underside of the koi; leeches will attach themselves here quite often, as no scales are present. Areas such as the face, mouth and the ball joints of pectoral fins are also highly prone to attack.

Prevention

It is important that all new plants are inspected for leeches and their eggs before they are introduced to a pond. Unfortunately, however well each new plant is inspected, it is virtually impossible to ensure that all possible hiding places on the plant are checked thoroughly. Live food is another common source of leech infestation, and the best course of action here is to avoid the use of live food, and opt for treated frozen "live food" instead. If live food is used, it is essential that the food is thoroughly inspected for any signs of leeches. You should also sieve the food in the hope of preventing any leeches from passing through the sieve. The other common cause of leech introduction into a pond is the presence of wildlife, such as frogs, birds and waterfowl. As it is very hard to stop these from visiting your pond, all that can realistically be done is to avoid encouraging birds and ducks to the pond, and to inspect koi regularly for possible signs of infection.

Treatment

It is very hard to eradicate a leech infestation entirely once it has taken hold. If you can legally

The life cycle of the fish leech *(Piscicola geometra)*

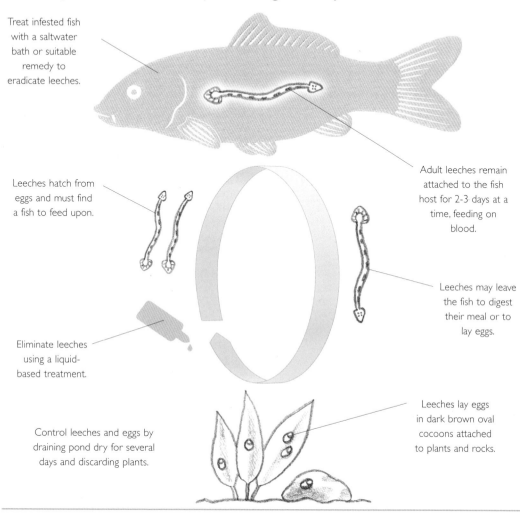

Treat infested fish with a saltwater bath or suitable remedy to eradicate leeches.

Adult leeches remain attached to the fish host for 2-3 days at a time, feeding on blood.

Leeches hatch from eggs and must find a fish to feed upon.

Leeches may leave the fish to digest their meal or to lay eggs.

Eliminate leeches using a liquid-based treatment.

Leeches lay eggs in dark brown oval cocoons attached to plants and rocks.

Control leeches and eggs by draining pond dry for several days and discarding plants.

obtain them, organophosphate-based treatments can be used, but the sale of these products is banned in many countries, including the UK. Normally the treatment has to be repeated many times to ensure complete eradication, as the eggs are not always killed and further treatments are required to kill the leeches as they hatch. Other possible treatments for leech infestations include the use of salt baths, or potassium permanganate dips. However, these are not a long-term solution to the problem of leeches as they will only kill leeches on the treated koi and not those still in the pond, or ones hatching from eggs. The only sure way of completely eradicating a leech problem is to drain the pond and all filter systems, and allow the site to completely dry out. This kills all eggs and leeches. While this is taking place, every fish removed from the pond must be inspected and any leeches removed. Care should be taken that the whole leech is removed and that none of the attachment organs are left on the fish. Any that do remain should be plucked off using tweezers. As the leeches are taken off, it is worth treating the attachment area with propolis to prevent secondary infection from occurring. Once returned to the pond, a careful eye must be kept on these areas for secondary infections. If they appear, a further topical treatment should be applied, and advice sought from your vet or local koi health specialist.

MYXOBOLUS (NODULAR DISEASE)

Nodular disease occurs when koi become infected with myxozoan parasites, namely *Myxobolus*. This disease can affect koi externally on the body, fins and gills, or internally when organs and muscles are affected. Gill and internal infections are the most harmful as these may go unnoticed for some time; by the time they are spotted irreparable damage may have occurred both through the initial illness and from secondary infection. This disease can be highly contagious so it is best to avoid buying any koi showing symptoms, and to remove any infected koi to a quarantine facility. This may prove problematic as the disease takes many months to develop so koi with early stages of infection are often difficult to identify.

Identification

As the name nodular disease suggests, lumps appear either externally or internally. These lumps – or cysts as they are correctly termed – may be up to 5mm (0.2in) in diameter and have

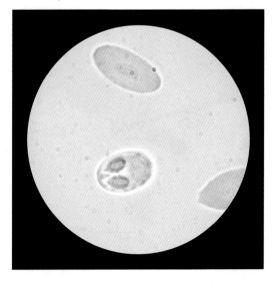

Above: *Myxobolus* seen under a microscope. As this is not an infection which is commonly experienced, a specialist will be required to make an exact identification.

a white or yellow appearance. They are not uniform in shape, some are circular while others may be elongate or irregularly shaped. These cysts contain many thousands of tiny parasitic spores which, when released, may be eaten by other koi so spreading the disease. When internal organs and muscles are affected by nodular disease, spores may be released in the fish's waste. These spores can infect invertebrate hosts which in turn are eaten by the koi, so causing further infection.

Above: This koi is showing swelling around the gills which is exaggerated on one side.

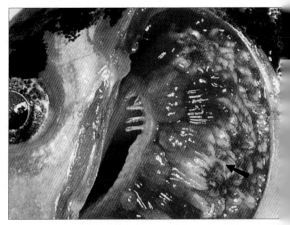

Above: A koi with an advanced gill infection caused by the *Myxobolus* parasite is shown.

Prevention

The best prevention against this disease is to avoid the introduction of infected koi, so ensure that all purchases come from a reliable source. Any koi showing any of the symptoms mentioned should be avoided. While they are not conclusively proof of myxobolus, the disease can be so infectious and damaging to a collection of fish that it wiser to err on the side of caution, and so to avoid acquiring the koi in question. It is sensible also to avoid the use of live food, as this could be a secondary host for spores released by already infected fish. If you do want to feed live food, it may be best to opt for a frozen type as these are generally treated and sterilized to destroy pathogens.

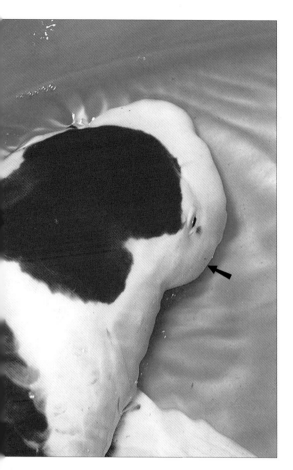

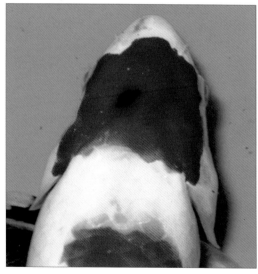

Above and right: Here two different koi can be seen both exhibiting swelling around the gills and face. From looking at these pictures it is quite obvious why this disease is sometimes referred to as "frog face".

The two most harmful instances of myxobolus occur when the gills are infected. Sometimes the gills become so swollen that they press against the gill cover (operculum), or the gills become infected with secondary bacterial infections which inhibit their ability to take up oxygen. Due to the swelling which occurs around the gills, myxobolus is commonly called "swelling cheek disease" or "frog face". A koi infected with nodular disease may show a number of others symptoms besides the white or yellowish cysts on the body. These include excess production of mucus, lethargy, or lack of hunger which over time causes the koi to look emaciated. It may also spend more time around areas rich in oxygen, such as airstones or water returns to the pond.

Treatment

There is no treatment for this disease currently available, so as soon as it is identified all infected fish must be moved to a quarantine facility. This should be kept exclusively for these fish to prevent the infection of any other fish in quarantine. The koi should be closely monitored and, if their condition worsens, the best course of action is to destroy all of them using an approved and humane form of euthanasia, as they will not recover. It may even be better to destroy all infected koi straight away rather than prolonging the agony by placing them in quarantine. Once this disease has been identified, it is essential that the whole system is sterilized and cleaned thoroughly before restocking.

PAPILLOMA AND CARP POX

Papilloma and carp pox are viral infections which tend to affect koi in periods of lower water temperature. Young koi less than one year old tend not be affected by papilloma and older koi sometimes seem to grow out of it. This is a relatively harmless disease and it does not pose a major threat to your koi. Carp pox and papilloma also have a very low level of infection and so one fish in a pond may show symptoms while the others remain healthy.

Above: This fish has carp pox on the head and face, which is one of the most common areas for it to be found. Despite being unsightly, it will seldom prove a serious health threat to your koi.

Above: A close-up of a pectoral fin showing a small area of carp pox. Fins are areas which are prone to carp pox.

Identification

Carp pox is easily identified by the hard, white, waxy lumps which appear mostly on the fins of the fish and occasionally on the head. On Doitsu or leather koi, carp pox may also be found on the body as it tends to be found on areas lacking scales. Carp pox is often described by professionals and hobbyists alike as if a white candle had been lit and the hot wax allowed to drop onto the koi. Papillomas are similar in appearance to carp pox with large areas appearing on the fins, especially around the hard leading ray. Elsewhere they tend to be smaller with an average size of around 5mm (0.2in), and may be present all over the koi in quite large numbers in some cases. Like carp pox, they may have a white waxy appearance; however, you may also notice tumour-like growths which look red or pink.

Prevention

Carp pox and papilloma are only a problem in cold water temperatures and so, if these can be avoided, you should not experience these diseases. Even if you do suffer an outbreak, it should not be any real cause for alarm as these viral infections are harmless. The worst effect is the unsightly appearance which your koi will take on while the virus is active.

Treatment

There is no cure for carp pox; however, an increase in water temperature may cause the virus to subside and the white waxy lumps to disappear, as the increased water temperature enables the koi to mount an effective immune response against the virus. An increase of around 10°C may be sufficient, however care should be taken to implement this increase over a period of days and even weeks with an increase of 1°C being made every one to two days. Rapid temperature increase should be avoided as this will be very stressful for the fish and could result in other diseases occurring, especially parasite infections such as whitespot. The symptoms of carp pox may well disappear with this increase in temperature, but this does not mean that the koi in question is free from the disease. White waxy lumps may suddenly appear again in the future, generally during a period of lower water temperature.

Papilloma responds in the same way as carp

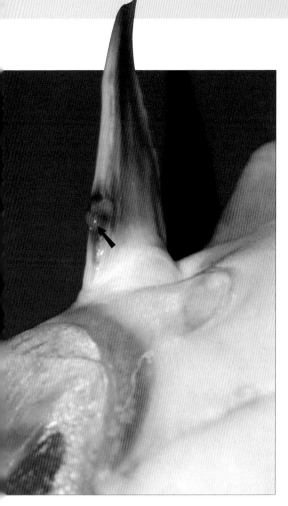

Above: This carp has a papilloma growth on its pectoral fin, which has started to cause an infection on the front leading ray. Consequently it requires removing.

pox: an increase in water temperature normally cures the koi. However, you may need to increase the temperature to over 25°C (77°F). The same precautions should be taken when increasing the temperature as mentioned above. This measure should cause the growths on the koi to disappear over a period of seven to ten days. Papilloma may reveal itself by the presence of tumours with a reddish to pink appearance. These may need to be removed surgically, a job which should be done by a vet or your local koi health specialist. The areas from where these tumours are removed should be topically treated with malachite green and propolis, for example. In extreme cases when a large number are removed, secondary infection may occur which will require additional treatment. Advice should be sought from your local koi health specialist in this case.

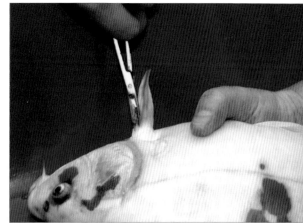

Above: A vet or koi health specialist must carry out this task.

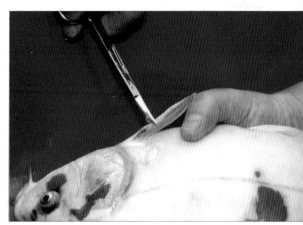

Above: Sterilized scissors are used to cut away the papilloma.

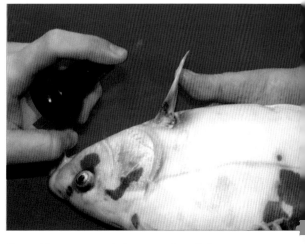

Above: After surgery, topical treatment is applied.

POP-EYE (EXOPHTHALMIA)

This is a condition which affects either one or both eyes, and causes them to stand out from the body as though they were mounted on stalks. If just one eye is pronounced, the chances of a serious problem and losses resulting are much less than if both eyes are affected as this may suggest a more serious (and possibly internal) problem. Pop-eye can be caused by a number of factors including parasitic infections, viral infections, bacterial infections, poor water quality, nutritional deficiency, internal problems and even physical damage.

Identification

Pop-eye is not usually a highly contagious condition and so only one koi may show symptoms at any one time; however, the underlying cause will determine if the condition will prove infectious or not. The tell-tale signs of pop-eye are unmistakable – the eyes stand out from the body, and in extreme cases this can be by over 10mm (0.4in). Remember that a koi's eyes normally protrude slightly from the body, so before assuming that a fish has pop-eye compare it with a known healthy koi. If it is pop-eye, it is vital to establish what the cause of the problem is. Stress is the most common trigger and poor water quality is the main culprit. This should be the first avenue to investigate. If water quality proves fine, think about any changes that have occurred; even events like the introduction of one or two new koi can be enough to trigger pop-eye in some fish.

You may also find that a particular koi develops pop-eye at certain times of the year every year, and this may simply coincide with seasonal changes in water temperature. If you also notice that areas of scales are lifting, or if the koi has gone off its food, is starting to waste or there seems to be swelling, it could be that a bacterial or viral infection is causing the problem. It could also be linked to the onset of dropsy. Internal problems are another trigger and these can be anything from a build up of fluid, to organ failure or even a tumour. As these causes are internal, it is often difficult to identify them precisely. As long as they do not result in the onset of a more serious bacterial infection or even dropsy, the condition may still clear up of its own accord.

Prevention

Simple good husbandry is a must – if excellent water conditions are maintained at all times, and other stress factors are avoided, the likelihood of pop-eye developing are dramatically reduced. The use of a pond heating system can also help in reducing stress as a constant temperature can be maintained throughout the year. The use of a good well-balanced koi food will also help in prevention as this condition can be triggered by a poor diet, especially if the vitamins A and/or E are lacking. When buying new koi, avoid any showing signs of pop-eye.

Treatment

As pop-eye is generally not contagious, it is not important to isolate the affected koi. In fact the koi generally improve faster if kept in their normal environment as this will generally have better filtration and be more stable than most quarantine or isolation facilities. Try to get at the underlying cause. Often a simple water test will show a high level of ammonia, and once this has

The eyes of this young koi are starting to stand out from the head.

Right: This koi has severe pop-eye, and at this advanced stage it should easily be identifiable in your pond by the protrusion of either one or both eyes.

Left: Pop-eye in its early stages can be hard to spot, and may go unnoticed for a while. However, early identification can lead to more successful treatment.

cases, antibiotic eye drops may be suggested. For more severe cases antibiotic injections will be required and it will be necessary to anaesthetize the koi in question to avoid any undue stress. Usually only one koi will be affected even if a bacterial or viral infection is responsible. However, if other koi start to show symptoms you may wish to treat the pond with a anti-bacterial medication such as Acriflavine at the dose recommended on the bottle (as this will be dependent upon the strength of the solution mix), or potassium permanganate at the dose of 1.5g per 1000 litres (220 gallons), or Chloramine T at the dose of 1g per 1000 litres (220 gallons) or an off-the-shelf product intended for bacterial infections. If both eyes are protruding and scale lifting and swelling are noticed, the koi may have dropsy and the recommended treatments for dropsy should be followed. Another option is to give the fish a salt bath of 100g (3.5oz) of salt per 4.5 litres (1 gallon) of water for 10 minutes. This will help to release any fluid which may be causing internal pressure. This can be done once a day for three consecutive days.

been remedied via small water changes with conditioned, dechlorinated tapwater allied to a reduction in food levels until optimum water conditions are re-established, the condition will normally cure itself. Once this, and other possible causes such as poor diet, have been ruled out, it may be necessary to treat with anti-bacterials as a bacterial problem may be behind the outbreak. If bactericides are required, seek advice from a qualified professional as to what should be used, and at what dose, and how it should be administered. In non-advanced and localized

SWIMBLADDER DISORDERS AND AIR GULPING

A fish's swimbladder is the organ which is used to maintain buoyancy and stability in the water, and a koi with symptoms of a swimbladder disorder will have difficulty in swimming normally. Swimbladder problems can occur simply of their own accord or they can be triggered by another health problem, such as a tumour, egg retention, internal fluid build-up, or even bacterial infection. In such cases once this problem is cured, the chances are that the swimbladder problem will also disappear as long as no internal damage has occurred to the organ itself. The most common cause of swimbladder disorder is a rapid decrease in temperature. This is why many koi keepers with unheated ponds will experience this problem during the colder months of winter, only to find that it rectifies itself once spring arrive.

Air gulping occurs when a koi takes in too much air to the extent that it becomes bloated. As a consequence it may start to show the same symptoms of a swimbladder disorder. This condition, however, normally corrects itself after a short period of time.

Below: Here a large Chagoi suffering from a swimbladder disorder is unable to move below the water surface.

Identification

Typical symptoms of swimbladder problems result in a koi either floating at the surface or sitting on the bottom of the pond, and in some cases even listing from side to side. The koi will still be able to swim but the effort required to do so may prove far greater than normal, and once stationary the koi may simply float or sink back to its previous position. Koi may also swim with their tail end higher, looking as if they are permanently in a nose dive position. Generally a swimbladder disorder on its own is not a cause for any great alarm. In most cases an affected koi will survive quite happily, although it may maintain an unusual position in the water. However, if the fish is unable to take food, or if it spends large amounts of time on the bottom and develops pressure sores that will prove susceptible to secondary infection, it may be necessary to consider euthanasia for the fish. If you suspect that air gulping is the cause of the buoyancy problems, you should notice that the affected fish only suffers with these problems periodically, unlike a true swimbladder problem which will continue to cause the fish problems until the disorder is rectified.

Above: A koi with swimbladder problems may not just sink or float within the pond; it may also have trouble maintaining an upright position in the water, as shown here. For a conclusive confirmation that the swimbladder is the cause of this, a vet may have to perform an X-ray.

Prevention and Treatment

The reason that we have grouped these two topics together is that many of the possible treatments for swimbladder problems are in fact preventative measures. The best course of action to prevent swimbladder problems from occurring is to maintain a stable temperature throughout the year, and the use of a pond heating system is the ideal way of doing this. If your pond is not heated and a koi develops swimbladder problems, you may want consider installing a heating system and then raising the temperature slowly by one or two degrees C every day or so. The affected koi can be left in the pond as swimbladder disorders (unless they are the result of another infection) are not contagious.

Another measure to help the koi to regain the correct function of its swimbladder is to lift it off the bottom and maintain it in a floating net or cage within the pond. This should be relatively shallow to keep the koi in question near the surface. Salt baths are another option – a dose rate of 22g per litre (3.5 oz per gallon) should be used for ten minutes. This can be done up to three times, with a bath being given on three successive days. Should bathing prove to be impractical, salt can be added to the pond at a dose rate of 3g per litre (0.5oz per gallon). However, be sure to test the salt levels and ideally reduce them to zero before using other medications, such as formalin. Formalin and salt work in the same way by stripping parasites and mucus from the koi's skin, and if you use both at the same time the fish may be burnt. If the affected koi is of particular value, it may be worth locating a specialist fish vet as he may try to reinflate or deflate the swimbladder. However, this procedure may have only limited success and must always be carried out be a qualified person.

With regards to air gulping, the best approach is to limit situations in which air is taken in, which happens most commonly during feeding. Nowadays a feed mix comprising 50 per cent floating and 50 per cent sinking food is recommended and this combination should help to reduce the occurrence of this problem, as no air will be taken from the surface when the fish consume a sinking food. Indeed you might want to use only sinking food, but take care then to ensure that the food is not extracted from the pond by bottom drains or pumps before the koi get a chance to eat it.

TAPEWORM INFESTATIONS

There are numerous species of tapeworm, but the main species that affects koi is a member of the *Bothriocephalus* genus, *Bothriocephalus acheilognathi*. These seldom prove a threat to koi, and can be almost impossible to detect because they are present in the intestines of the koi, so making external signs of an infestation hard to spot until its later stages. As the worm develops in the intestine, the host koi may appear very thin and undernourished, and in extreme cases you may see the parasitic worm exiting the vent of the koi. Obviously, when purchasing, avoid any koi showing these signs of an advanced infestation.

Life Cycle

Bothriocephalus are parasitic worms and in their adult stages they attain lengths of 15-23cm (6-9in) and have a body width of 3mm (0.1in) within the intestine of a koi. They have a white ribbon-like appearance, but are generally only seen when a fish undergoes a post-mortem. Before they reach this size they must complete a complex life cycle. Firstly a fish already infected with a tapeworm excretes waste containing eggs of the internal worm into the water, and after a time they turn into free-swimming larvae. These newly hatched larvae must then find a host in which to develop further. This host is often a

The life cycle of a tapeworm (*Bothriocephalus*)

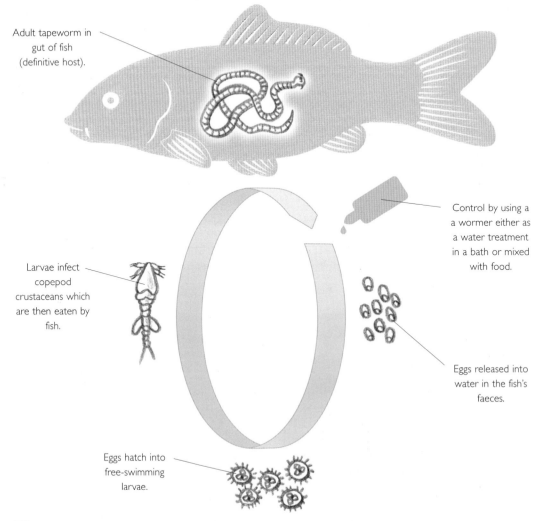

Adult tapeworm in gut of fish (definitive host).

Control by using a a wormer either as a water treatment in a bath or mixed with food.

Larvae infect copepod crustaceans which are then eaten by fish.

Eggs released into water in the fish's faeces.

Eggs hatch into free-swimming larvae.

Right: The typical koi hobbyist will be very unlikely to see a tapeworm. Generally they are only observed when a post-mortem is performed,

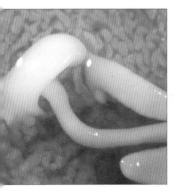

Above: Tapeworms in koi can reach up to 23cm (9in) in length inside the intestine of the fish.

copepod which may simply eat the larvae, which triggers the next stage of development. A copepod is a free-living crustacean (and hence is related to anchor worms and freshwater fleas), which may be naturally present in any body of water, but in a pond they are generally introduced on plants or live food. If the copepod happens to be eaten by a koi harbouring the larvae, there is chance of infection.

Prevention

The best preventative measure is to avoid the introduction of any koi which already have an infestation of *Bothriocephalus* sp. But as there are seldom external signs of infection, in reality this can prove very difficult. The next step to take is to ensure that the copepod host is not present. This is difficult because copepods may just suddenly appear, but steps can be taken to keep their numbers low to prevent such an event. You can avoid adding plants to your pond, and steer clear of live food as both may harbour copepods. If you do favour plants and live food, make sure that you disinfect them first. Improved maintenance of your pond, resulting in a decrease in the organic matter present, may also help, i.e. aim to improve the discharges of your filters to remove fish waste. Finally, avoid introducing koi from wild lakes

and rivers as these will have been more exposed to parasites such as *Bothriocephalus* sp.

Treatment

In a well-maintained pond the hosts needed to complete the life cycle of tapeworms are not always present and so treatment is not needed. If a newly purchased koi is infected with a tapeworm, infection of your other koi is very unlikely as long as copepods are not present. After a time the internal worm of the infected koi will die, and thus reinfection cannot occur. Overall these worms are a small threat to the average pond keeper and as long as a good, clean and well-maintained system is kept they are unlikely to be encountered. They are more of a problem for the fish farmer and breeder. Should you feel that treatment is required, you may wish to use a proprietary worming treatment either as a water treatment at the rate recommended by the manufacturer, or mixed with the food – in which case seek expert advice. Some wormers can be purchased as an injectable solution which may prove more effective on larger koi. Such an injection should be given intra-muscularly and assistance should be sought from your vet or local koi health specialist who will determine the dose rate for the koi in question and administer it.

TRICHODINA

Trichodina is an external parasite which is found commonly on all koi varieties, especially at times of temperature change, such as autumn going into winter when the water temperature falls, and again when winter moves into spring and the temperature rises. *Trichodina* is also found more profusely in poorly maintained systems where mulm and sediment have been allowed to build up in the pond and filter.

Identification

Trichodina is a protozoan parasite which is only visible under a microscope, as its average size is just 0.07mm (0.003in). It looks like a small circle from which a number of hooks will be seen, inside a larger circle and it may be spinning and moving at quite high speed. *Trichodina* live on the skin of the fish and attach themselves to a host koi by the use of hooks and holding discs.

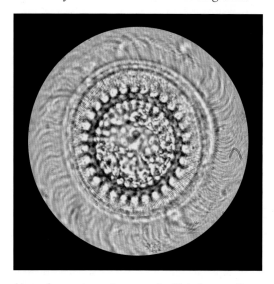

Above: Seen under a microscope, the *Trichodina* parasite looks like a small circle with hooks attached.

Large numbers of trichodinids can damage the koi's skin making it prone to attack by bacteria. This in turn aids the growth and spread of *Trichodina* as they will use these bacteria as a food source. *Trichodina* will readily swim from koi to koi, and, if conditions allow, will multiply quickly by a process of division. Mature infected koi may not show any obvious signs of disease despite having a heavy infestation. Koi under one year of age are more susceptible to severe *Trichodina* infestation and they may exhibit

numerous symptoms. The initial indication that something is wrong is generally flicking and rubbing as the fish tries to relieve the irritation caused by these parasites. This behaviour can lead to physical damage which is vulnerable to secondary infection from bacteria and fungus. Younger koi (under one year) will show symptoms very quickly while koi aged two years and more may not show any adverse signs until the infestation levels become much higher.

Other than flicking, the first thing that may draw your attention to a possible *Trichodina* problem will be the fact that the koi start to float just below the surface of the pond. Some koi will look emaciated, and quite often it seems as if the body has become too small for the head of the fish. You may also notice that the koi develops a whiteish appearance, especially around the head area. This is due to excessive amounts of mucus being produced, and in severe cases this mucus may envelop the whole fish causing it to become very lethargic and weak. In such cases it is normally pulled towards any drains or skimmers within the pond. *Trichodina* can also attack the gills and then you may well see your koi seeking the oxygen-rich water around waterfalls or airstones. You may occasionally also see the koi shake its head rapidly as if it were trying to remove a blockage. With gill infestations the fish become very lethargic and weak, and they also will be drawn towards skimmers and drains.

Below and above right: A koi with a *Trichodina* infection – the skin tissue around the eye has been eaten away.

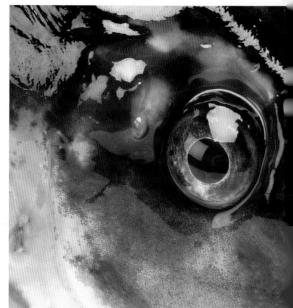

If not spotted early, areas of damage caused by *Trichodina* are susceptible to secondary infection.

Prevention

The installation of a heating system in the pond will help prevent fluctuations in temperature, and thus remove the prime times when *Trichodina* may be a problem. Good husbandry and regular inspections of the filters also ensure that only limited amounts of debris are allowed to collect, as debris build-up can contribute to heavy infestations. Finally *Trichodina* will happily travel from koi to koi and may be introduced on plants, live food, wildlife and new fish. So steps should be taken to disinfect any plants or live food, and you should avoid purchasing any koi showing the symptoms of *Trichodina*. If in doubt, a period of quarantine or a precautionary bath (see below) should be employed before introducing the new purchase to your existing collection.

Treatment

If left untreated severe outbreaks of *Trichodina* will kill. Even if it is not fatal, the bacterial infections which generally follow often are. If you suspect *Trichodina*, a skin scrape will need to be carried out and examined under microscope. If a positive identification is made, an appropriate course of medication needs to be followed. For *Trichodina* infections use potassium permanganate at a dose of 1.5g per 1000 litres (220 gallons). This can be repeated if required at five to seven day intervals for three weeks maximum.

An alternative to the use of potassium permanganate is to give a two per cent salt bath – 20kg of salt per 1000 litres (44lb per 220 gallons) for ten to twenty minutes. It is also important that any secondary infections are topically treated with propolis plus a suitable bactericide. If severe ulceration starts to appear, further treatment may be required and this should be discussed with your vet or koi health specialist.

WHITESPOT

Whitespot, as this disease is often known, is caused by the protozoan parasite *Ichthyophthirius multifiliis*. This disease is a common problem which will be encountered by most koi keepers, and is easily dealt with if identified early. Whitespot is temperature-dependent and infections are only likely to occur when the water temperature is below 28°C (82°F). The whitespot parasites will attack a koi by breaking through the top layer of skin (epidermis) and gills, and then attaching themselves to the koi, where they feed on blood and skin tissue by continually moving in a circular manner. Once the parasite has reached maturity, it will fall from the fish and seek a suitable area of the pond to attach itself, where it will develop into a cyst, which is the reproductive stage.

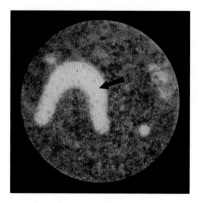

Above: The whitespot parasite as viewed through a microscope on a skin scrape.

Whitespot reproduces by division, and within this cyst many hundreds of new whitespot parasites are produced. At this early stage they are highly infective. These new whitespot or "swarmers" will then leave the cyst and become free-swimming as they try and find a new host to attack. If, however, no host is found within 48 hours they will die. If a new host is found, the whitespot will resume the attack by breaking through the top layer of skin, and they will remain in situ for up to 20 days (possibly more), before the cycle starts all over again. This life cycle is governed by temperature – the complete process takes longer at lower temperatures, and in winter months in an unheated pond the parasite may lay dormant for many months. By contrast, at higher temperatures the whole life cycle is speeded up – it can take place in as little as four days at temperatures of 21°C (70°F).

Identification

Very early stages of whitespot may not produce any visible external signs other than changes in your koi's behaviour. You may notice that a fish starts to clamp fins, becomes lethargic and occasionally rubs against the bottom and walls of the ponds. If these symptoms are noticed, a skin scrape should be performed to allow accurate diagnosis. In later stages of whitespot disease, a few white spots may appear on your koi, and over time these will increase in number so that it looks as if someone has sprinkled salt over the body of the koi. As these white spots increase in number, your koi may start to lose their appetites, and rub vigorously against objects in the pond to try and relieve themselves of the irritation caused by the parasites. They may also start to hang in the water and spend more time near areas of higher oxygen, such as airstones and water returns.

When the disease reaches an advanced stage the whole body of the koi may start to take on a whiteish appearance as large amounts of mucus are produced to try and relieve the irritation. The intensity of the flicking carried out by the affected fish may increase causing numerous physical lesions to appear, and secondary bacterial and fungus infections can set in. At this advanced stage the mature parasites start to leave the koi to reproduce, and areas will be exposed on the body which will be a target for secondary infection. If the disease has reached this stage, you will probably not only be dealing with whitespot, as other parasites and pathogens will take advantage of the situation and start to attack the infected koi. It is sometimes these secondary infections that kill the koi, if no suitable treatment is given.

Prevention

Whitespot will take advantage of situations in which koi become stressed and their immune response becomes weakened, so good husbandry and water management will help to keep the occurrence of this disease to a minimum. Whitespot is also triggered by water temperature change and is a common problem after new koi are added to a pond, as the water temperature is usually different and they will be stressed from transportation. Changes in water temperature are a major contributor to the occurrence of whitespot so the installation of a heating system for your pond will help in maintaining a stable water temperature. Whitespot may also be introduced on plants and live food, so always disinfect these before adding them to the pond. This can be done by dipping the roots of plants and immersing live food in a potassium permanganate bath of 0.8g per 4.5 litres (1 gallon) for five minutes. However, this may have a detrimental effect on more delicate plant species, so it is better to avoid adding plants and live food if possible. Alternatively keep them in a fish-free environment for a week at a temperature of 21°C (70°F) or above as this will cause any cysts to develop into swarmers which will soon die in the absence of fish to infect.

Treatment

Unfortunately when whitespot has reached its mature stage at which it is visible, it is relatively immune to treatment as it is embedded between the top two layers of skin. So when treating

whitespot you must aim to kill the free-swimming stages. There are many off-the-shelf medications formulated for treating whitespot and these can be used with good results. Alternatively malachite green can be used – the dose rate will depend upon the concentration of the mix. The final method of treatment is to increase the water temperature to over 28°C (82°F); this should be done slowly at a rate of 1°C per day to avoid stress caused by rapid temperature change. This temperature should be maintained for a week, in order to terminate the life cycle of whitespot. Do remember that secondary bacterial and fungal infections may have occurred and these will need topical treatment with fungicides, bactericides and propolis. Koi which survive an attack tend to develop a degree of immunity to the parasite.

Whitespot life cycle (*Ichthyophthirius multifiliis*)

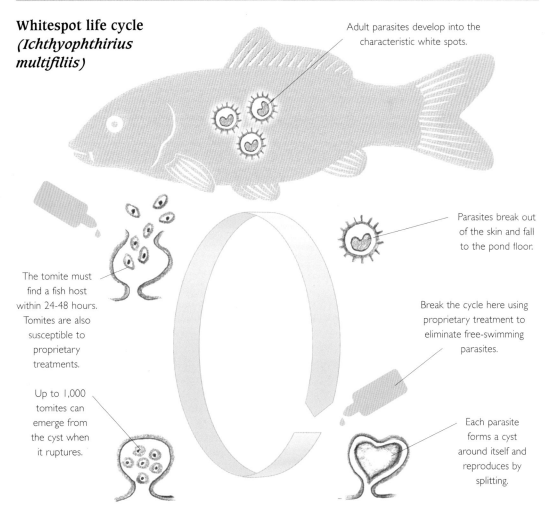

Adult parasites develop into the characteristic white spots.

Parasites break out of the skin and fall to the pond floor.

The tomite must find a fish host within 24-48 hours. Tomites are also susceptible to proprietary treatments.

Break the cycle here using proprietary treatment to eliminate free-swimming parasites.

Up to 1,000 tomites can emerge from the cyst when it ruptures.

Each parasite forms a cyst around itself and reproduces by splitting.

125

OTHER HEALTH PROBLEMS – AN OVERVIEW

Blood Parasites

These are not often a problem for the general koi keeper, and in fact the chances of them even being identified are slim, because a koi needs to go through an extensive post-mortem for an exact identification to be made. Signs of this type of infection include loss of appetite leading to

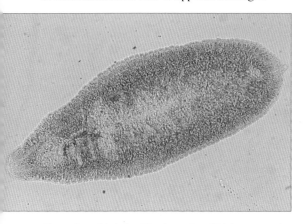

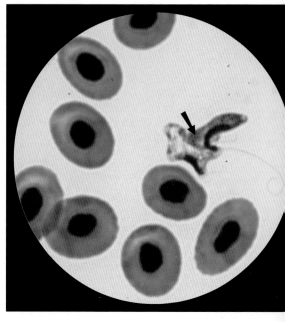

Above: *Sanguinicola* is a blood parasite which is very rarely experienced as a problem by the average koi keeper. Here it can be seen viewed under a microscope .

Above: For an exact identification of *Trypanoplasma* to be made a specialist must be contacted. Once again, this is seldom a problem for the average koi hobbyist.

rapid weight loss, an emaciated appearance, gill damage, internal damage, and even pop-eye. All these are common symptoms of numerous other diseases which makes positive identification of these parasites even harder. If you want to research blood parasites further, the common culprits are *Trypanosoma* and *Trypanoplasma* which can be spread by leeches in a pond. The other blood parasite which may be encountered is the bloodworm *Sanguinicola*. In its developmental stages this needs an aquatic snail as an intermediate host. So eradicating the presence of all snails will help to prevent this parasite from causing problems. Blood parasites are extremely hard to treat. If a positive identification is made, seek professional advice from either your vet, the laboratory which carried out the tests, or a suitably qualified professional as to the best course of treatment.

Dragonfly Larvae and Frogs

In their larval stage dragonfly live in water, and so your pond is an ideal environment for them to grow to maturity. Although not a threat to large, mature koi, small fry and juvenile koi may be

attacked by predatory dragonfly larvae. It is virtually impossible to stop dragonfly from visiting your pond and so all you can do is to check regularly for the presence of larvae. However, a typical unplanted koi pond is unlikely to be the chosen habitat for dragonfly; they are far more likely to seek out a heavily planted or more natural pool. The other way these creatures can find their way into your pond is on plants and live food, so extra care should be taken to ensure that such items are thoroughly washed and checked before being added.

Very occasionally frogs may also prove a problem in the mating season when they may become over-amorous and try and attach themselves to an unsuspecting koi. Although in most cases the frog will soon realize its mistake and let go, physical damage may occur and this may require subsequent treatment. In very extreme cases it has been said that frogs can attach themselves so tightly to the fish that they actually block the gills and can suffocate the koi – it must be stressed that this is extremely rare. In the unlikely event that you witness a frog attaching itself to a koi, give it a chance to let go of its own accord, and then take steps to remove the frog by hand. It is impossible to prevent wildlife from visiting your pond; all you can do is keep a watchful eye, and perhaps make the pond unattractive to wildlife to discourage their presence.

Fish Tuberculosis (TB)

This is another disease (caused by mycobacteria) which is very unlikely to affect the average koi keeper. If it ever is identified, great care should be taken when dealing with it, as this disease is a zoonosis, meaning that there is a chance of infection spreading to humans. Signs of a possible infection of fish by mycobacteria include rapid weight loss and the apparent wasting of the infected koi, combined with a drastic loss of appetite. Again symptoms include many other signs which are also indicative of other more

common diseases, and these are more likely in most instances to be the culprits rather than fish TB. These symptoms include areas of reddening on the skin, which may then turn into small ulcerations, pop-eye, excessive periods of hanging in the water, clamped fins, and possibly erratic swimming behaviour. The only way an exact diagnosis can be made is to send away a fish for testing. If you get a positive identification, seek advice from your vet. Regrettably even koi which show no symptoms may be carrying the infection, so many consider the best course of action is to destroy all current stock, and then thoroughly disinfect the whole system and any equipment used with it. Then allow it to dry thoroughly before restocking. However, although many cases may go undetected and undiagnosed, this disease appears to be very uncommon in koi and should not be a major cause of alarm.

Above: Improbable as it may seem, cases have been reported of over-amorous frogs attaching themselves to unwary koi during the mating season. They usually let go without any human intervention being needed.

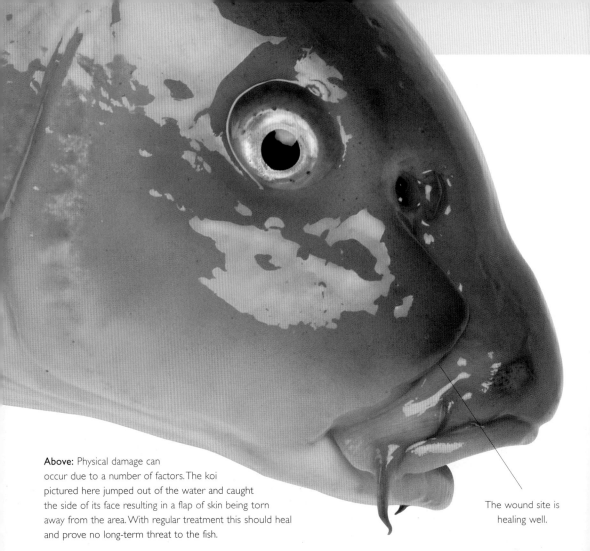

Above: Physical damage can occur due to a number of factors. The koi pictured here jumped out of the water and caught the side of its face resulting in a flap of skin being torn away from the area. With regular treatment this should heal and prove no long-term threat to the fish.

The wound site is healing well.

Physical Damage

This is a common problem for the koi keeper, and can be caused by anything from bumping into sharp rocks, bad netting, spawning activity, and poor transportation to attack by predators, such as herons, magpies or crows. The best step to take to avoid the occurrence of physical damage is to reduce the objects in the pond on which the koi can damage themselves. If predators like herons are a problem, consider netting the pond or installing a suitable deterrent device. If spotted early most physical damage can easily be treated with topical application of malachite green and propolis. However, if unnoticed for any length of time, bacterial or fungal infections may develop and these may need further treatment, possibly including the use of anti-bacterials and fungicides. Obvious signs of physical damage include missing scales, areas of reddening, split fins, and grazes on non-scaled areas, such as around the mouth or all over Doitsu koi.

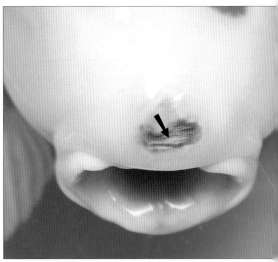

Above: This koi has damage around the mouth which may have happened either in transit (bag rub) or due to feeding around the edge of the pond and rubbing its face.

Sleeping Sickness of Koi

This is a problem which may be experienced by koi keepers with an unheated pond in the very cold months of winter when water temperatures may fall to only a few degrees above freezing. It is not a clinical disease as such, rather a term that is used to describe a particular behavioural abnormality. This condition usually only affects young koi – koi over two years of age may not show any symptoms at all. Typically the koi appear to be dead, and simply lie on the bottom showing no signs of movement. The cold temperature has the effect of dramatically reducing their metabolism so they may not appear to be breathing as the gill movement is so slight. However, when stimulated the koi will move slowly but only for a short time, before relapsing into their previous condition. This condition can be treated by adding salt to the pond and raising the water temperature to at least 21°C (70°F). If sleeping sickness is suspected, the temperature can be raised rapidly at a rate of 3-4°C every day or two as prolonged exposure to low temperatures dramatically reduces the chances of recovery from this condition. While doing this salt can be added at a dose rate of up to 6kg per 1000 litres (13lb per 220 gallons), but after ten days this will need to be reduced to a lower level through water changes. Although this condition is sometimes experienced by the hobbyist, it is more of a problem for farmers and breeders who keep vast stocks of young fish. If not treated quickly, losses should be expected.

Sunburn

Koi with areas of white pigmentation are susceptible to sunburn, and this is characterized by a reddening of the white pigment; in extreme cases blistering may occur. The best way to stop this happening is to provide adequate shade over the pond. The whole pond need not be covered but at least an area of it should be. An alternative approach is to build a pergola over

Above: Though they look dead, these fish are just suffering from sleeping sickness. As year-round heating becomes more popular with the serious koi hobbyist, outbreaks of this condition become less likely.

the pond, and use greenhouse shading or shaded polycarbonate to reduce the levels of direct sunlight which can get to the pond. This will have the added benefit of reducing green water and blanketweed growth. If a koi does develop sunburn, avoid the use of harsh medications on the affected area as this may aggravate the situation. The simple application of propolis should be sufficient to clear things up. Just keep an eye on the affected koi to ensure that no secondary infections occur, such as fungus or bacterial infections. Should these arise, take the necessary steps to treat them, i.e. further topical treatment, or in the case of bacterial infection seek expert advice.

TREATMENTS

In this final section the ways in which you can treat your koi will be described and illustrated. This section also explains what medications and treatments are available, what they look like, and how they should be used. Many of the treatments can be obtained from your local koi specialist or vet. However, in recent years some countries have started to impose tight controls on certain medications. For example, in some countries, including the UK, the use and sale of organophosphates are banned, while in others the use of chemicals such as malachite green is under tight control. Many branded medications are available which claim to be as effective as these banned chemicals. So if you live in a country where there are controls in place, permitted off-the-shelf products will have to be your next (and only) option. As improvements are continually made, they may well prove a good option too.

It is vital that you find a good vet or koi specialist, and form a strong relationship with them to ensure that you can obtain medications and services when needed. If all other avenues of treatment fail, it may be necessary to use antibiotics as a last resort and these will have to be obtained from your local vet. However, before antibiotics are ever used, a full sensitivity test must be obtained by taking a swab. Administering the wrong antibiotic is as bad as giving none at all, and if it is given for a prolonged period it will encourage a resistance to that particular drug to build up. The only exception is when a koi is so ill that the delay in waiting for swab results is unacceptable and immediate selection of the "best guess" antibiotic is needed. It must be stressed that antibiotics should not be used without the guidance of your vet or koi health specialist. Do be aware that the treatments mentioned here are all potentially harmful if they fall into the wrong hands, and so all medications and treatments must be kept securely. Make sure that:

- Medicines are kept out of the sight and reach of children and animals.
- All bottles are clearly marked, with the appropriate health and safety information.
- All bottles have a safety lid to prevent children

from opening them, should they fall into their hands. **Never** mix up a powder-based medication and, finding that you have some left, decant it into an empty soft-drinks bottle!
- When not in use, the storage area where all medications are housed should be locked.
- After treatment, be sure to tidy away thoroughly making sure that any spillages are cleaned up, and any unused medication and used apparatus, such as syringes, are disposed of in the correct way

In addition, when using these treatments it is essential that you take all necessary steps to protect yourself and the surrounding area. Many of the treatments will stain anything with which they come into contact and these stains can prove virtually impossible to remove. Any buckets or containers which are used for mixing will be stained, so it is a good idea to keep separate containers which are just for pond use. Furthermore any buckets or watering cans which have contained other chemicals, like weedkiller, should be avoided. You should wear rubber gloves, and ideally an apron or some form of protective clothing. When using some medications, such as those which are powders or give off fumes, it is also advisable to wear a face mask, as well as ensuring that the treatment area is well ventilated. Finally the wearing of eye protection is sensible, as many chemicals can cause serious injury if they get into your eyes, and wash your hands after handling chemicals.

Before actually administering any medication, it is vital that the expiry or use-by date should be checked as many chemicals may become more toxic with time or simply be ineffective. When administering any of the treatments described, be sure to allow yourself enough time to do it carefully. Once you are happy that you have made all necessary preparations, you can start treating your koi. But please remember, this should always be under the guidance of, and for some procedures the supervision of, your vet or koi health specialist.

Right: Here an area of infection is receiving topical treatment to encourage healing.

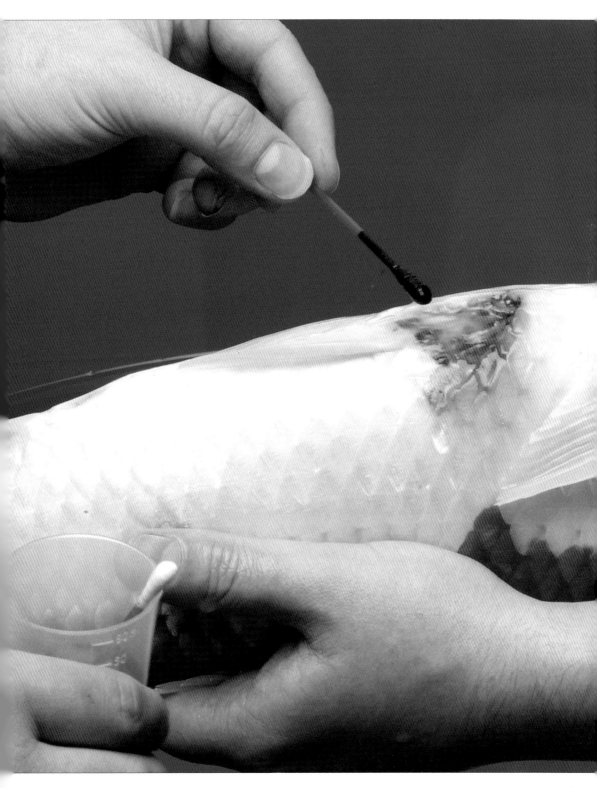

SEDATING YOUR FISH

Times may arise when it is necessary to sedate (anaesthetize) your koi either for treatment or simply to allow easier handling. There are many reasons for sedating your koi including:

1 To calm a koi down and prevent it from struggling and hurting itself.
2 To reduce levels of stress to which a fish is exposed during a procedure.
3 To suppress pain, as many sedating agents have analgesic properties.

It is important to remember that fish probably do experience pain. Anyone who has applied a topical treatment to a open wound is likely to confirm that the koi may flinch or struggle as it is applied, so it must be sensing some form of discomfort, which may be interpreted by us as pain. Therefore it is important that all steps be taken to limit exposure to situations which may prove painful. This is where sedating agents become a useful tool for both vets and skilled koi health professionals when certain procedures are being undertaken.

The actual process of sedating a fish is one which needs to be learned and thus initially your vet, or koi health specialist, must carry out the procedure. It is only after careful guidance and training from such professionals that you will be able to sedate your own koi successfully. Remember sedating your koi is both a stressful and potentially dangerous procedure for the fish – if too much sedating agent is used and the fish is left in it for too long, it will die. Proper training in the use of sedating agents is vital.

Available Sedating Agents

Numerous sedating agents are available but the most popular for use with koi are MS222 (also known as tricaine methane sulphonate, TMS), 2-

1: Pour enough water into a container to cover the koi.

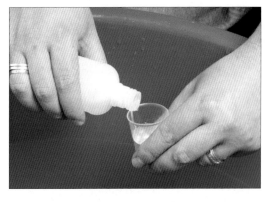

2: Measure out the sedating agent and mix in thoroughly.

3: Place the koi to be sedated into treated water.

4: As the koi is sedated, it will start to list on to its side.

phenoxyethanol (or phenoxytol as it is more commonly known), and benzocaine although this must be dissolved in acetone before it can be used. Other sedating agents are available under various brand names depending upon the manufacturer. This type of product must be obtained from a specialist koi dealer or vet.

IMPORTANT NOTICE

If you wish to take a skin scrape or even a swab from a fish, do not sedate it as this may have the effect of reducing the number or activity of any parasites or bacteria present. This may lead you to think that the fish is either clean or harbours only dead parasites or bacteria.

Once suitably trained in using sedating agents by your vet or koi health specialist, the process of sedating (anaesthetizing) a fish is as follows:

1 Measure an amount of pond water into a suitable container, such as a blue bowl large enough for the fish. The amount of water should be kept to a minimum but be enough to completely cover the fish in question.

2 Add enough sedating agent for the volume of water in the bowl, and then mix thoroughly. If using phenoxytol this may take some time because of the oily nature of the liquid. In some cases it may be impossible to dissolve it fully.

3 Once the sedating agent is fully mixed, catch the fish to be treated and move it to the bowl. Once the fish is in the mixture it is vital that you keep a careful watch on its behaviour to ensure that it is removed at the right time. You should see the following signs:

i Fish swims around normally, but reactions start to become slower.

ii Fish stops swimming but is still able to maintain its position in the water.

iii Fish starts to sway from side to side but when upright it can just maintain its position in the water. Gill movement may appear to be slow.

iv Fish starts to lie on its side for longer periods, and appears to be unable to correct its position to upright. However, upon placing your hand in the water to lift the fish, it will try and swim off.

v Fish becomes completely motionless, apart from very slow, and sometimes irregular, gill movement. As this point the fish should not make any attempt to struggle and thus it can be lifted from the bowl ready for treatment or inspection.

If you were to leave the fish in the sedating agent longer, it will eventually lead to cardiac arrest. Thus sedating agents can be used as a humane way of destroying sick or badly damaged fish by simply leaving them in the mixed solution for an hour or two (see page 135).

4 Once you have finished with the sedated fish, it can be returned to the pond or a recovery tank or bowl which should contain the same water as the pond. The water at this point should be heavily oxygenated to aid the recovery process. If using a recovery tank or bowl, the sedated koi should be kept in here until normal breathing is established. When returning the fish to the pond it is advisable to hold the fish in a stream of air to provide a rich supply of oxygen to the gills. The fish can also be gently coaxed back and forth in the water to aid the water flow over the gills. After a couple of minutes the fish should start to show signs of returning to normal, i.e. fin movement, and regular gill movement. At this point you can simply let the fish swim away into the pond. However, keep an eye on it to ensure that it does not get pulled towards any drains or other water outlets while it is regaining its full strength. This whole process usually takes five to ten minutes after which it should have completely recovered and returned to normal.

Above left and right: If the sedated koi does not come around by holding it in a stream of oxygen-rich water, use your fingers to open and shut the mouth gently

Left and above: To speed recovery after sedation, a fish can be gently massaged between the pectoral fins and moved to and fro in the water to improve water flow over the gills.

5 If for some reason, the fish does not come round when put back in the pond the following steps should be taken. While holding the fish in the water by an airstone or venturi, use your fingers to open and close the mouth gently. This helps to push oxygen-rich water over the gills. While doing this move the fish back and forth in the water, as this again helps the flow of water over the gills. You may find it easier to do this by holding the fish belly up, and you may also rub the area between the pectoral fins gently, as this will assist the passage of water over the gills and speed up recovery. Another procedure which might be employed is to use a small pump or pipette to push water into the mouth and over the gills. It may take some time for a fish to come round, but do not give up. Even after one or two hours, in most cases you can get the fish back!

6 Once you have finished with the sedating agent it should be disposed of. Under no circumstances should it be tipped into the pond; instead it should be safely poured to waste.

This information is only given as a guide. It is essential that, until you are properly trained in the use of sedating agents, a vet or koi health specialist must be employed to carry out the procedure. Once you are trained, you will start to notice how different sizes, sexes and varieties of koi react differently when being sedated. It seems logical that a small fish will go over quicker than a larger fish, but if the larger fish has a high fat content, the reverse may be the case as fat absorbs the sedating agent quicker. You will learn how to adjust the dosage to allow for a fish to be sedated quickly, or if dealing with a large number of fish, when to add more sedating agent as each fish absorbs an amount of the original solution from the water. Using sedating agents is a expert skill and professional assistance is required to learn the procedure. However, knowing how to use sedating agents correctly is valuable. It will increase the number of koi that you can coax back to full health, simply because of the extra time that you will have to administer treatments while they are out of the water, and reduce levels of stress and pain that the fish will experience.

Euthanasia

This subject is often not discussed and this leaves the koi keeper having to make the decision on how best to humanely destroy a diseased or injured koi without appropriate guidance. Some unsuitable methods have been practised but these cause the koi much suffering. Unsuitable methods of euthanasia include:

- Slow freezing by placing the fish (in a container of water) in a domestic freezer. Although still routinely practised, it is now considered unacceptable.
- Dropping the fish into very hot/boiling water.
- Leaving the fish to die out of water.
- Snapping the fish's backbone.

Basically, there are two acceptable methods for putting down a fish:

Sedating Agent Overdose

This is the preferred method for most situations. Fish sedating agents such as MS222 and benzocaine can be administered at a lethal overdose level. MS222 is ideal as it dissolves readily in water. Benzocaine on the other hand must be made up as a "stock" solution in alcohol or acetone before further dilution in water to achieve the desired strength. Ideally, ask your local vet or koi health specialist to perform euthanasia on your fish for you.

If, however, you have no option but to perform this procedure yourself, then ensure you administer the correct dosage of anaesthetic, and seek expert guidance if in any doubt. Select a clean water-tight receptacle that is large enough to accommodate the koi comfortably without it having to bend its body or expose any part of its skin above the water. You will need to know the volume of water added to gauge how much anaesthetic to use. You can fill the receptacle with clean pond water. If using an alternative water source, ensure the water is at the same temperature as the koi's pond. The actual dose of sedating agent required will vary according to the size of fish, the water temperature and other factors. As an approximate guide, 0.3 to 0.5g per litre of MS222 will kill most types of fish. Add the koi after mixing in the sedating agent and cover the receptacle. The sedating agent may take 15-20 minutes to kill the fish (sometimes longer) but it is recommended to leave the fish in it for an hour or so, just to be sure. Closely inspect the fish to ensure that all bodily activity (including movement of the gill covers and mouth) has fully ceased before removing it. As a final measure to ensure that the koi is dead, it can be concussed.

Concussion

If no sedating agent is to hand and a fish needs to be put out of its misery quickly, then death by concussion must be considered. The koi is removed from the water and its body (not the head) wrapped in a sheet of soft tissue paper. The fish is gently held on a firm solid surface and its head struck with a heavy object. The aim is to swiftly and fatally damage the brain. This may seem barbaric but is actually fast and effective when performed correctly. If you feel at all uneasy about this procedure, don't attempt it; a half-hearted strike may be unsuccessful and cause even more suffering.

Left: An anaesthetic overdose provides a humane way of killing a severely injured or diseased fish.

TOPICALLY TREATING WOUNDS

This is a treatment that you may need to administer to your koi quite often. Depending on the severity of the condition being treated, you may need to set aside time once or twice a week for it to be done. Topical treatment means treating the area on a fish that is affected rather than treating the whole pond. The advantages are that you are not subjecting the pond to continual treatment which may encourage resistance to certain medications to build up, and also you are treating the affected areas directly which means they can be inspected and cleaned regularly and so should heal quicker. The need for topical treatment may arise after physical damage has occurred, perhaps during spawning or netting, after a parasite infection when scales may have been dislodged by flicking against the pond to try and relieve the irritation, or after a bacterial infection when ulcers have appeared which need to be kept clean while antibiotics take effect.

The actual medication used for the topical treatment varies. Numerous proprietary sprays and ointments are available off the shelf. If these do not appeal, malachite green can be used as an effective topical treatment. It is used undiluted and applied to the area with a cotton-wool bud. When using malachite green gloves should always be worn to protect your hands from

exposure to it. An alternative to malachite green, or something to be used in conjunction with it, is propolis spray. This is a natural product made by bees which has beneficial healing and anti-oxidant properties. Propolis can be purchased off the shelf in numerous forms, and is in fact found in many of the products offered commercially for the topical treatment of koi. Propolis can simply be sprayed or painted onto the affected area. If the area to be treated is quite badly damaged or resistant to healing, you may wish to apply malachite green or a proprietary brand of topical treatment first, followed by the propolis. When carrying out topical treatment the following procedure should be followed, in conjunction with any guidelines given on the product being used:

1 If the koi is small or easily handled, you may not need to anaesthetize it. Or you may enlist a helper to hold the koi while you administer the topical treatment. However, if the koi is large or the area to be treated looks like it may require some additional attention before the topical treatment is applied, it is best to anaesthetize the koi.
2 Place the koi on a wet towel, and cover its tail and head with the towel as this will help to keep the fish calm. It may be out of the water for some time.

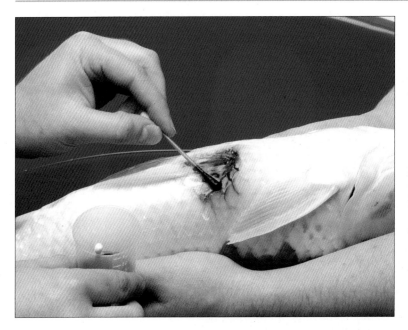

Above left and right: Here a cotton-wool bud is used to apply a topical treatment to an area of infection or physical damage.

Above: Before any topical treatment is applied, check that there is no build-up of fluid under the scales. If the scales are lifted, a small amount of pressure can be applied to help release the fluid.

3 Inspect the area and remove or trim any scales as required. If any of the scales are lifted and feel spongy to the touch, apply a little pressure to them. If any fluid is released, continue to do this until no more fluid appears. You may find it best to do this by running your finger from head to tail over the affected area. You are releasing trapped fluid from under the scales which may contain high levels of bacteria and prevent the affected area from healing. If the area to be

treated is on the head of your koi and there are any loose flaps of skin, these should be cut away with a sterilized pair of scissors. Stitching by a vet may be an alternative option.
4 Take a cotton-wool bud and gently run it over the affected area to remove any excess fluid or moisture.
5 The site can now be treated with your chosen topical treatment. Care should be taken if working near the mouth, eyes or gills to ensure that the medication does not come into contact with these areas. The gills are perhaps the most vulnerable organs here and extra care should be taken to avoid contact with them.
6 Having finished applying the topical treatment, the koi can be returned to the pond. It will, however, need to be treated again in three to four days' time to keep the area clean and encourage healing. As the affected area starts to heal, the frequency of these treatments can be reduced and eventually stopped.

For quick healing to be achieved, the water in which the koi are kept should be maintained at a temperature of at least 18°C (64°F) or above and in optimum condition. This temperature (or higher) combined with excellent water quality will promote healing and speed up recovery.

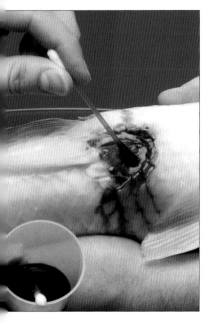

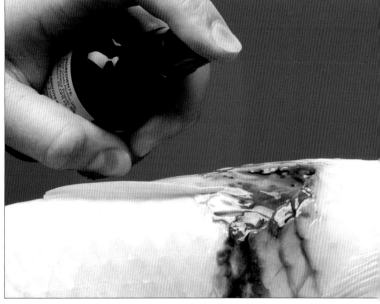

Above: Then propolis spray is applied after the topical treatment.

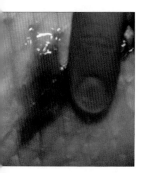

smooth to the touch. If the scale has been dead for some time, algae may be found growing on its rough surface. Some scales may just have dead areas. The way you treat them differs and advice should be sought from a vet or koi health specialist as to the best course of action. The easiest way to check for dead or damaged scales is to run your finger very lightly over the surface of the fish. Any scales which are dead will feel rough all over while ones with just dead areas will be smooth except for the places where the scale is starting to die.

Generally the best way to deal with dead scales is to remove them, but this should not be attempted without the guidance of a vet or your koi health specialist, and ideally they should be employed to carry out this procedure until you are properly trained and confident in performing such tasks. If you leave dead scales in place they may become sites of infection. As long as the scale pocket is not damaged when the scale is removed, there is a high chance that the scale should re-grow although this may take many months and even years. If the scale does re-grow,

1: To check for the presence of any dead scales, very gently run your finger over the surface of the fish. Dead scales will feel rough to the touch.
2: If scales have to be removed for medical reasons, or are lost due to infection or physical damage, the area will develop scar tissue which will be visible once it has healed.

Removal of Scales

While applying any topical treatments to your koi, it is advisable to inspect the area being treated for other potential problems such as dead or damaged scales. Dead scales have the texture of sandpaper unlike a healthy scale which is

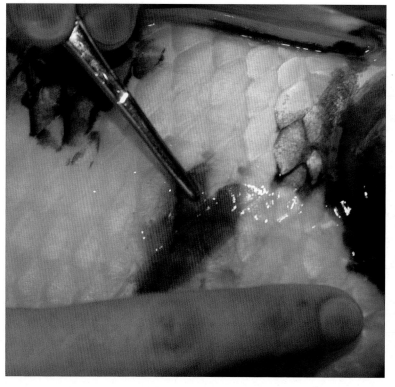

it may not be the same colour as the rest of the area from which it was removed nor exhibit the same intensity of colour.

However, if damage has occurred to the scale pocket through infection or incorrect removal of a dead scale, you may find that new scales do not appear. Instead you are left with a smooth area of skin, which ends up looking like a scar. Some scales may not be completely dead but just contain an area which has died. If this is the case the vet or koi health specialist may choose when treating it to trim the scale by cutting away the dead area rather than removing the whole scale. After either complete removal of a dead scale or trimming of a dead area from a scale, a constant watch should be kept to ensure that no secondary infections occur.

Below (1-3): Here a koi health specialist can be seen removing a dead scale with a sterilized pair of tweezers. This should speed up the recovery of the koi, and may help to prevent further infection from occurring around the site from which the scale was removed.

Treating Fin Damage

When examining areas of fin damage caused by an infection, such as fin rot, through exposure to high ammonia or nitrite levels, or because of physical injury, you may find that the fin or fins are only slightly damaged with small tears and that there are no – or only slight – areas of redness. The best approach here is usually to apply a suitable topical treatment. However, if a fin is very red and inflamed, or the infection has reached the base of the fin and is starting to spread into the body, additional treatment will be required and this must be performed by your vet or local koi health specialist. If the fins are heavily frayed and look inflamed and red, but the problem has not reached the body, it may be necessary for the fins to be trimmed to remove the infection. If the infection has reached the body, there is a chance that some of the bones which are present in the fins may need removing. This is not a procedure for the hobbyist, and a koi health professional or vet should always be employed to carry out any such tasks, and advise on any follow-up treatment.

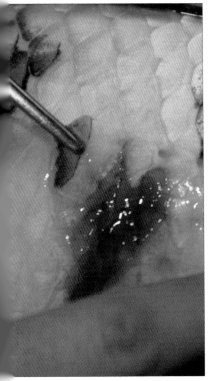
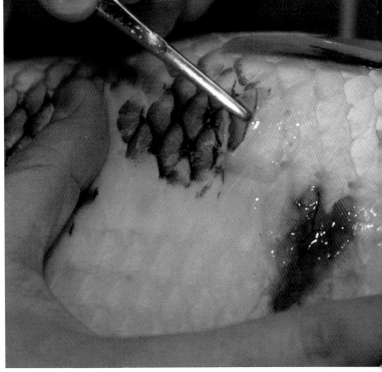

ADMINISTERING ANTIBIOTICS AND INJECTING KOI

Although many antibiotics can be mixed with food, this is generally not the best way of administering them as a sick koi may not be eating. Guidance and advice should always be sought from your local vet or koi health specialist before any decision is made about the use of anti-bacterial medications on sick fish. They may advise that the treatment should be administered in the form of an injection. Very experienced koi keepers may feel confident enough to inject their own fish, but this is potentially a hazardous procedure so we would recommend that you take advice from your vet or koi health specialist on

so they should only be used as a last resort after all other avenues of treatment have been exhausted. It is also worth bearing in mind that whenever antibiotics are injected there is also a small associated risk of secondary infection at the injection site as the skin is punctured when the needle is inserted. You must weigh the koi to be injected in order to work out the correct dose, and for this an accurate set of scales is needed. It is easier to weigh your koi if it is sedated as this will both reduce stress and prevent damage from occurring by the fish thrashing about while on

Above: This is a 1ml syringe and is typical of what a vet or koi health specialist will use to inject a sick fish.

the best course of action. In many countries antibiotics are not readily available over the counter but must be purchased from a vet who may need to see the fish for legal reasons before he will prescribe the necessary drugs. If you are experienced enough to perform injections yourself, it is a good idea to acquire syringes when picking up the antibiotic as they may also have to be obtained from a vet. Ideally use 0.5ml insulin syringes which come with a pre-attached needle. For bigger koi which require larger amounts of antibiotics you may be better off with a larger syringe which has a separate needle.

There is always a risk involved with antibiotics, and some can have a harmful effect on internal organs, especially the kidneys, and

the scales. It is vital that either your vet or koi health specialist assists with the sedating procedure unless you have been properly instructed in how to do it yourself. Once the koi is weighed your vet will be able to calculate the exact dose of the required antibiotic required. Although weighing is the only way of getting an accurate measurement, it can be stressful to the koi, and it is time-consuming to do. For this reason some people use the size of the fish to estimate its weight and work out dosages accordingly. If you choose this option, the following size-to-weight ratios may be used. Please note these figures are only guides, and if the koi is over- or underweight adjustment may be required.

Gauging Weight	Below 15cm (6in) or less, fish are too small to inject.		
In order to work out injection dosages, your koi should either be weighed, or you may use the size of the fish to calculate the required dose, using a table like this. These figures are only guides.	**Size**	**Male**	**Female**
	30cm *(12in)*	0.6kg *(1.3lb)*	0.8kg *(1.8lb)*
	35cm *(14in)*	1kg *(2.2lb)*	1.25kg *(2.75lb)*
	45cm *(18in)*	1.5kg *(3.3lb)*	1.9kg *(4.2lb)*
	50cm *(20in)*	2kg *(4.4lb)*	2.5 to 3kg *(5.5 to 6.6lb)*
	55cm *(22in)*	3kg *(6.6lb)*	4.5kg *(10lb)*
	60cm *(24in)*	4kg *(8.8lb)*	5.5kg to 6kg *(12.1 to 13.2lb)*
	70cm *(28in)*	5kg *(11lb)*	7kg *(15.4lb)*

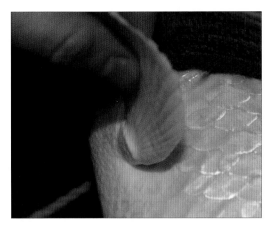

1: Here a koi health specialist can be seen preparing the pectoral muscle ready for injection.

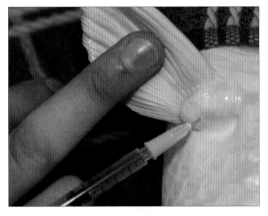

2: The health specialist is now administering the chosen antibiotic via an intra-muscular injection.

3: Finally the injection site is massaged gently to help the dispersion of the medication.

It is best to perform the injection straight after you have weighed the koi to avoid having to sedate it again. Once the koi is sedated, it can either be laid on a wet towel or held against the side of the bowl in which it was sedated, although this does require some practice to get right and should only be attempted once you are confident at handling koi. An injection can be given in two different ways, although intra-muscular injection is normally the safest. Seek advice from your vet or local koi health specialist as to the best method of application. If inexperienced in this procedure, employ your vet or koi health specialist to do it. The preferred delivery route will be influenced by the type of sedating agent to be given and by the nature and location of the bacterial infection to be treated.

Intra-muscular Injection

This involves the injection of antibiotics into the muscle tissue of your koi, and it can be done in a number of locations. Two of them do present problems, however: these are in the dorsal muscle, which is located just below the front ray of the dorsal fin, and the caudal muscle, which is located between the anal fin and the caudal fin below the lateral line. In order to inject in these positions you have to insert the needle underneath a scale and as there is always a risk of infections entering injection sites, this may lead to one or more scales being lost. These injection sites are in prime locations on a koi and any infection would have a dramatic effect on the aesthetic and monetary value of the fish. If, however, you still choose to inject into one of these locations, be sure that the needle is pointing towards the head of the koi.

Another location for intra-muscular injection is in the pectoral muscle which is located under the pectoral fins. This makes an ideal injection site as it is situated underneath the koi. If any infection of the injection site should occur, there are no scales to be lost, and any scarring will not be easily noticeable. An injection should only be carried out by someone suitably qualified to perform the procedure, such as your vet or local koi health specialist, and the procedure will be conducted in the following way.

1 The koi is sedated.
2 The fish is laid on a wet towel, or held upside down against the side of the bowl in which it was sedated, out of the water.

3 The pectoral fin is rotated so that it is facing away from the body and held there, causing the pectoral muscle to become tense. The injection site is swabbed and cleaned.

4 The loaded syringe is held pointing towards the tail of the koi at a 45-degree angle to the body.

5 The needle is gently pushed into the centre of the taut pectoral muscle; if any firm resistance is felt, the syringe will be pulled out slightly.

6 The contents of the syringe are injected, and then the needle is pulled out.

7 Once the needle is removed, the muscle is gently massaged to encourage dispersion of the antibiotic. If the pectoral fin is just released and the muscle naturally contracts, some of the antibiotic may be expelled from the injection site.

Below: Here a trained koi health specialist is performing an intra-peritoneal injection. Due to the potential risks involved, this method of injection should only be performed by a vet or trained koi health specialist.

8 Finally a suitable topical treatment may be applied to the injection site. A slight discharge of blood may occur, but this should cause no undue alarm.

Intra-peritoneal Injection

This involves injection into the peritoneal space or body cavity located behind the pelvic fins but before the vent and anal fin are reached. With this method of injection there are added risks, as if the location of the injection site is wrong, serious and potentially fatal damage to internal organs may occur. Consequently it is recommended that such injections should only be carried out by, or under the very close guidance of, your vet or local koi health specialist.

Antibiotics and Bactericides

Antibiotics should be stored according to the manufacturer's recommendations, and as a very general rule this is at room temperature below

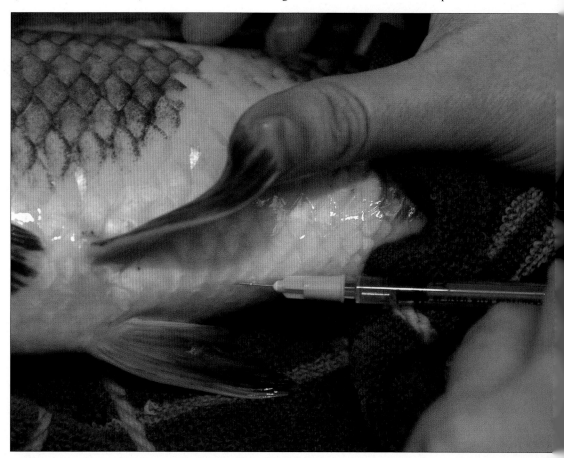

25°C (77°F). A few require refrigeration. It is important to remember that antibiotics have different shelf lives once opened and this shelf life must be strictly observed, along with any other special storage recommendations. Most antibiotics as a rule have to be used within 28 days, but always follow the manufacturer's recommendations. There are numerous anti-bacterials available but really these should only be considered as a last resort after all other possible avenues of treatment have been exhausted, and after guidance from your vet or local koi health specialist.

Before rushing off to your vet for these drugs, it is important to remember that a swab should be taken and sensitivity test carried out and the results shown to your vet so that he can suggest the correct antibiotic or bactericide to use. Guidance should be sought from an experienced fish health consultant regarding the timetable involved in processing the swab when it is sent away for the sensitivity test. In some situations when a fish is extremely ill, the delay in waiting

Above: A fish such as this which is displaying signs of severe emaciation may well be suffering from a bacterial infection that will need to be treated with anti-bacterial medications. In such cases, take advice from a vet.

for the results to come back may prove fatal. In these situations the recommendations of your vet or koi health specialist will be highly valuable. Also it is important to remember that the overuse of antibiotics in itself is an unwise practice, as it may result in antibiotic resistance building up in the bacteria affecting your fish.

To sum up, the use of antibiotics to treat infections should only be considered as a last resort, and then only after guidance from a vet. It pays to take time to discover a vet near you who has experience of fish health problems. Along with advice on antibiotics and medications, he or she will be able to offer many other important professional services, such as x-rays and ultrasound to look for organ abnormalities and tumours, endoscopy, histological examinations, post-mortems and various surgical procedures.

TREATMENT BATHS AND DIPS

S ome of the diseases discussed in section 3 can readily be treated with baths or dips, usually either a salt bath or a potassium permanganate dip. When using a bath or dip treatment, do take care to follow the guidelines described below; if unsure, seek advice.

Salt Baths

These are an ideal way to treat numerous infections and may be administered to a single fish or to all the koi in the pond. It is vital to use the correct salt – this should be cooking salt not table salt. Table salt contains bleaching agents and other impurities which may harm your koi. Not only is salt suitable for bath treatments, but it can also be added to the pond in very low temperatures when other medications prove ineffective, and when dealing with a condition that responds well to such pond

treatment. As a general rule, however, avoid adding salt to your pond as it will limit your use of other medications, such as formalin. Salt does not degrade in the pond and the only way it can be removed is through water changes. So salt is best suited to bath treatments for individual koi. The strength of the salt bath will vary depending upon the condition being treated, although as a guide 22g per litre of water (3.5oz per gallon) for 10 minutes is a standard dose. This is how to give a salt bath.

1 Measure enough water into a viewing bowl or other suitable container to cover the koi to be treated. This should be pond water not tapwater! Ideally put in an airstone as well to provide the fish with sufficient oxygen in the bath.
2 Measure out the right amount of salt in relation to the volume of water in the bowl in which the

1: Add the required amount of salt to some pond water.

2: Having added the salt, mix it thoroughly.

3: Start timing as soon as the fish enters the water.

4: Fish may list in the water while being treated.

koi is to be treated.

3 Thoroughly mix and dissolve the salt.

4 Transfer the koi into the salt bath. As soon as it is in the water, be sure to have a stopwatch to hand to time how long it should remain in the bath. Ten minutes is the maximum time that fish should spend in the bath.

5 While koi are in a salt bath they may appear to be stressed and many may float on their sides as if they were dead. Do not be alarmed by this, and leave the fish for the duration of the bath. This is purely the effect of the salt and once the koi is taken out of the bath it should make a quick recovery.

6 After the designated time remove the koi from the salt bath and return it to the pond. The water used for the salt bath should then be poured to waste.

Potassium Permanganate Dips

These are much harsher than salt baths and are generally used when a specific problem, such as a parasite, is identified. Potassium dips may be used simply as a preventative measure such as when introducing new koi to your pond to ensure that no parasites are present. It is a messy procedure, so take adequate steps to protect yourself and the surrounding area from being stained by the chemical. As with salt baths, the strength of the dip required depends upon what you are dipping for, but a standard dip for most parasite infections is 100mg of potassium permanganate per litre (0.016oz per gallon) for five minutes. This is how to give the dip:

1 Measure enough water into a viewing bowl or other suitable container to cover the koi to be treated. This should be pond water not tapwater! As potassium permanganate oxidizes in water, it is recommended that airstones be added before the chemical is mixed into the water.

2 Measure out the right amount of potassium permanganate for the dip. To help reduce the oxidizing properties of the chemical, you may wish to mix it first in warm or hot water and add an airstone to this mixture. Leave it for 20 minutes before adding it to the bath.

3 Transfer the koi to be treated into the dip; if airstones are to hand add these to the dip while the koi are in it. Again, use a stopwatch to time how long the fish is in the water. This chemical stains so watch out for any splashing.

1: A measured amount of potassium permanganate is being poured into a treatment bath.

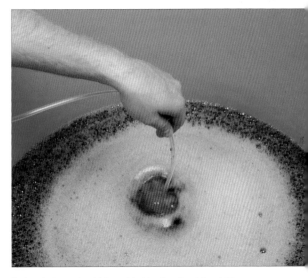

2: An airstone should be added to the dip at least 20 minutes before the koi is placed into it.

4 While koi are in the dip they may appear to be very stressed and many may float on their sides as if they are dead. Don't be alarmed, just leave them for the duration of the dip. This is purely the effect of the chemical and once the koi are taken out of the dip they should make a quick recovery. However, weak koi may not survive the dip, but in such cases the chances are that these koi would probably have died shortly, even if the dip had not been used.

5 After the designated time has passed, remove the koi from the dip and return it to the pond. This is a messy business so once again wear protective clothing. The water used for the dip should then be poured to waste.

POND, TOPICAL AND ALTERNATIVE TREATMENTS

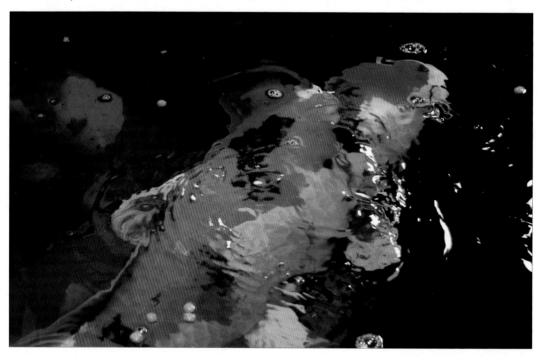

Many chemicals mentioned in section 3 can be used to treat the whole pond, and/or used as a topical treatment. These commonly come as either a liquid or in powder form. Some of the treatments covered here are not explicitly mentioned in section 3, but they provide a useful alternative to those which are recommended, and may be preferred by some koi keepers who are already familiar with them. Of course, many more treatments than are mentioned here are commercially available. In all cases it pays to take advice from your koi health specialist or vet regarding the most effective treatment to use.

Whether you are treating the whole pond or simply topically treating a wound, it is vital that precautions are taken regarding the safe handling of the product. This may involve wearing gloves or working in a well-ventilated area, or even wearing a face mask. Once these precautionary steps are taken to protect yourself, it is critical that the correct amount of medication is measured out for the required treatment. If the whole pond is being dosed, you must know its volume in litres or gallons. Ideally this figure should have been obtained when the pond was built and filled, normally by using a flow meter. However, if you have not done this or perhaps have moved into a house with an existing pond, the volume of water will have to be worked out as best you can. The easiest way to do this if the pond is of a square or rectangular shape is to measure the length and width, take an average depth, multiply these figures together to give a measurement in cubic feet and multiply this by

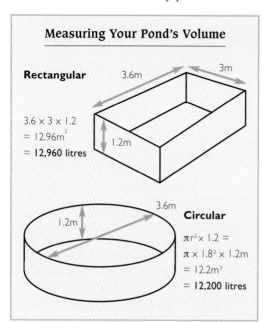

Measuring Your Pond's Volume

Rectangular   3.6m   3m

$3.6 \times 3 \times 1.2$
$= 12.96m^3$
$= 12,960$ litres

1.2m

Circular   3.6m

1.2m

$\pi r^2 \times 1.2 =$
$\pi \times 1.8^2 \times 1.2m$
$= 12.2m^3$
$= 12,200$ litres

up to a maximum of three times.

Notes: Formalin goes off, and the easiest way to check for this is to ensure that there are no white crystals or lumps present in what should be a clear liquid. If any are seen, dispose of the substance immediately. When handling formalin care should be taken to avoid skin contact and breathing in any fumes. Formalin should never under any circumstances be used with potassium permanganate. If using in a pond which already contains salt, advice should always be sought from your koi health specialist before applying this treatment.

Hydrogen peroxide 3 per cent solution

Clear liquid. Used as a cauterizing agent (will seal the wound and stop bleeding) as a topical treatment.

Dose rate: Not appropriate.

Topical use: Apply to the affected area with a cotton-wool bud. Should only be used when advised to do so by a vet or health specialist due to the hazardous and potentially harmful nature of this product.

Bath use: Not appropriate.

Frequency: As advised.

Notes: A very powerful treatment which should only be used when directed, as it can cause severe tissue damage which may hinder rather then help the healing process if used inappropriately. When treating, avoid getting this substance on the gills or other sensitive areas, such as the eyes.

Malachite green

Crystals but commonly sold now as a very dark green liquid in its dissolved form. Should never be handled neat in its crystal or powder form as it is highly toxic if breathed in. An excellent treatment for whitespot if used alone, plus a topical treatment. When used with formalin an excellent all-round general pond treatment.

Dose rate: Varies depending upon solution strength and manufacturer.

Topical use: Simply apply to the area with a cotton-wool bud as required.

Bath use: Not appropriate.

Frequency: When using as a pond treatment once every five to seven days up to a maximum of three times. Same applies if using with formalin.

Notes: Always wear gloves when working with liquid malachite green.

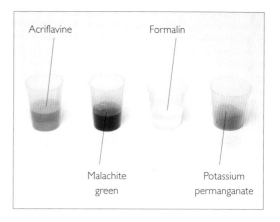

Acriflavine   Formalin

Malachite green   Potassium permanganate

Potassium permanganate

Can be brought as liquid or in crystal form – purple in colour. Mainly used as a pond or bath treatment for numerous diseases, particularly parasites or bacterial infection. Can also be used as a topical treatment where it acts as a cauterizer; but it is potentially harmful and should only be used when advised to do so by your koi health professional or vet.

Dose rate: Numerous dose rates are used. The standard dose is 1.5g per 1000 litres (220 gallons), but as potassium permanganate is rendered inactivate by organic debris in the pond, dose rates may vary depending upon the levels of organic debris present. The more debris present, the less effective the treatment will be.

Topical use: Mix a very small amount of potassium permanganate crystals with water to create a slurry, which can be applied with a cotton-wool bud. Acts a cauterizer so should only be used when bleeding occurs as it will seal the skin and stop the bleeding. Should only be used when advised by a vet or koi health specialist.

Bath use: 100mg per litre (0.016oz per gallon) for five minutes. This is very strong but effective. If treating weak fish you should expect losses, but those which survive the bath will probably make a full recovery. Don't exceed five minutes!

Frequency: As a pond treatment it can be repeated up to a maximum of three times leaving five to seven days between each dose. As a bath, use as required, but avoid excessive use.

Notes: Potassium permanganate should never be mixed with formalin. If using in a pond which already contains salt, advice should always be sought from your koi health specialist before applying this treatment.

Propolis

A topical treatment and food additive. Generally available in spray form or as a liquid with a brush for easy application. If using as a food additive, different concentrations are available.
Dose rate: Not appropriate.
Topical use: Apply to the affected area as required.
Bath use: Not appropriate.
Frequency: As required.
Notes: A natural product produced by bees. Can be mixed daily with food to improve your koi's immune system and overall health.

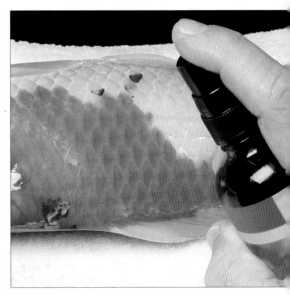

Above: Propolis spray makes an excellent topical treatment either on its own for small superficial damage or used in conjunction with a proprietary topical treatment for more severe areas of infection.

Above: Two different versions of propolis – the smaller bottle is a spray for wound treatment while the larger bottle is a food additive.

Salt

White granules. Used to reduce osmotic pressure as a pond treatment and help reduce stress levels. Also used as a bath to reduce parasite levels.
Dose rate: The amount of salt used varies from 7g (0.25oz) per 4.5 litres (1gallon) up to 6kg (13.2lb) per 1000 litres (220 gallons).
Topical use: Not appropriate.
Bath use: Strength of bath varies, standard doses are between 85-100g (3-3.5oz) per 4.5 litres (1 gallon) for ten minutes.
Frequency: Pond treatment will normally be a one-off, unless you want to maintain a specific

level, in which case salt will need to be added after water changes. To determine how much is required, the salinity will need to be monitored using a hydrometer or salt tester, but these only offer a limited level of accuracy and ideally an electronic salt tester or TDS (total dissolved solids) meter should used. If given as a bath, everything depends upon the condition being treated. Generally one bath a day for three days is the maximum.
Notes: Salt is an effective treatment at all water temperatures. The disadvantage of adding salt to your pond is that it will not biodegrade and the concentration can only be reduced through water changes, while continued salt use can lead to salt-tolerant parasites as is thought to be the case with trichodinids. If you wish to use other medications when salt is also present in the pond, advice should always be sought from your vet or koi health specialist.

General Advice

The use of medication in your pond can have an effect on the filtration system so it is vital after any course of treatment to perform extra water tests, and to take the necessary steps to improve the water quality. You must follow the guidelines

Above: Salt is an excellent bath treatment, and is easily measured.

printed on the packaging, or seek professional advice from your vet or local koi specialist before dosing your pond. In the very unfortunate event of overdosing a pond, you will soon notice drastic

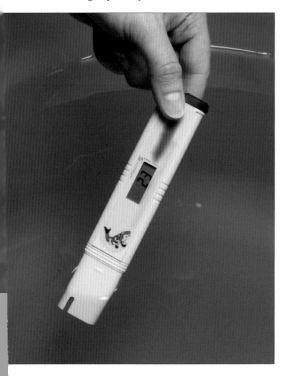

behavioural changes in your koi, such as gasping, jumping, erratic swimming movements, or at the other extreme they may start to float or sink to the bottom and list from side to side. If this does happen, your first step should be to start to change water and increase aeration and continue to do so until your koi start to behave normally again. For routine pond maintenance no more than 10 per cent of the water should be changed at any one time to avoid causing stress to the fish and, if the pond is heated, lowering the temperature too rapidly. However, in the event of an overdose, it may be necessary to change larger volumes of water to dilute the quantity of medication present more quickly. Even then, try to avoid changing more than 40 to 50 per cent of the water at a time.

The treatments described above are only a small selection of what are available for the koi keeper. Most manufacturers of koi products produce their own range of medications which can be used effectively to treat most conditions which the koi keeper will experience. This is helpful as not all of the treatments mentioned are readily available worldwide, as different countries have different regulations regarding acceptable medications.

This has led to increased interest in alternative approaches, and the use of probiotics. These are not medications as such, but friendly bacteria which are introduced into the pond via a liquid product. In very simple terms these friendly bacteria eat and live on the harmful bacteria or their food source and so help to create a healthier environment for the koi. Probiotic foods have also become popular. It must be stressed that many of these new alternative approaches are still in their infancy and thus have yet to be fully evaluated for their claimed benefit. Food additives such as propolis and specific vitamin supplements are also popular, although if a good quality branded food is purchased in the first place, their use is not essential. All of these approaches aim to improve your koi's overall health and so reduce the incidence of disease, and hence the need to use medication.

Left: If salt is added to the pond, it is vital that the strength of salinity is known as some treatments cannot be used with salt. Here a digital salt meter is being used to check the salt level in the water.

SHOULD YOU QUARANTINE OR NOT?

Quarantining new koi purchases is a matter of personal choice. It is also a subject that arouses much discussion. You can argue that if you buy from a reputable dealer who has already kept the koi in quarantine for some time before sale, an additional quarantine period is not required. However, then you must make sure that koi are only purchased from a single, or very limited number of, sources – otherwise the risk of problems arising increases dramatically. Others argue that you should quarantine all new purchases for between four and eight weeks as the stress of transportation and the change in water quality from the dealer's ponds to your pond alone creates a need for an additional quarantine period. This argument is valid, but to be effective the quarantine facilities need to replicate your main pond; if that is not the case, when the koi are finally moved into your main pond they will undergo the same stresses that they would have when purchased.

existing stock if it infects your pond, it is becoming a decision to which more people are saying "Yes". The problem with quarantining is simply this: in most instances the factors which contribute to a koi succumbing to serious diseases are stress, poor water quality, and environmental change. Now while in an ideal world every koi would be quarantined in optimum conditions, the majority of quarantine tanks are actually small units with limited filtration, often located inside a shed or garage. This causes two problems. Firstly, the size and set-up of a typical quarantine system does not create the ideal environment for your koi, and it is very difficult to keep the filters mature, as you do not want to keep fish in the quarantine tank all the time as these may develop their own infections which could be passed on to newly purchased stock. Secondly, because of the location and positioning of most quarantine systems, they tend to take second place to your main pond, and they suffer as a consequence.

How can this problem be overcome? The ideal solution is to have a large quarantine system – a second pond in fact, not necessarily landscaped and decorated, but holding at least 4500 litres (1000 gallons) of water, heated

Above: This koi is suffering from an attack of fungus. The virtue of running a quarantine system is that you can isolate such fish to lessen the chances of disease transmission.

Should you quarantine or not? There is no definitive answer to this, but as more people become aware of devastating diseases like KHV, which can require you to destroy all of your

and containing all the filtration equipment that you would consider putting in your main pond, and perhaps even some extra units, such as ozone and UV sterilizers. Unfortunately this is beyond most people's budgets and they just do not have room for such a set-up. Thus a compromise should be sought and this can take the form of a quarantine facility, but one which is

not necessarily for isolating newly purchased koi. Instead this facility may be used to move koi from your main pond when they succumb to infection and require specialist treatment, such as very warm water, regular injections, or the introduction of medication which may be detrimental to the filter system. If, however, a fish only has physical damage or an isolated infection which requires topical treatment, it is better to leave your koi in the main pond as they will recover more quickly there, and only move them out as a last resort.

When buying new koi, you should be able to trust your dealer if the business is reputable. The dealer should be able to tell you when the fish were imported, what they have been treated with, any problems which they might have experienced, if they have been temperature-tested for KHV, and if the farm they have come from has been tested for KHV. Ultimately a reputable koi dealer will not knowingly sell diseased or infected stock, as the consequences for the business would be catastrophic. So when choosing your principal source for new koi, take time to get to know the staff and look at the

Above: This well-maintained quarantine system belongs to a private koi keeper. It has all the filtration equipment that you would normally find associated with a main koi pond.

stock. You should not see large numbers of dead koi in the display ponds, nor lots of fish with evident signs of injury or damage. The koi which are for sale should all be lively and readily looking for food, and appear in overall good health. Try to speak to regular customers and see how they have found koi purchased from this dealer. Ask if they have ever quarantined any purchases and, if not, have they ever experienced health problems.

With all this information to hand you should be able to buy your koi in confidence and be happy to introduce them to your main pond without the need for any extended quarantine programme. Your own quarantine facilities can be used more as a treatment-cum-isolation tank for any serious infections which need separate treatment. In the end there is no "right" answer. It is a matter of personal preference guided by the advice of your local koi dealer who will help you to make your final decision.

CONCLUSION

Koi health should not be a daunting subject. Many of the diseases described in this book can easily be prevented by careful, thorough system maintenance and good husbandry. The single biggest cause of disease is stress and if this can be kept to a minimum, the outbreak of health problems will be dramatically reduced. The largest stress factors in your koi pond are poor water quality, temperature fluctuation, overstocking, bad handling, frequent netting, and poorly maintained filtration systems. If these factors can be closely monitored and maintained in optimum conditions, you are well on your way to creating a healthy and stable environment in which your koi will thrive.

Diseases do unfortunately occur, no matter how well your pond is maintained. However, if correct identification is made quickly and the appropriate course of treatment followed, the common complaints which the koi keeper will experience can be cleared up quickly and easily. Of course, there are some conditions which do require more specialist treatment and are harder to cure; however, these will only affect a handful of koi keepers, and so should not be a cause for general alarm. It is all too easy to convince yourself that your koi have a rare and serious condition, but the chances are that they do not.

When using this book to identify symptoms, always start with the common problems, such as parasites or mild bacterial infections. A lot of the diseases which affect koi exhibit very similar symptoms, but it makes sense to start with the obvious diseases in trying to make an exact diagnosis. Correct identification is the key to the treatment and successful cure of all koi diseases, and so as much time and effort should be put into making the diagnosis as into the treatment itself. The trap here is that you will do the easy things, like taking a skin scrape which requires little time

or expense, but forget to take a swab, which has to be analysed by an independent laboratory for a charge. It is only when all the necessary tests have been carried out that an accurate diagnosis can be made, and the correct course of treatment selected.

As you come to the end of this book, you should now be able not only to identify what is causing many of

The goal of all koi keepers – beautiful and healthy fish swimming gracefully for our pleasure.

the health problems covered, but also to be able to treat it accurately and thoroughly and keep losses to a minimum. Despite this, it is always advisable to seek the opinion of a suitably qualified vet or koi specialist before administering any treatments. We hope that you will have been persuaded to buy a microscope and install heating in your pond. These are costly items and

unfortunately this tends to put some people off, but then these same people will quite happily spend a similar amount of money on a new fish. Remember, the investment made in heating and a good microscope will easily pay for itself in time, as these items will help you to keep the pond healthier, identify any problems quicker, and ultimately save more koi when disease does occur.

Finally, perhaps the most important point to stress is that everyone has a different opinion and different experiences. What works for one person will not always

work for another. When dealing with the health of your koi, it is vital that you decide whose advice you are going to follow, and stick to it. Far too often fishkeepers will take advice from numerous sources and then mix up the recommendations, following different advice from different

people. This is asking for trouble. If you decide to use the treatment methods outlined in this book, it is vital that they are followed as described. Don't use them in conjunction with other treatments as this could cause complications. Conversely, if you are currently pursuing a course of treatment and want to change to one of the treatments suggested in this book, seek advice before doing so. When you have fully assimilated the advice offered in this book, you should be in a much better position than you were beforehand to provide your koi with a high standard of health care, but always discuss things in full with your local koi specialist, and do not be afraid to ask for their help and advice. Finally keep the book by you as a source of reference and enjoy your koi!

INDEX

Note: Page numbers set in *italic* type refer to picture captions; page numbers set in **bold** type refer to a main A-Z disease entry.

A

abdomen, swollen **88**
acclimatization 11
acidosis 13
acriflavine 54, 65, 81, 86, 117, **148**, *149*
additives, mineral and vitamin 25, 85
adrenaline 10
Aeromonas (bacterium) 60, **62-65**, *62, 65*
agar dish 48, *48*
age, old 86
air gulping **118-119**
air pumps 18, 20, 21, 37, 50, 52
airstones 18, 30, 44, 76, 79, 80, 82, 103, 113, 122, 124, 144, 145
algae 14, 18, 28, 96, 97, 101, 138
alkalosis 13, 14
ammonia 12, *12*, 13, **14-15**, 16, 34, 57, 81, 116, 139
anaesthesia 117; *see also* sedation
anchor worm 58, *59,* **66-69**, *66, 67, 68, 69,* 84
life cycle *67*
antibiotics 48, 49, 64, 79, 80, 117, 130, **140-143**, *141*
overuse of 47
Apiosoma (parasitic gill disease) 58, **70-71**, *70*
Argulus (fish louse) *56,* 58, **72-75**, *72, 74*
life cycle *73*

B

bacteria, aerobic *12,* 15, 18, *18,* 21, 57, 148
bacterial infection 27, 46, 48, *48,* 49, **56-57**, *57, 63, 64,* 67, 69, 71, 72,

74, 76, 78-81, 82, 85, 86, 88, *88,* 92, 93, 94, 95, 99, 103, 116, 117, 118, 122, 123, 124, 125, 128, 129, 136, 141, 148, 149, 154
Aeromonas 60, **62-65**, *62, 65*
diagnostic guide **60-61**
Flavobacterium columnare 62, **78-81**, 94
prevention of **63-64**
treatment of **64-65**
bagging for transportation 50-53, *50, 51, 52, 53*
behaviour, abnormal 96
behavioural changes 44, 92, 124, 151
blanketweed *12, 16,* 17, *18,* 20, *73,* 97, 101
bloodworms *24,* 25
body, swollen 86, *86,* 116, 117
Bothriocephalus acheilognathi (tapeworm) **120-121**, *120, 121*
life cycle 120-121, *120*
bowl, viewing 30, 36, *36, 37, 37,* 38, 39, *39,* 40, 41
Branchiomyces (gill rot) **100-101**
breeding 84

C

carbohydrates 23
carbon dioxide 14, 17, *32*
carp pox 61, **114-115**, *114*
carrying fish **39-41**, *40;* see also handling
Chilonodella (external protozoan parasite) 58, 70, **76-77**, *76, 77*
chloramine T 65, 81, 101, 117, **148**
chromatophores 32
circulation system **34-35**
colour, loss of/discoloration 80, 106, 108; *see also* pigmentation

columnaris disease 60, **78-81**
copepods (tapeworm host) *120,* 121
costia 58, **82-83**, *82, 83*
cotton wool (fungal disease) **94-95**
cotton wool mouth rot 78, 80, *80, 81,* 94
cysts 112-113

D

Dactylogyrus (gill fluke) *56,* **102-105**, *102, 103*
life cycle *103*
damage, physical 30, 36, 42, 46, 47, *55,* 57, *57,* 94, 126, **128**, 128, **136-137**, 150
dechlorinator 15, 19, 97, 99, 117
diagnostic guide **58-61**
digestive organs **33-34**
Doitsu (leather koi) 14, 40, 128
dormancy 19
dragonfly larvae **126**
dropsy 15, 60, *61,* 62, **86-87**, *86,* 88, 116, 117

E

egg retention 60, **88-91**, *88,* 118
eggs 17, 35, 91
environmental conditions influencing development of 84
fungal infection of 94, 95
electric shock 84, *84,* 85
emaciation *70,* 71, 83, 93, 105, 113, 122, *143*
environmental changes 10-11
Epistylis (protozoan parasite) 58, **92-93**, *92, 93*
Ergasilus (gill maggots) **99-100**
life cycle *100*
euthanasia 86, 88, 91, 113, 118, 133, **135**, *135*

columnaris disease 60,
exophthalmia **116-117**, *116, 117*
eyes 34, 149
deformed 84
exophthalmia **116-117**, *116, 117*
gas bubbles around 96
parasites around *58,* 66
pop-eye 61, 62, 96, **116-117**, *116, 117*
protruding 86, *86*
sunken 79

F

fatty acids 23
feeding 8, 20, **22-25**, 86
automatic feeding equipment 25
during low oxygen levels 18
during treatment 148
overfeeding 23, 25
recommended quantity of food 25
underfeeding 25
water temperature, according to 24, *24*
fertilizer 12
filter media, biological 21, 95
mechanical 20
filters 14, 20, 101, 121, 123, 152
biological 148
cleaning 21
denitrification 12, 17
discharges 82
failure of 15
leeches in 110, 111
maintenance of 15, 71
sand 96, 97
vegetable 12, *16,* 17
ultraviolet (UV) 20, 97, 147
filtration systems 8, 12, *12,* 20, *57, 73,* 116, 150, 154
biological 13, 15, 18
ozone 8
fin rot 15, **78-79**, *78, 79,* 139
fins *33,* **34**, 40

clamped 44, 70, 76, 80, 82, 93, 124, 127
damage to 14, 139
fungal infection of *61, 94, 95*
gas bubbles in 96, *96, 97*
growths on 88
lumps on 114
missing 84
parasites on 66, 70, 72, *72,* 110, 112
reddened 82, 139
split 128
treatment of damage **139**
fish lice 56, **72-75,** *72, 74,* 84
life cycle *73*
Flavobacterium columnare (bacterium) 62, **78-81,** 94
Flexibacter columnaris see *Flavobacterium columnare*
flow meter 85
flukes 54, 59, **102-105,** *102, 103, 105*
gill 56, **102-105,** *102*
life cycle *103*
skin **102-105,** *105*
food 54
additives 25, 85, *150,* 151
floating 119
sinking 119
storage of 25
foods **22-25**
bread, brown 24, *24*
colour-enhancing 24
flake *23*
floating sticks 22, *23*
freeze-dried/frozen *24,* 25, 110, 113
high-protein 24
incorrect 85
lettuce *22,* 24, *24*
live 25, 110, 113, 121, 123, 124, 125
oranges 24, *24*
paste 22, *23*
pellets 22, *23*
prawns 24, *24*
sinking 22-23
wheatgerm-based diet 24
formalin 54, 71, 77, 82, 105, 119, 144, **147-8,**

149, *149*
fountains 18, 19, 21
"frog face" *see Myxobolus*
frogs **126-127,** *127*
fry 17, 126
feeding of 85
fungal disease/fungus **57,** *61,* 64, *65,* 67, 71, 72, 74, 76, 78, 80, 82-83, 92, 93, **94-95,** *94, 95,* 103, 107, 122, 124, 125, 128, 129, 148
Branchiomyces (gill rot) **100-101**
diagnostic guide 61
Saprolegnia 94
fungicide 83, 95, 125, 128

G
garlic *24*
gas bubble disease *60,* 61, **96-97,** *96, 97*
gill maggots 58, 98, **99-100,** *99*
life cycle *100*
gill rot 78, **79-80,** *79,* **100-101**
gills *17,* **32-33,** *32,* 34, 45, 96, 137, 149
bacterial infections of 148
colour change/loss 80, 109
damage to 14, 99, *103,* 108, *109*
discoloration of 101, 103
disorders 61, **98-101,** *98, 101*
filaments, disintegrating or rotting 99, *101,* 108, *109*
flukes *56,* **102-105**
gas bubbles on 96
grey 99
holes in 101
hyperplasia 15
missing plates 84
movement
erratic/irregular 13, 76, 83, 105
rapid 18, 44, 79
parasites *56, 58,* 66, 67, 70-71, *70,* 76, 112, *112, 113,* 122
rotting 101

samples, taking 101
sticky **98-99**
white patches on 92
gonads **35**
Go Sanke varieties 106, *106*
Gyrodactylus (skin fluke) **102-105,** *105*

H
handling *30,* **36-41,** *40, 41,* 154; *see also* carrying
heart **34-35**
heater, floating 19
heating 91, 95
heating systems 8, **26-27,** 35, **54,** 63, 71, 76, 82, 93, 105, 116, 119, 122, 124, *129,* 154
heat exchanger 26, *26*
in-line electric heater 26, *27*
hi-kui disease 61, **106-107,** *106*
hormones to induce spawning 91
hydrogen peroxide **149**

I
Ichthyobodo necator (costia) (external protozoan parasite) **82-83**
Ichthyophthirius multifiliis (whitespot) **124-125,** *124*
life cycle *125*
immune system 11, *11,* 16, 19, 26, **35,** 56
imported fish *11,* 68, 109
injections **140-143,** *140, 141, 142*
intestine **33-34**
introduction of new stock 15

J
jumping 16, *37,* 39, 151

K
KHV (koi herpes virus) 56, 61, **108-109,** *108, 109,* 152, 153
kidneys **33,** 35, 140
failure of 85
koi herpes virus (KHV)

56, 61, **108-109,** *108, 109,* 152, 153

L
lateral line **32,** *34*
leather koi (Doitsu) 40, 114
leeches 59, *59,* **110-111,** *110, 111*
Lernaea (anchor worm) **66-69,** *66, 67, 68, 69*
life cycle *67*
lethargy 113, 122, 124
lightning strike 84, *84,* 85
liver **33-34**

M
maggots, gill 98, **99-100,** *99*
maintenance **20-21,** 30, **54,** 81, 82, 93, 95, 105, 106, 121, 151, 154
malachite green 54, 64, 68, 71, 77, 78, 81, 82, 93, 95, 105, 115, 125, 128, 130, 136, **149,** *149*
malnutrition 84, *84,* 85
medications 11, 14, 30, 63, 84, 136, 146
administration of 130
anti-bacterial 65, 86, 117, 128, 140
anti-fluke 105
anti-parasite 69. 71, 77, 125
at low temperatures 19, 27
dispensing 147-148, *148*
gill, proprietary 101
organophosphate-based 74, 84, 100, 105, 130
overdose 84, *84,* 151
safety 130, 146
storage 148
medicine chest 54
Melaleuca (herbal extract) 64
methylene blue 95
microscope 30, **42-43,** *42, 43,* 44, 45, *45,* 54, 56, *56,* 57, 66, *70, 74,* 76, *76,* 78. 82, *82,* 92, *92,* 99, 102, *102,* 103, 112, *122,* 123, *124,*

154, 155
electron 56, *108*
lenses **42**, *42*
slides **43**
styles of **42**
milt 35
minerals as constituent of
food 23
mouth
fungal infection of 94
parasites affecting 66,
67, 72, 99, 110
ulcers around 62
mouth rot 78, **80**, *80, 81*
movement, erratic 67, 74,
79, 127, 151
mucus 32, 35, 44, *45*
covering gills 99
damaged 15, 94
effects of formalin on
119
excess 13, 45, *58,* 62,
70, 74, 76, 79, 80, 82,
103, 105, 108, 113, 122
sloughing 80
mycobacteria 127
Myxobolus (nodular
disease) 54, 59, **112-
113,** *112*

N

net 54
pan 30, 36, *36, 37*
plastic bag **39,** *39,* 40
seine 38
sock 30, 36, **38-39,** *38,*
40
netting 10, *11,* 20, 30,
36-39, *36, 37, 38, 39,*
154
damage caused by 94
new hole disease 62-63
nitrate 12, *12,* 13, 14, **17,**
57
nitrification 12, 17
nitrite 12, *12,* 13, **16,** 17,
17, 57, 139
nitrogen cycle *12*
nitrogen gas 12, 57
supersaturation 96, 97
Nitrobacter (bacteria) 12,
12
Nitrosomonas (bacteria)
12, *12*
nodular disease
(*Myxobolus*) **112-113,**
112

O

oesophagus **33-34**
operculum 32, 33, 113
lifted 103
ulcerated 62
orfe 69, 74, 84, 100
organophosphates 69, 74,
84, 100, 105, 111, 130
osmoregulation 10, *32,*
33, 103
oxygen 12, *12,* **17-19,**
17, 32, 33, 34, 35, 44,
50, 52, 53, 81, 86, 99,
107, 122, 148
effects of temperature
on 17, *17*
levels in summer *18*
levels in winter *18*
meter 18
supersaturation 96, *96,*
97
oyster shells, crushed 14
ozone units 21, **28,** *28,*
63, 152

P

papilloma 61, **114-115,**
115
parasites 16, 19, 27, 30,
42, 43, 44, 45, 46, *55,*
56, 57, 81, 84, 85, 93,
94, 114, 116, 119,
136, 145, 148, 150,
154
anchor worm (*Lernaea*)
58, *59,* **66-69,** *66, 67,*
68, 69, 84
Apiosoma (parasitic gill
disease) 58, **70-71**
Argulus (fish lice) *56,*
58, **72-75,** *72, 74*
blood parasites **126**
Chilodonella (external
protozoan) *38,* 58, 70,
76-77, *76, 77*
costia (external
protozoan) 58, **82-83,**
82, 83
Dactylogyrus (gill
flukes) *56,* **102-105,**
102, 103
diagnostic guide **58-59**
Epistylis (external
protozoan) 58, **92-93,**
92, 93
Ergasilus (gill maggots)
99-100, *99*

fish lice *56,* **72-75,** *72,*
74, 84
flukes 54, *56,* 59,
102-105, *102, 103,*
105
gill maggots 58, **99-
100,** *99*
Gyrodactylus (skin
flukes) **102-105,** *105*
Ichthyophthirius
multifiliis (whitespot)
124-125
leeches 59, **110-111,**
110, 111
Lernaea (anchor worm)
58, *59,* **66-69,** *66, 67,*
68, 69, 84
Myxobolus (nodular
disease) 59, **112-113,**
112
Piscicola geometra
(leech) 111, *111*
Sanguinicola
(bloodworm) 126, *126*
tapeworm *58,* 59, **120-
121,** *120, 121*
temperature, effects on
93
Trichodina (external
protozoan) *55,* 59, 70,
80, **122-123,** *122,*
123, 150
Trypanoplasma (blood
parasite) 126, *126*
Trypanosoma (blood
parasite) 126
whitespot 54, 58, *59,*
67, 80, 114, **124-125,**
124, 124, 149
worms 88
PCR (polymerase chain
reaction) test 108
peat, aquatic 14
photosynthesis 17, 57, 96
pigmentation 106
pipework, purging 20
Piscicola geometra (leech)
110-111
life cycle *111*
plants 12
excessive growth of 14
ponds
heated 19, 21, 24, *26,*
72, 81, 91, 151
unheated 26, 27, 68,
91, 118, 124, 129
pop-eye 61, 62, 96, **116-

117,** *116, 117,* 127
potassium permanganate
54, 65, 71, 77, 81,
105, 111, 117, 123,
125, **145,** *145,* **149,**
149
predators 128
pressure sores 19, 118
probiotics 63, 151
proflavin hemisulphate 65,
148
propolis 25, 54, 64, 68,
71, 74, 77, 78, 80, 81,
83, 93, 95, 105, 111,
115, 123, 125, 128,
129, 136, **150,** *150,*
151
proteins 23, 24, *24,* 25,
34
pumps *16,* 20, *27,* 119
failure of 15

Q

quarantine 29, 36, 86, 95,
109, 112, 113, 116,
123, **152-153,** *153*

R

redox potential meter 28
reproductive organs **35**
residual-current device
(RCD) 85
Rhabdovirus carpio
(spring viraemia of
carp) **109**

S

salt 54, 149, **150**
baths 71, 77, 80, 82,
86, 93, 99, 101, 111,
111, 117, 119, 123,
144-145, *144,* 150,
151
pond treatment 14, 16,
71, 77, 82-83, 119,
129, 150
Sanguinicola (bloodworm)
126, *126*
Saprolegnia (fungus) 94
scales **32,** *33,* 35, 40, 44,
45
dead *65,* 138, *138,*
139, *139*
dislodged 136
lifting *61,* 62, 64, 68,
80, 81, 86, 92, 116,
117, 136, *137*

loss of *64*, 81, *92,* 128
parasites affecting 66, *66*
removal of dead 64, *65,*
  138-139, *138, 139*
sedating agents 41, 44,
  54, **132-133**, 134, 135
sedation 10, 41, 46, 64,
  68, 78, 95, 107, **132-**
  135, *132, 133, 134,*
  140, 141
septicaemia, haemorrhagic
  62
sex, determining 88, *91*
sight **34**
skimmers, protein 20, *20,*
  28, *29*
skin **32**, 33, *33,* 35
  abrasions 82
  cancer 106
  columnaris disease 60,
  80-81
  discoloration of 80, 106
  flukes **102-105**, *105*
  fungal infection 94
  hi-kui 61, **106, 107**,
  106
  irritation 44, *61*, 67,
  71, 76, 82, 105, 122,
  124, 136
  lesions on *61*, 74, 110,
  124
  lifting 96
  opaque appearance of
  70, 76
  parasites affecting 70,
  76-77, **102-105**, 122-
  123, *122*, 124-125,
  124, 125
  pigmentation loss 106,
  106
  reddening 13, 15, 62,
  82, 92, *92,* 109, 127, 128
  rough 76
  ulcerated 62, *63,* 93,
  95, 109, 123, 127, 136
  white patches 92, *92*
skin scrapes 30, 36, 41,
  44-45, *44, 45,* 46, 49,
  54, 56, 67, 70, 76, 82,
  92, 99, *102*, 103, 123,
  124, *124*, 154
sleeping sickness 19, **129,**
  129
snails, aquatic 126
spawning 91, 94, 95,
  128, 136
  hand 91

spine, curvature of 60,
  84-85, *84, 85*
spinning technique **41,**
  41, 44, 47
spirulina 25
spleen 35
spring viraemia of carp
  (SVC) 61, **109**
steroid creams 107
stocking levels 13, 54, 63,
  71, 76
  overstocking 10, 11,
  15, 18, 62, 154
stress 8, **10-11,** 12, 13,
  19, 36, 38, 40, 45, 56,
  62, 82, 86, 93, 94,
  114, 116, 124, 140,
  148, 150, 154
sunburn 106, **129**
SVC (spring viraemia of
  carp) 61, **109**
swabs 30, 36, 41, **46-49,**
  46, 47, 54, 57, 62, 63,
  64, 65, 78, 79, 80, 81,
  99, 130, 143, 150, 154
"swelling cheek disease"
  see Myxobolus
swimbladder **33**
  disorders of 23, 61, 86,
  88, **118-119**, *118, 119*
syringes 140, *140,* 141

T

tapeworms 54, *58,* 59,
  120-121, *120, 121*
  life cycle 120-121, *120*
test kits 13
  ammonia 14
  oxygen 18
  water hardness 14
trace elements 23, 25
transporting fish 30, **50-**
  53, *50, 51, 52, 53*
treatments 30, 57, **130,**
  146-151
  anti-bacterial 57, 62,
  64-65, 79, 80, 81,
  105, 117, 123, 125
  anti-fungal 95, 107
  anti-parasite 82, 84,
  93, *103*
  for lice *73*
  organophosphate-based
  69, 84, 100, 105, 111,
  130
  topical, **136-139**, *136,*
  137, 146, 149, *150*

worming *120,* 121
Trichodina (external
  protozoan parasite) 54,
  55, 59, 70, 80, **122-**
  123, *122, 123,* 150
Trypanoplasma (blood
  parasite) 126, *126*
Trypanosoma (blood
  parasite) 126
tuberculosis, fish (TB) **127**
tubifex 25
tumours 60, **88**, *88,* 91,
  115, 116, 118, 143

U

ulceration 46, 47, 49, 62,
  63, 64, 93, 95, 109,
  123, 136
ultraviolet (UV) clarifiers
  64, **28-29**, *29*
ultraviolet (UV) sterilizers
  8, 64, 152, **28-29**
ultraviolet (UV) units 21

V

vaccination 56
vacuum cleaners 21, *21*
viral infections 85, 88,
  116, 117
  carp pox 61, **114-115,**
  114
  diagnostic guide **60-61**
  KHV (koi herpes virus)
  108-109
  papilloma 61, **114-115,**
  115
  spring viraemia of carp
  (SVC) 61, **109**
viruses **56**, 67
  diagnostic guide **60-61**
vitamins 23, *24,* 25, 116,
  151
volume, measuring pond
  146-147, *146*

W

water
  acidic conditions 13
  algal problems 14
  alkalinity 13, 14
  ammonia level 12, 13,
  14-15, *15*
  analysis 19
  anti-bacterial additives
  79, 80
  antibiotic additives 49
  buffering 14

carbonate hardness
  (KH) 12, **14**, *14*
  changes *12,* 15, 18, 82,
  83, 97, 101, 105, 117,
  151
  chemical contents of 19
  freezing 19
  general hardness (GH)
  10, **14**
  metal content 19
  nitrate level 12, 1, **17**
  nitrite level 12, 13, **16,**
  17
  oxygen level **17-19**,
  18, 21, 81, 98, 99,
  105, 107, 148
  effects of temperature
  on 17, *17*
  in summer *18*
  in winter *18*
  pH values 10, 12, **13-**
  14, 17, *17,* 148
  purifier 19
  quality 8, 9, 10, **12-19**,
  21, *25,* **28**, 30, 46, 49,
  54, 62, 76, 81, 82, 84,
  86, 94, 98, 105, 116,
  137, 150, 154
  recommended levels
  16
  tapwater 19, 21, 71,
  96, 117
  conditioners 71
  temperature 10, 13, *15,*
  18, *18,* **19**, *19,* 21, 24,
  24, 25, 26, 27, 30, 35,
  62, 63, 68, 71, 72, 76,
  77, 78, 82, 86, 91, 93,
  96, 105, 108, 114,
  115, 116, 118, 119,
  122, 124, 125, 129,
  137, 144, 151, 154
  testing 8, 10, *12,* 13,
  20, 82, 95, 99, 116,
  119, 150
waterfalls 18, 21
weight, gauging *140*
weight loss 68, 76, 127
whitespot 54, 59, *59,* 67,
  80, 114, **124-125**, *124,*
  149
  life cycle *125*
wounds 128, **136-137**,
  146, 149, *150*

Z

zeolite 15

Further Reading

Andrews, Dr Chris, Exell, Adrian and Carrington, Dr Neville *The Interpet Manual of Fish Health* (Interpet Publishing, 2002)

Hickling, Steve, Martin, Mick, Brewster, Bernice and Fletcher, Nick *Koi – A colourful and comprehensive celebration of these beautiful ornamental fish* (Interpet Publishing, 2002)

Jepson, Lance *Koi Medicine* (TFH Kingdom Books, 2001)

Johnson, Erik L. *Koi Health and Disease* (1997)

Kuroki, Takeo *Manual to Nishikigoi* (Shuji Fujita, 1981)

Lammens, Maarten *The Koi Doctor – your guide to keeping healthy koi* (A-Publishing/KINDAI bvba, 2004)

Nishikigoi Manual – Nishikigoi varieties and their diseases (published in Japanese with an English parallel text) (All-Japan Nishikigoi Promotion Association in association with Kinsai Shuppan)

Post, Dr George *Revised and Expanded Textbook of Fish Health* (TFH Publications, 1987)

Rinko magazine (published monthly by Shin Nippon Kyoiku Tosho Co., Ltd, Japan)

Untergasser, Dieter *Handbook of Fish Diseases* (TFH Publications, 1989)